Work Staggering for Traffic Relief

THE STAGGERED WORKING HOURS PROJECT
OF THE CITY OF NEW YORK

THE POLICY COMMITTEE

JOHN V. CONNORTON, Chairman
City Administrator

JOSEPH E. O'GRADY
Former Chairman, The New York City Transit Authority

WILLIAM F. R. BALLARD
Former Chairman, The City Planning Commission

LYLE C. FITCH
President, The Institute of Public Administration

LUTHER H. GULICK
Chairman of the Board of Trustees,
The Institute of Public Administration

THE STEERING COMMITTEE

HENRY COHEN, Chairman
Director, New School Center for New York City Affairs

WILLIAM LASSOW
The New York City Transit Authority

JOSEPH LEIPER
The New York City Department of City Planning

MARVIN ROTH, Secretary
The Hospital Review and Planning Council

THE PROJECT STAFF

LAWRENCE B. COHEN, Director

ECONOMIC AND INDUSTRY STUDIES

Frederick W. Cleveland	Jerome E. Komisar	Richard Perlman
John N. Gartner	Eugene Lerner	Natalie Sirkin
Shirley Johnson	Dean W. Morse	John E. Ullman

SOCIOLOGY STUDIES

Amitai Etzioni	Immanuel Wallerstein	Terence K. Hopkins

ASSISTANTS

Harriet Greenberg	Roberta Simmons	Elaine R. Meyer

TECHNICAL STUDIES

Norman Agin	Cyrus Derman	Sylvain Ehrenfeld
	Morton Klein	

ASSISTANTS

Sol Drimmer	Arthur D. Johnson	Simon Teitel
M. Barry Dumas	Allen Lanoue	Sunder Singh Thakur
Marvin Fishman	Alvin Shulman	Steven Young

PRAEGER SPECIAL STUDIES IN
U.S. ECONOMIC AND SOCIAL DEVELOPMENT

Work Staggering for Traffic Relief

AN ANALYSIS OF MANHATTAN'S CENTRAL BUSINESS DISTRICT

Lawrence B. Cohen

FREDERICK A. PRAEGER, Publishers
New York · Washington · London

The purpose of the Praeger Special Studies is to make specialized research monographs in U.S. and international economics and politics available to the academic, business, and government communities. For further information, write to the Special Projects Division, Frederick A. Praeger, Publishers, 111 Fourth Avenue, New York, N.Y. 10003.

FREDERICK A. PRAEGER, PUBLISHERS
111 Fourth Avenue, New York, N.Y. 10003, U.S.A.
77-79 Charlotte Street, London W.1, England

Published in the United States of America in 1968
by Frederick A. Praeger, Inc., Publishers

© 1968 by Lawrence B. Cohen

Library of Congress Catalog Card Number: 67-25240

Printed in the United States of America

PREFACE

The Staggered Working Hours Project of the City
of New York was created, late in 1959, to investigate
the feasibility of work staggering in Manhattan's
central business district.

The immediate origins of the Project go back to
1955, when a cursory review of the problem was undertaken by Henry Cohen and Marvin Roth, then with the
staff of the Division of Administration of the Office
of the Mayor of the City of New York. Their analysis
indicated that even though a sizable amount of work
staggering already existed, the public transportation
system operated with very high peak loads during the
morning and evening rush hours. Many persons had
been advocating a program of staggered work hour as
a panacea for relieving congestion in the subway system. It was therefore felt that a definitive study
should be undertaken to assess the feasibility of
further staggering work hours in the central business
district of New York City to evaluate its potential
effectiveness in relieving transit congestion.

A research proposal was developed which received
financial support from the Rockefeller Brothers Fund
and the City of New York. Substantial additional support in the form of computer time and service was made
available by the New York City Port Authority and
Columbia University.

The organization of the Project consisted of a
Policy Committee, a Steering Committee, and the
Project staff. The Policy Committee exercised general
direction and responsibility over the Project. Its
members were the City Administrator, the Chairman of
the New York City Planning Commission, the Chairman
of the New York City Transit Authority, and the President of the Institute of Public Administration.
The Steering Committee, made up of representatives of
each of these cooperating agencies, served as the

supervisory body. The staff of the Project, consisting of professional personnel, assistants, and other service employees, were responsible to the director.

The research program was designed by the Project staff and approved by the Steering Committee. It was thereafter carried out by the staff. This report was prepared by the Director of the Project, who bears sole responsibility for it.

It would be impossible to name all the individuals who contributed to this study. They number in the thousands and include the 1,572 individual respondents of the sociological survey, the officials of the more than 230 firms in the sample, the thousands of firms and their officials who provided schedule information, and the many other firms who permitted members of the Project staff to make studies of their scheduling. Their generosity of time, effort, and expense is gratefully acknowledged.

The Project Director takes this occasion to express his personal gratitude to the individuals whose direct collaboration made possible the execution of the study. The members of the staff--professional as well as others--displayed remarkable qualities of talent and loyalty to this long and often stubborn undertaking. A very special debt of thanks is owed to the Steering Committee--Chairman Henry Cohen, William Lassow, Joseph Lieper, and Secretary Marvin Roth. It would be difficult to imagine, much less assemble, a more generous, competent, and persevering supervisory committee.

L. B. C.

CONTENTS

		Page
PREFACE		v
LIST OF TABLES		xi
LIST OF FIGURES		xvii

Chapter

1	AN INTRODUCTION TO WORK STAGGERING	1
	The Design of the Study	4
	The Problem of Inquiry	8
	A Theory of Feasibility	18
	Data and Sources	24
	Conclusion	28
2	HOW MUCH CONGESTION? HOW MUCH RELIEF?	29
	The Measure of Subway Traffic	30
	Evaluation and Adjustment of the Cordon Counts	42
	The Accuracy of the Cordon Counts	56
	The Standard of Subway Traffic	65
	The Prevailing State of Subway Congestion	71
	The Relief of Subway Congestion	85
	Conclusions	88
3	CBD INDUSTRY AND WORK SCHEDULES	90
	The CBD	91
	The CBD Work Schedule	104
	Summary	115
	A Comparative Analysis of the Major Industry Divisions	115
	Evaluation	125

Chapter		Page
4	THE MODIFIABILITY OF WORK SCHEDULES-- FUNCTIONAL CAPABILITY	134
	Schedule Modifiability	138
	Units of Employment	148
	Alternative Start Times	151
	Functional Capability of Schedule Change	164
	Industry Groups and Their Schedule Alternatives	176
	Conclusions	182
5	ACCEPTABILITY OF SCHEDULE CHANGE	185
	The Sociological Study	186
	Personnel Constraints on Modifiability	229
	Conclusions	244
6	FORECASTING CORDON COUNTS	245
	Work Schedule and Cordon Count-- The Present Relationship	246
	The Forecasting Equation	277
	The Forecasting Equation and Its Application	298
	Cordon Counts Without Congestion	302
	Summary	312
7	FEASIBLE WORK SCHEDULES	314
	The Feasible Schedules	317
	The Constant Schedules	321
	The Varying Schedules	323
	The Final Schedules	326
	The Stop Time Schedules	343
	Conclusions	350
8	THE FEASIBILITY OF WORK STAGGERING	351
	Evaluation	352
	The Modifiability of Work Schedules	352

Chapter	Page
The Acceptability of Schedule Change	355
Relief of Congestion	358
Other Modes of Transit	374
Tolerance and Resistance	380
Durability	382
What If . . .	385
Conclusion	392

APPENDIXES

LIST OF APPENDIX TABLES   397

Appendixes

		Page
A	THE CORDON STATIONS	409
B	THE SHAPE OF TRAFFIC FLOW	412
C	THE OCTOBER, 1962, CORDON COUNT	416
D	OPERATIONS DURING THE OCTOBER, 1962, CORDON COUNT	419
E	CORDON INTERVAL PATTERNS	422
F	THE TRUNCATION ADJUSTMENT	426
G	THE ADJUSTED CORDON COUNTS	436
H	CAPACITY	442
I	PER CENTS OF PASSENGERS, BY CORDON STATION AND INTERVAL	452
J	EXCESS PASSENGERS AND SPACE	454
K	THE MAJOR INDUSTRY DIVISIONS	463
L	TABLE OF MODIFIABLE INDUSTRIES	502
M	INDUSTRY GROUPS AND THEIR SCHEDULE ALTERNATIVES	514

Appendixes

		Page
N	THE LATENESS ADJUSTMENT	543
O	SUBWAY RIDERS	558
P	THE ARRIVAL ADJUSTMENT	561
Q	THE TRAVEL TIME-CORDON INTERVAL ASSIGNMENT TABLES	573
R	COMPARISON OF ALTERNATIVE ADJUSTMENT FACTORS	587
S	THE RELATIONSHIP AND FORECASTING EQUATIONS DERIVATION, DIMENSION, DATA TABLES	590
T	THE DEGREES OF THE ARRIVAL ADJUSTMENTS	615
U	CBD CORDON COUNTS AT COMFORT LEVEL	620
V	EFFECTS OF SCHEDULE CHANGE ON THE INDUSTRY GROUPS	630
	ABOUT THE AUTHOR	647

LIST OF TABLES

Table   Page

1   Per Cents of Each Transit Mode's 24-Hour Total Entering the CBD During 7:00-10:00 A.M.   15

2   Per Cents of People Entering the CBD, by Mode, 7:00-10:00 A.M. on a Typical Business Day   17

3   The Peak Intervals of Each Cordon Station, Entering the CBD   39

4   October Cordon Counts, by Borough Origin and Total, Entering the CBD Between 6:20 and 10:00 A.M., 1959-63   43

5   October Cordon Counts, by Borough Destination and Total, Leaving the CBD Between 3:20 and 7:00 P.M., 1959-63   43

6   Capacities of Principal Types of Subway Cars   67

7   Excess Passengers Entering the CBD, by Cordon Station and Interval, October, 1962   74

8   Excess Passengers Leaving the CBD, by Cordon Station and Interval, October, 1962   75

9   Excess Space (Equivalent to Passengers) Entering the CBD, by Cordon Station and Interval, October, 1962   77

Table   Page

10   Excess Space (Equivalent to Passengers)
      Leaving the CBD, by Cordon Station
      and Interval, October, 1962   78

11   Net Excess of Passengers Entering the
      CBD, by Cordon Station   80

12   Equivalent Net Excess Passengers
      (Before Final Correction)   87

13   Required Reductions in Total CBD Cordon
      Counts, by Interval, Preliminary and
      Corrected   88

14   Number of Firms and Employees in
      Manhattan's Central Business District,
      by Major Industrial Division,
      September, 1958   94

15   The September, 1958, Employment in
      Manhattan's Central Business District,
      by Major Industry Division, as
      Modified by the Staggered Working
      Hours Project   99

16   Selected Scheduled Starting-Stopping
      Times of Work, Regular Weekdays:
      Estimated Numbers of Employees of
      Manhattan's Central Business District   110

17   Selected Scheduled Starting-Stopping
      Times of Work, Regular Weekdays:
      Estimated Per Cents of Employees of
      Manhattan's Central Business District   111

18   Per Cents of People of the CBD and
      Major Industry Divisions Scheduled
      to Start and Stop Work During Peak
      Periods   121

xii

Table   Page

19   Per Cents of CBD Employees Starting
      and Stopping Work During Rush Hours,
      by Major Industry Divisions   124

20   Covered Employment in Manhattan During
      the Month of September, 1958 to 1964   128

21   Per Cent of Employment in Selected
      Major Industries in Manhattan,
      September, 1958 and 1964   130

22   Numbers of People in the Wholesale
      Trades Starting and Stopping Work
      at Various Times   155

23   Number of People in the Wholesale
      Trades Starting and Stopping Work
      at Various Times Under an 8:30
      Start Time   156

24   Summary of Functional Capabilities of
      Schedule Change   173

25   The Nonmodifiable Industries   174

26   Special Industries   176

27   Total and Modifiable Employment in
      CBD Industries   179

28   Alternative Schedules of Industry
      Groups by Preference   183

29   Per Cents of Sample Preferring Changed
      Starting Times, by Minutes of Change   190

30   Per Cents of Sample, by Present Start
      Times, Who Prefer Other Start Times   193

31   Willingness to Start Earlier or Later:
      Per Cents of Sample by Minutes of
      Change   195

Table   Page

32   Per Cents of Sample, by Present Start
      Times, Willing to Start Various
      Amounts Earlier and Later   198

33   Per Cents of Men and Women Willing to
      Start Earlier and Later   199

34   Per Cents of Occupational Groups
      Willing to Start Earlier and Later   200

35   Per Cents of Sample, by Type of
      Establishment and Industrial
      Subdivision, Willing to Start
      Earlier and Later   201

36   Tolerance to Earlier and Later Starts:
      Per Cents of Sample by Minutes of
      Change   203

37   Tolerance to Earlier and Later Starts:
      Per Cents of Each Present Start Time   204

38   Tolerance to Earlier and Later Starts:
      Per Cents of Men and Women   205

39   Tolerance to Earlier and Later Starts:
      Per Cents of Occupations   206

40   Tolerance to Earlier and Later Starts:
      Per Cents by Type of Establishment
      and Industrial Subdivision   207

41   Summary: Per Cents of Preference,
      Willingness, and Tolerance, by
      Earlier and Later Starts   209

42   Opposition to Schedule Change
      (Nontolerance)   212

43   Anticipated Nontolerance of Schedule
      Change and Quits   217

Table		Page
44	Per Cents by Residence Borough Willing to Start Earlier and Later	224
45	Per Cents by Residence Borough Tolerant of Earlier and Later Starts	225
46	Present and Preferred Start Times, by Per Cents of Occupation	234
47	Present and Preferred Start Times, by Type of Establishment	235
48	Present and Preferred Start Times, by Office Type Industries	236
49	Personnel Constraints on Schedule Modifiability--Per Cent of Each Present Start Time Who Will Tolerate Each Alternative Start Time	242
50	Effects of an 8:30 Start Time on Schedules of the Wholesale Trades-- Functional Capability Adjusted by Personnel Constraints	243
51	Office Absentee Rates, Annual Daily Averages, 1958-62	256
52	The Reconstructed Cordon Count	276
53	The Comfort Level of the Total CBD During Selected A.M. Intervals, Entering the CBD	305
54	The Present and Optimum Work Schedules of the CBD	308
55	Computed Cordon Counts Produced by Optimum Work Schedules	310

Table		Page
56	Deviations from Standards of Four Congested Intervals, by Congested Cordon Counts, Produced by Optimum Work Schedules	312
57	The Constant Schedules, by Industry Group	321
58	The Net Changes in the Numbers of People in the Constant Schedule Groups at Each Start and Stop Time	322
59	The Varying Schedules, by Industry Group	324
60	The Net Numbers of People of the Variable Schedule Groups, by Each Combination, Changing at Each Start and Stop Time	327
61	The Five Feasible Schedule Combinations	328
62	The Net Changes in Numbers of People of All Groups, by Each Combination, at Each Start and Stop Time	329
63	The CBD Work Schedules Produced by the Five Feasible Combinations	330
64	The Forecasted Cordon Counts Resulting from the Five Combinations, by Each Degree of Travel Practice	332
65	The Deviations of the Five Feasible Combinations from Cordon Count Standards, by Degree	333
66	The Numbers and Per Cents of People Whose Schedules Are Changed Under Each of the Five Combinations, by Minutes of Change	344
67	Per Cent of Reduction in Congestion in Four Intervals, by Each Schedule Combination and by Degree of Change in Travel Timing	372

xvi

LIST OF FIGURES

Figure   Page

1   Entrances to the Central Business
       District (CBD)   14

2   Number of Passengers Entering the CBD
       During Each 20-Minute Interval from
       2:00 A.M. to Noon, as Reported in
       the October, 1962, Cordon Count   37

3   Number of Passengers Leaving the CBD
       During Each 20-Minute Interval from
       1:00 to 9:00 P.M., as Reported in
       the October, 1962, Cordon Count   40

4   Number of Passengers Entering the CBD
       Between 6:20 and 10:00 A.M., as
       Reported in the October Cordon
       Counts, 1959-63   44

5   Number of Passengers Leaving the CBD
       Between 3:20 and 7:00 P.M., as
       Reported in the October Cordon
       Counts, 1959-63   45

6   October Turnstile Registrations,
       24 Hours, 6:00-10:00 A.M., and
       3:00-7:00 P.M., 1952-63   48

7   Monthly Averages of Turnstile
       Registrations, 1959-63   50

8   Per Cents of Total Employment, by
       Census Tract   103

9   Comparative Location of Employment,
       by Industry Division   117

Figure   Page

10   Covered Employment in Manhattan During
        September, 1958-64   129

11   Cordon Count Entering the CBD and
        Number of People Starting Work   249

12   Participants in the Relationship   252

13   Cordon Station-to-Work Activities   253

14   Number of People Who Work in the CBD,
        by Scheduled Start Time and by
        Present-at-Work and Actual Start
        Time   261

15   Number of People Who Work in the CBD,
        by Scheduled Start Time, by Present-
        at-Work and Actual Start Time, and
        by Subway Cordons Crossings   264

16   Number of People Who Work in the CBD,
        by Scheduled Start Time, by Present-
        at-Work and Actual Start Time, by
        Subway Cordons Crossings, and by
        Arrival Time   265

17   Actual and Computed Cordon Counts   273

18   Capacity and Cordon Count   287

19   Capacity, Cordon Count, and Absolute
        Demand   289

20   Number of People Scheduled to Stop
        Work from 3:30 to 6:00 P.M. at
        Present and According to the Maximum
        and Minimum of the Five Feasible
        Combinations   346

21   Number of People Scheduled to Start
        Work Between 7:30 and 9:30 A.M.
        and to Stop Work Between 3:30 and
        6:00 P.M., According to the First
        Feasible Combination   348

Figure   Page

22   Location of Factory Employment   468

23   Location of Employment of the
      Transportation, Communications,
      and Public Utilities Division   472

24   Location of Employment of the
      Wholesale Trades   478

25   Location of Employment of the
      Retail Trades   482

26   Location of Employment in the
      Finance, Insurance, and Real
      Estate Division   486

27   Location of Employment in the
      Services Division   492

28   Location of Employment in Governments   499

xix

Work Staggering for Traffic Relief

CHAPTER **1** AN INTRODUCTION
TO WORK
STAGGERING

Large cities throughout the world suffer from
rush hour traffic congestion. The congestion occurs
in all kinds of transportation facilities--subways,
buses, railroads, highways, streets--conveying people
to and from their centers of employment. It also occurs in other facilities which service the people who
work in the centers: restaurants, shops, and the
like. A possible cause of rush hour congestion may
be found in work schedules--the times people are required to start and stop work.

The work schedules of an area are deeply imbedded in its industry and culture. Places of employment fix their work schedule at times which enable
them to maintain contact with suppliers, services,
customers, and the local labor market. The schedules
of an area thus form an intricate and delicate net-
work in an economic complex which may extend over the
entire world. The people who work in the area become
habituated to the prevailing pattern of starting and
stopping times. They and their families--as well as
the social, cultural, entertainment, educational, and
political institutions--organize their days around
prevailing work schedules. Work schedules locate
places of employment in time, just as the physical
facilities situate them in space.

The notion of work staggering attacks the problem of rush hour congestion by modifying work schedules, the source of people's travel times. If work
schedules can be suitably rearranged, the flow of
people to and from work will be distributed more
evenly. Thereby, the height of the traffic peaks,

1

both morning and afternoon, may be reduced. Hopefully, the amount of schedule change need not be
very great. Its maximum extent might even be limited
to the range of schedules actually prevailing in the
area.

The simplicity of the notion vanishes almost immediately when examined more closely. Work stag-
gering--even a minimal amount--can produce profound
economic changes because industries have intricate
relationships within an area and with the outside
world. It requires changes in people's daily habits
of life and, as a consequence, in the timing of all
kinds of community activities--potentially a profound
social change. The feasibility of work staggering is
sharply constrained by the fixed--essentially im-
mutable--conditions of an area, such as the location
of its places of employment, residential areas, and
its existing systems of passenger transportation:
roads, streets, subway lines and stations, and the
like. These are some of the many direct factors which
complicate the otherwise simple and obvious notion of
work staggering.

One step removed from these direct and instrumental factors are still other complicating ones. It
is virtually certain that any change in community
practice as deeply rooted as work schedules cannot
possibly satisfy or benefit everyone. There are bound
to be segments of industry and population--both within
the affected area and outside--which are disadvantaged
by such changes. The extent of the disadvantage will
range from trifling inconvenience at having to adjust
to change, to possibly severe economic or social dislocation. The best that can reasonably be hoped for
in work staggering is an "on balance" advantage to
the community as a whole, with minimal damage.

Finally, the relief of transit congestion through
work staggering may be feasible on all counts, yet may
not be the soundest solution to the rush hour problem
of a particular area. There may be other solutions
which will prove more acceptable on various grounds
to the community. The discovery that work staggering

is feasible raises an issue of public policy. It
does not settle the issue.

These are some of the complexities of work staggering. They suffice to show that work staggering is
not a general nostrum for rush hour traffic. Its
feasibility depends upon--and must be wrought from--
a city's own unique circumstances. This study will
show how the feasibility of work staggering was
tested for Manhattan's central business district.
The method--but not the results--ought to be applicable to other places.

Work staggering will be shown to be a feasible
way of relieving rush hour transit congestion to and
from Manhattan's Central Business District (CBD).
There are, in fact, several possible ways of changing
work schedules in the CBD which will have the desired effects on transit traffic. This conclusion
emerges clearly from the investigations reported in
the ensuing chapters. It simplifies, perhaps excessively, an exceedingly complex set of findings.
To present them adequately--to expose them to a critical review by the community and to minimize the risks
of misunderstanding--it is necessary to describe the
structure of fact and analysis upon which the result
is based.

This chapter will formulate the problem of feasibility, the method by which it may be solved, and the
kinds of information which are required to solve it.
The second chapter will establish the measures and
criteria of congestion in the subway system. Chapter 3 will present the work schedules of the CBD.
The modifiability of schedules by CBD industry will
be set forth in Chapter 4. This will be followed in
Chapter 5 by an exposition of the acceptability of
schedule change on the part of the people who work in
the CBD. Chapter 6 develops the method by which
changes in work schedule will be converted into their
effects on subway traffic. This method is put to use
and its results are given in Chapter 7. The final
chapter of the study evaluates the feasibility of
staggering work hours in the CBD.

THE DESIGN OF THE STUDY

This study presents the report of an inquiry into the question: Is work staggering in Manhattan's Central Business District (CBD) a feasible way of relieving transit congestion during the morning and afternoon rush hours? The goal of the inquiry was to answer the question as objectively as possible, not to "prove" one side of the question or the other. The inquiry also imposed one additional burden upon itself in the event work staggering appeared feasible: to produce, as part of the proof, a feasible program for the CBD.

The idea that work staggering might relieve rush hour congestion is fairly old and very enticing. Organized efforts to stagger hours were made in cities both in the United States and abroad as early as the 1920's, and possibly even during World War I. It is likely that the idea itself was proposed even earlier, when mass transit began to be installed to carry working populations into the industrial and business centers of large cities. As rush hour congestion grew under the pressure of continuously expanding employment--given the fixed facilities of mass transit--work staggering emerged as an obvious way of sparing the cities the heavy additional capital cost of enlarging their transit systems.

There were at least two serious earlier efforts to stagger working hours in Manhattan's CBD. At the end of 1926, Dr. Louis I. Harris, then Commissioner of the Department of Health, established a Committee on the Staggering of Traffic. In letters to people named to the Committee, Dr. Harris explained his initiative. "The reason for this anxiety on the part of the Health Department is to prevent the transmission of respiratory infections which are so common where overcrowding exists." The Metropolitan Life Insurance Company undertook an extensive survey of work hours which covered 800,000 people employed south of 72nd Street and its statistician, Mr. Louis I. Dublin, developed fairly detailed proposals for work staggering by CBD industries. The outcome of

this effort is not disclosed by the available records.

The Commerce and Industry Association of New
York, Inc., took the next initiative toward work
staggering in 1948. With the cooperation of the
Board of Transportation and the Department of Commerce of New York City, it made a survey of work
hours and of attitudes of CBD firms to work staggering. It produced a report on August 16, 1948, with
findings about hours and attitudes. There seems to
have been no further effort to implement work staggering after the report was issued.

Apart from these two undertakings, there is
evidence that the city government maintained a fairly
continuous interest in the possibilities of work
staggering. Succeeding administrations are reported
to have talked privately and informally with large
CBD employers with the view of pursuading them to
introduce staggering for their own staffs. The government itself staggered its own agencies' hours from
time to time. Available records indicate that there
was considerable staff interest in work staggering
during 1956. By 1958, the subject had engaged the
close attention of the City Administrator, whose
active interest culminated in the present study.

Work staggering aroused considerable interest
during World War II. The Transportation and Communication Department of the United States Department
of Commerce published two small pamphlets on staggering. One was Staggered Hours, dated November,
1941; the other Staggered Hours--Supplementary Report, dated February, 1942. There are reports that
actual work staggering plans were introduced into a
number of cities, including Providence, Rhode Island;
Buffalo, New York; Atlanta, Georgia; Los Angeles and
San Francisco, California. Efforts to obtain information from these cities, however, proved unrewarding.
The most notable experience occurred in Washington,
D.C., which instituted a program during the war, and
again in the early 1960's.

A number of European cities have reported upon
their efforts to stagger hours. London, England,
dates its first formal interest as early as 1920.
Its principal activity however was launched in 1956,
with the formation of the Committee for Staggering
of Working Hours in Central London. In France, a
national committee was established by the then Min-
ister of Transport and Public Works, M. Buron. It
is called "Le Comité National Pour L'Etude et La
Promotion d'un Aménagement des Horaires de Travail"
(CNAT). The committee produced a general plan for
work staggering by French cities. There are also
reports of programs in Paris, Metz, and Strasbourg.
Information has also been received that work staggering was introduced in the city of Moscow, but published reports are not at hand. A preliminary report on the London program notes initial progress
toward staggering work hours. Other than this, the
results in the European cities are not part of the
public record.

This history contains some valuable experience
for work staggering which later undertakings must
carefully consider. Perhaps its most persistent theme
is the absence of a record of results. Except for
Washington, and to a lesser extent London, the prior
efforts in New York and elsewhere are resoundingly
silent about their achievements. From this alone, the
present study has drawn a fundamental lesson. The
feasibility of work staggering depends not only upon
its ability to relieve congestion--presumably all the
earlier efforts could do this--but also equally upon
its suitability--to all who are affected, directly
or indirectly--as a program of schedule change.
This aspect of staggering receives minimal attention
in the available reports, and yet it is probably the
principal reason that most programs were not effectively implemented, the promised traffic improvements
notwithstanding.

The present study contrasts with the earlier

efforts in several salient characteristics.* It is
a feasibility study, not a combination study and action program. As such, it is concerned solely with
investigating the feasibility of work staggering as
a preliminary step to consultation with the community,
reaching a policy decision and implementation. It is
thus a very large expansion of one part of the undertakings mentioned above. Different from the others,
this one is a research study, utilizing the techniques of various disciplines concerned with the
phenomena involved in staggering. It is, by contrast,
not a survey of opinions about the feasibility of
staggering, nor the results of deliberations of experts or knowledgeable people about the conditions
and problems of the CBD, nor the product of negotia-
tions or persuasion among parties of interest to
staggering and schedule change. All of these may
follow the issuance of the present study. They did
not contribute to its preparation. It is thus independent of employers, employees, organizations, government, and other responsible agencies in its design, execution, and results.

As the subject of a research inquiry, work staggering poses a problem: How is its feasibility to be
determined? This problem of method arose at the outset of the present study, and it continued vital and
pressing until the work was brought to a conclusion.
It involves, among many other things, the definition
of the problem of inquiry, a theory of work staggering and criteria of feasibility, and the researches
and investigations to produce the required information. It will prove helpful to introduce the study
by presenting these elements of the design of inquiry.
Not only will they furnish a guide to the rest of the
report; they will present the first of the assumptions
and constraints which shape the inquiry and its ultimate results.

---

*The literature on work staggering is sparse.
Although it appeared after this study was completed,
mention must be made of the article by Mathew J. Betz
and Jankie N. Supersad, "Traffic and Staggered Working
Hours," Traffic Quarterly (April, 1965).

THE PROBLEM OF INQUIRY

The question which the study undertakes to answer was stated at the beginning of this section: Is
work staggering in Manhattan's CBD a feasible way of
relieving transit congestion during the morning and
afternoon rush hours? This is the problem which the
inquiry is designed to solve. It contains a number
of terms which have to be clarified, if for no other
reason than that they can be defined in various ways.
The inquiry adopted its own definitions and thereafter proceeded to use them. Hence, it is crucially
important--if the study and its results are to be
understood--that its definition of the question be
made explicit.

Three of the terms will be defined here. They
are: work staggering, Manhattan's CBD, and transit.
In the section to follow, the meaning of feasible
will be established. It constitutes the theory of
work staggering. The remaining terms--relief, congestion, and rush hours--will be defined in Chapter
2, when the transit data are presented.

Work Staggering

Work staggering is an arrangement of work schedules which has one distinctive characteristic. The
people who work in a given place--a firm, a neighborhood, a larger area--start and stop work at different
times (but within a relatively small interval) instead
of all at the same time. Work staggering may take
place within a single establishment or among establishments. If within an establishment--often called
internal staggering--employees of a single firm are
scheduled at different times. Many firms practice
internal staggering as a way of handling congestion
in elevators and other entering and leaving facilities. Staggering also occurs within a geographic
area, among the firms and establishments located
there. This is called external staggering and it reflects the different starting and stopping times of
the individual places of employment. Both kinds of
staggering, internal and external, may obviously occur in any given area.

This is the way the present study defines work
staggering. It accords with the definition used in
other studies and in the literature upon the concept
of work staggering, particularly as it applies to
the researches and to the ultimate formulation of
possible programs. These constraints and the reasons
for imposing them must be made explicit.

First and foremost, a program of work staggering,
as projected by this study, must be wholly voluntary.
Any program which may be discovered as feasible will
imply, as a necessary condition, that the industries
and the people who work in them adopt the proposed
schedules by their independent decisions, without
coercion by any outside agency, especially not by
government. This does not mean that every individual
will be free to accept or reject a feasible work
schedule. This is not the case now, nor does it have
to be contemplated as part of the study of feasibility. (The notion of voluntary staggering means that
the various entities of the CBD which make decisions
about schedules will also exercise their prerogatives
in respect to any work staggering proposal, and that
the proposal will not be imposed by decree--even if
that were possible--upon any such decision making
bodies.

SWHP
most
be:

This stricture of a voluntary program is in one
sense simply a recognition of social reality. There
simply is no way by which work staggering could be
forcefully imposed upon the community. But in another
sense it sets the tone and a viewpoint which will per-
vade the studies of schedule modifiability to be reported in Chapters 4 and 5. Modifiability of schedules, whether by firms or individuals, will always
imply voluntary acceptance by those empowered to
make the responsible decisions.

A second constraining factor evolves out of the
first one. If work staggering is to be voluntary, it
has to minimize the amount of dislocation and adjustment which will be required of industry and the community. This means that the number of people whose
schedules would have to be changed should be kept to
a minimum; and for them, the amount of change must
also be as little as possible.

This constraint was made salient by a suggestion received very early in the study. It recommended that consideration be given to the possibility of large-scale modifications in work schedules with their consequences for changed patterns of daily living. The suggestion was based on the observation that the daylight work day causes a great deal of economic and social waste to contemporary society. It restricts the use of all facilities--productive as well as consumer--to limited portions of the 24-hour cycle. It compels most people to be indoors during the healthier portions of the day and to take their leisure at night. It prevents people from engaging in leisure time activities which would benefit by daylight, including artistic, educational, and athletic pursuits. Much of this restraint made sense in earlier epochs, but under contemporary technological conditions, most work can be performed at night as well as during the day.

It might be tempting to broaden the scope of the problem to encompass such vast possibilities as reorganizing contemporary living. But the temptation must be rejected, and for obvious reasons. The objectives of work staggering and of such a radical rescheduling of life are very different and would raise altogether different kinds of problems for research and analysis. Within the terms of reference of staggered working hours, the extent of change must be minimized on principle.

The third constraint adopted by this study pertains to the final form of work staggering. It may be summarized by a slogan: pattern not patchwork. To be feasible, a plan of work staggering must propose a scheduling system for the CBD whose simplicity and clarity will make it immediately comprehensible to the community. The model for this concept is the traditional stereotype of the bankers' hours, or of the 9:00 to 5:00 office schedule. A plan which consists of many detailed and individual schedules without an obvious design--a patchwork, not a pattern--will prove exceedingly difficult to implement and should be accepted with the greatest of hesitation, if at all. This constraint is much more than a particular

taste for order and regularity in results. It comes
from a view of work staggering as a pervasive change
in the working and personal lives of the community
and which must therefore make sense on the face.

As a direct consequence of this point of view,
a decision was made early in the study to forego any
attempt at internal staggering. Not only is this too
minute a matter to handle by such a study, it is
something which can best be left to the discretion of
the individual enterprise. Provision will be made
within the over-all conception of schedule change to
allow for internal staggering. This will be explained
in Chapter 4.

These three constraints delimit this study and
its ultimate conclusions in ways which will emerge
as the account proceeds. Without question they dis-
pose of possible staggering plans a priori, and without further consideration. But the belief is strongly
held, that they improve the quality of the final product.

The CBD

The place this study situates work staggering--
both the research and the ultimate proposals--is designated as Manhattan's Central Business District. It
is defined here as the total area between the East
and Hudson Rivers and between the Battery and a northern boundary at approximately 63rd Street.* It covers

_____

*The boundaries of the CBD--which are also in-
cluded in it--are as follows: the south side of 63rd
Street from the East River to York Avenue; the west
side of York Avenue from 63rd to 64th Street; the
south side of 64th Street from York to Third Avenue;
the east side of Third Avenue from 64th to 63rd
Street; the south side of 63rd Street from Third to
Fifth Avenue; the east side of Fifth Avenue from 63rd
to 59th Street; the south side of 59th Street from
Fifth to Eighth Avenue; the west side of Central Park
West from 59th to 62nd Street; the south side of 62nd

about 9-1/3 square miles. This is the New York City
Department of City Planning's definition of the CBD.

The reasons for choosing the CBD as a place for
work staggering are self-evident. It is an area of
maximum density of employment, and it is the hub of
public transit systems. It is thus the center of
transit congestion originating in work schedules.
Accordingly, bounded on three sides by natural bar-
riers and on the fourth by a perceptible change in
land use, it is a clearly demarcated area within
which to locate a work staggering program.

Some question may be raised about the appropriateness of these boundaries, especially for the study
of work staggering. The United States Bureau of the
Census defines a somewhat smaller CBD, eliminating
(approximately) the areas east of Third Avenue and
west (partly) of Eighth and (partly) of Tenth Avenues
lying below Canal Street. Its statistics apply to
its definition of the CBD. The larger area was used
by this study because it is more appropriate from
the viewpoint of destination and because there are
essential transit and employment statistics available
for it.

A more serious issue arises in respect to the
downtown Brooklyn section, the area lying directly
across from lower Manhattan. It is also a dense
employment area, and from the viewpoint of transit,
it is a peak destination area connected to and continuous with lower Manhattan. It was excluded from
the study, however, for several reasons. It would have
added seriously to the complexity of the problem,
both by increasing the intricacy of the required
computational procedures and by the demands for additional data. From the viewpoint of staggering, the

_____

Street from Central Park West to Amsterdam Avenue;
the west side of Amsterdam Avenue from 62nd to 66th
Street; the south side of 66th Street from Amsterdam
Avenue to the Hudson River.

East River introduces a valuable time lag which, if coupled with schedule change in Manhattan, can function as a built-in staggering device. Finally, in the actual computations of work staggering, significant account is taken of the Brooklyn area as a transit destination, as will be explained fully in Chapter 2.

For a study involving transit, a destination area as large as the CBD's 9 1/3 square miles must sometimes be broken up into smaller subdivisions. Several ways of subdividing the CBD are available. For example there are traditional neighborhoods, such as the Grand Central area, the financial district, the civic center, Chelsea, Penn Station, Murray Hill, and the others. These would be very useful for the present study but for one deficiency. They do not correspond to the geographic bases of available statistics. This practical criterion dictates the use of census tracts as subdivisions of the CBD. These are formulated by the Bureau of the Census of the United States Department of Commerce. Figure 8 presents a map of the CBD, subdivided according to census tracts. Statistics of industry and employment are available on a census tract basis. Whenever areas smaller than the total CBD are needed, the census tracts serve as the units.

Transit

Many different modes of transit are used to enter and leave the CBD. They include: automobiles and taxis, buses (local and interurban), trucks, the subways, PATH tubes (formerly the H & M), railroads, and ferries. Figure 1 shows all the entrances to the CBD by transit modes. The streets, highways, bridges, and tunnels carry vehicular traffic--cars, buses, taxis, and trucks. The modes with rights of way-- railroads, subways, and tubes--are specifically named on the Figure, as are the ferry routes.

All of the modes experience congestion during the rush hours. They differ, however, in the relative size of their peak loads. Table 1 presents each

FIGURE I
ENTRANCES TO THE CENTRAL BUSINESS DISTRICT (CBD)

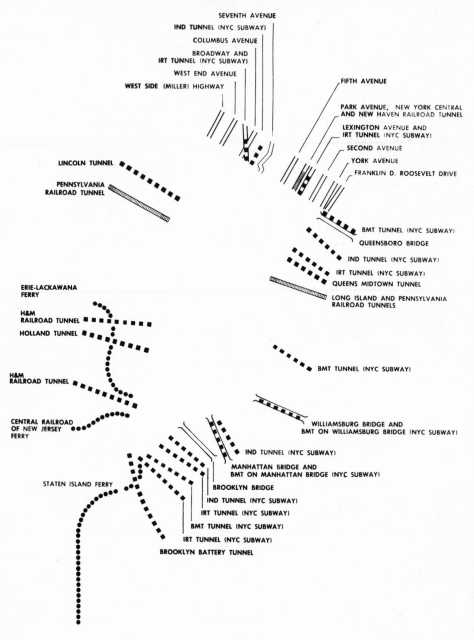

mode's percentage of people entering the CBD during
7:00-10:00 a.m. (as a per cent of its 24-hour total).
The percentages are indicative of peak load characteristics, not of congestion as such.   The higher the
per cent, the greater the concentration during the
three hours; the lower, the greater the dispersion
of traffic over the twenty-four hours.   Thus, the
railroads and ferries are characteristically rush
hour systems; they carry, respectively, 70 per cent
and 69 per cent of their total daily incoming passengers during the rush hours.   The subways and tubes
follow closely with 59 per cent.   The buses bring in
42 per cent of their daily totals during this period.
Autos, taxis and trucks have the least acute peak,
carrying only 24 per cent of their 24-hour totals
during the three rush hours.   The various modes have
peak load problems in that they are heavily utilized
during the 7:00-10:00 a.m. period, and underutilized
to varying degrees during the rest of the twenty-four
hours.   Even without further statistics, there is
enough evidence to indicate that they experience congestion, perhaps also to varying degrees, during the
rush period.

TABLE 1

Per Cents of Each Transit Mode's 24-Hour Total
Entering the CBD During 7:00-10:00 A.M.

Mode	Per Cent
Auto and taxi	24
Bus	42
Truck	24
Rapid transit[*]	59
Railroad	70
Ferry	69

[*] Includes subways and tubes.

Source: Hub-Bound Travel, Regional Plan Association,
December, 1961.

In determining the effects of work staggering upon congestion, this study will confine its numerical analysis to the subway system. All inquiries about measures and standards of traffic, of travel practices by the people who work in the CBD, and of other relevant transit factors will concern only the subway system. The computational model for converting work schedules into transit traffic and the computations which it produces will pertain only to the subways. Despite the occurrence of congestion on the other modes, they will not be subjected to the same kind of detailed quantitative analysis.

This course is justified by several considerations. First, the subways carry by far the greatest proportion of rush hour passengers. The passenger loads of the various modes are shown on Table 2. The subways and tubes together have 70 per cent of the total number of people entering the CBD during 7:00 to 10:00 a.m. The next closest are autos and taxis, with but 13 per cent or less than one fifth of the rapid transit share. Railroads carry only 9 per cent, buses 6 per cent, ferries 2 per cent, and trucks 1 per cent. These are the percentages of total incoming passengers, not the total who work in the CBD. Of the people who work in--but do not live in--the CBD, almost three fourths enter by subway alone (not including the tubes), according to the results of this study. Hence, by concentrating on the subways alone, most of the congestion is actually covered by the analysis.

Second, the analysis was confined to the subways in order to reduce the study to workable proportions. The importance of simplifying and reducing the size of the work will become apparent as the ensuing analysis of the subways are presented. To have included the other modes would have required far more research--the essential data do not exist for many of them--and would have necessitated exceedingly complicated computational procedures. The decision to limit the analysis to the subways was practically unavoidable.

TABLE 2

Per Cents of People Entering the CBD, by Mode,
7:00-10:00 A.M. on a Typical Business Day

Mode	Per Cent
Auto and taxi	13
Bus	6
Truck	1
Rapid transit*	70
Railroad	9
Ferry	2

*
Includes subways and tubes.

Source: Hub-Bound Travel, Regional Plan Association,
December, 1961.

        Second, the analysis was confined to the subways
in order to reduce the study to workable proportions.
The importance of simplifying and reducing the size
of the work will become apparent as the ensuing analysis of the subways are presented. To have included
the other modes would have required far more research--
the essential data do not exist for many of them--and
would have necessitated exceedingly complicated computational procedures. The decision to limit the analysis to the subways was practically unavoidable.

        But in taking this decision, an important assump-
tion is made by the study and it must be stated explicitly at the outset. It is that the effects of
work staggering upon the subways will correspond to
the effects on the other modes of transit, insofar
as they are disclosed by the computations. This assumption will be explored more fully in the final
chapter, when the conclusions of the study are presented.

Third, although the other modes are not subjected to any quantitative analyses, they are not neglected by the study. In various places, the passengers
of other modes are also given attention. And in the
final chapter, after the assumption of similarity is
explored, conclusions are reached with respect to the
other modes.

A THEORY OF FEASIBILITY

The main terms of the problem have now been laid
down. Work staggering has been defined as a planned
rearrangement of schedules by the places of employment of the CBD. Three general constraints were imposed upon any forthcoming program: voluntary acceptance, minimization of the extent of schedule
change, and a schedule pattern, not a patchwork.
Within the framework of these terms, what conditions
must a program of work staggering satisfy to be
judged feasible? What are the criteria of feasibility
and how can they be applied?

The feasibility of work staggering has to be
determined by a means other than directly trying out
a program. Experimentation is not possible on account of the numbers of people and the amount of
money and effort which would be required to carry it
out--if an experiment could actually be designed.
The only trial which can reasonably be anticipated
will take place after an affirmative answer is reached
that work staggering is feasible. Such a trial will
be the implementation of a massive community policy,
in many respects an irreversible one.

The only way to determine whether work staggering
is feasible is by means of a theory which can be
tested by the use of evidence and logical reasoning.
A theory, formulated on the basis of knowledge of work
staggering and of the universe in which it is to be
applied, will now be presented. It consists of five
statements, each of which deals with one of the crucial aspects of the subject. Each statement specifies the terms and conditions of feasibility and the

ways they are to be examined and evaluated. The
theory is capable of being tested empirically. The
five statements and their explanations now follow.

1. A sufficient number of places of employment
must be able to modify their work schedules.

The fundamental premise of work staggering is that
peak hour transit congestion can be relieved by suitable changes in work schedules. Actually, congestion
is "caused" by insufficient transit facilities in relation to demand, and it can be relieved in many ways--
by increasing the facilities or reducing the demand.
Work staggering, if feasible, may possess the advantage of reducing the demand for the facilities ef-
ficiently and with lower cost to the working people
and the community than other means. To bring it
about, work schedules have to be changed.

Work schedules belong to places of employment.
They are an arrangement between the employer and employees with respect to starting and stopping times.
A place of employment is presumed to be autonomous
in deciding its work schedule, but its decision will
certainly be influenced, if not actually determined
by forces and entities outside its formal decision
making processes. Whatever the source of its decision, the place of employment is the organizational
unit to which work schedules apply.

For work staggering to occur, the places of
employment must be able to modify their schedules.
The word "sufficient" in the statement implies
all the other characteristics which are essential
to modifiability. It includes the numbers of
people, their present schedules, their possible
alternative schedules, the locations of their
employment and residence, and other factors which,
when suitably combined, will produce the required modification in the flow of people to and
from the transit systems. There are specific requirements with respect to each of these characteristics,
but they cannot be stated in advance. They will depend upon the circumstances of the entire area which

emerge only as a result of a detailed quantitative
analysis.

The first statement focuses upon work schedules
as the instrumental factor in staggering and upon
their source, the places of employment. Unless the
places of employment can change their schedules sufficiently, there can be no work staggering.

2. <u>A sufficient number of people must accept</u>
<u>the required modifications in their work schedules</u>.

This statement refers to the people who work
in the area and whose schedules would be modified.
It includes owners, executives, professional, clerical, and manual employees--all, in fact, who are part
of the flow of traffic. Of this aggregate, a sufficient number must accept the required changes in
schedule.

The notion of sufficiency in this statement contains two intentions. First it refers to people in
whatever decision making capacities they have in
respect to their places of employment--as employers
or executives, or as union members who have access
to schedule decisions. A sufficient number of such
decision makers must accept schedule change for themselves and for their places of employment. Second,
it refers to a general level of acceptability of
schedule change on the part of the people who work
in the area. If establishments employing a sufficient
number of people are able to modify their schedules,
not all of their employees will be able to accept the
change. If adjustments have to be made by people
transferring away from jobs whose schedules have been
changed, the working population must contain a sufficient number of other people to whom the new schedules will prove acceptable. Work staggering must en-
visage such adaptations of people to schedules, and
hence the level of acceptability in the population as
a whole must be high enough to allow for the required
exchange of people.

3. <u>There must be at least one rearrangement of</u>
<u>schedules which will relieve the rush hour traffic</u>
<u>congestion</u>.

One term in this statement will be left unde-
fined--"relieve rush hour traffic congestion." Its
definition is crucial but it will have to wait until
Chapter 2. For present purposes it may be taken to
mean reducing the peak loads, leaving the specification of the upper limit of such loads to later decisions.

Feasibility requires that the change in schedules bring about the relief of transit congestion
during the rush hours. The statement envisages certain possibilities which will not satisfy this requirement. There may be various possible rearrangements of
schedules which will not relieve transit congestion.
This can occur because the schedule changes are insufficient in number or time, or because they are
distributed unsatisfactorily over the area. It is
also possible that the passenger carriers may be unable to accommodate the modified flow of traffic,
either financially or for other operating reasons.
Accordingly, it is essential to specify transit relief as a requirement which must be met if work staggering is to be judged feasible.

It goes without saying that the reduction of the
present traffic peaks must not be accomplished by
creating new ones earlier or later than those now
existing.

4. <u>A plan to stagger working hours must not</u>
<u>create an opposition capable of preventing its imple-</u>
<u>mentation</u>.

This fourth statement draws attention to the
places of employment, people, institutions, and other
aspects of life outside of those which are directly
involved in schedule change. A work staggering program is bound to produce effects outside the partici-
pating firms and employees. These effects must be
taken into account in assessing the feasibility of
any program.

There are two inescapable reasons for this concern. First there will be some firms, institutions,
or people who might be adversely affected by staggering and who occupy strategic economic, social, or
political positions in the community. They may be
capable of obstructing an otherwise tenable plan of
staggering. It would be of great practical value to
uncover, if possible, such potential sources of ob-
struction and opposition before a plan is implemented.

Second, the effects of work staggering may cause
disadvantages or costs to other firms, organizations,
places of employment, and people which may simply outweigh the gains which the program will produce. In
theory one can conceive of a balance which might be
constructed for the city or region and their component
entities, weighing all the favorable and unfavorable
effects produced by staggering. If it were possible
to compute this kind of balance, policy making could
then consider the appropriateness of a work staggering
plan on the basis of its net contribution to the
over-all welfare of the city and the region. Even a
little information on this subject would provide important material for public education, regardless of
the final conclusion of the study, for it would enable public officials to predict the effect of staggering on the various sectors of the community, and
on the community as a whole.

5. Work staggering, once instituted, must prove
durable.

The final statement considers transit traffic
after staggering has been introduced and after initial adjustments to it have been completed. Will the
relief of congestion be a momentary or short-lived
event, or will it last? If the relief of congestion
continues only for a short time, the program of staggering may be expected to arouse frustration and
disappointment among the people who have been asked to
shift their schedules. Thus before accepting the
feasibility of staggering there should be some assurance as to its durability.

Three possible factors may shorten the life of
traffic relief. The first would arise from changes

in some of the statistical magnitudes upon which
schedule feasibility would be calculated. These include particularly changes in employment, in the
relative use of the various systems of travel, and
in length of the working day. Changes in these factors could benefit or harm work staggering. They
might accelerate the relief of congestion or they
might worsen it, either alternative depending upon
the nature of the changes.

The second factor is that some firms may restore
their original schedules. In small amounts this might
not prove embarassing. Indeed, there is reason to
believe that small amounts might be offset by late
participation of other firms in the program after the
initial schedule change becomes apparent to them. If,
however, the move back acquires a momentum and many
firms restore their original schedules, the result
will be a return of the peak hour congestion.

The third factor would be the diversion of passengers to the old peak hours from sources other than
the firms which modified their schedules. When it becomes apparent that the peak loads have been reduced
and that the capacity of the transit systems are not
being fully utilized, it is possible that other traffic will tend to flow to the vacated hours, thereby
reinstating the congestion during the morning and
evening periods.

Conclusion

The five statements contain a comprehensive
theory and set of criteria by which to determine the
feasibility of work staggering. As a theory, the
statements describe the system in which work staggering is to be applied. Each statement identifies a
component of the system and shows how it contributes
to work staggering. These elements are: the places
of employment, the people who work in them, the
transit systems, the community and region, and time.

As criteria, the five statements establish conditions which work staggering must satisfy if it is
to be considered feasible. These conditions are:

modifiability of schedules, acceptability of schedule change, relief of congestion, tolerance toward
staggering, and durability. The criteria contained
in the statements are maximal; that is, they spell
out the most severe tests which work staggering must
meet to be considered feasible, and they imply that
every one of the conditions must be fully satisfied.
If any fails, then work staggering must be regarded
as not feasible.

A practical question is destined to arise in the
light of these maximal criteria. How far short of
meeting the maximum conditions may work staggering
actually fall and still be considered feasible? Some
aspects of the criteria will prove inapplicable to
work staggering in the CBD, largely because essential
data are lacking. At least one criterion can only be
partly satisfied. Some aspects of the criteria will
prove applicable after the results of the study are
made public, during a period of public review and
consultation. The choice will thus arise between
rejecting work staggering or finding it feasible
despite the lack of total compliance with the criteria. It ought not prove a difficult decision to
make--partly because reasonable judgments can be made
about the untested criteria, and partly because work
staggering may offer greater benefits than disadvantages even though a criterion cannot be fully satisfied. A judgment "on balance," may be clearly indicated. The evidence and reasoning will be fully
explored when the specific issue arises for decision.

DATA AND SOURCES

The theory of work staggering--as just set forth--
supplies the framework for the entire inquiry. It
furnishes a conceptual model of the universe in which
work staggering occurs, and from which a model may be
constructed by which to determine how changes in
schedule will affect the system, and how in turn the
system will affect a proposed plan of staggering.
It contains the criteria by which the feasibility of
any proposal may be evaluated. It also supplies the
specifications of data which are needed in order to

formulate and test work staggering programs. It is
thus an applicable theory--not necessarily the only
one--by which to pursue an answer to the question of
the inquiry.

It will become abundantly clear as the study
proceeds that a vast amount of information is required to put this theory to work. Ultimately, the
whole conception of the study rests upon numerical
computations which consume seemingly endless quantities of statistical data. In view of their importance, the principal data sources will be briefly
described. For convenience, they may be divided into two categories: the outside sources and the Staggered Working Hours Project.

The Outside Sources

Two major bodies of data were obtained from outside sources. They are: the statistics of subway
traffic furnished by the New York City Transit Authority, and the statistics of employment in the CBD made
available by the New York State Department of Labor
and the New York City Department of City Planning.
These data will be presented--and analyzed and eval-
uated--in Chapters 2 and 3, respectively.

The need for transit statistics arises out of
the third criterion of feasibility--the requirement
of relieving congestion. The statistics are used in
Chapter 2 to establish the present state of transit
traffic, and in Chapter 7 as a basis for estimating
the consequences of schedule change. They are also
used in Chapter 6 to develop computational models.

The statistics of employment are required for
applying three of the criteria: modifiability of
schedules, acceptability of change, and relief of
congestion. They furnish the quantitative weighting--
by numbers of people--to modifiable industries (Chapter 4), to acceptability (Chapter 5), and to the computations of transit traffic resulting from schedule
change (Chapter 7). They are also used elsewhere in
the study: in designing the researches and in developing computational models.

The Project's Researches

Four field studies were needed to provide the
rest of the information on which this inquiry is
built. They may be identified as: (1) the work
schedule survey, (2) the industry studies, (3) the
sociological study, and (4) the transit study. These
studies were organized on the basis of subject matter
and discipline, and not according to any of the criteria. They furnished the data both for applying the
criteria and for other problems which had to be
solved as part of the total inquiry.

The work schedule survey furnished the essential
information about prevailing work schedules in the
CBD. Work schedules are required in order to apply
the first and third criteria—modifiability of schedules and relief of congestion. They define existing
schedule conditions which are used in the study of
modifiability and in the computations of transit traffic. They provide the point of departure for establishing the changes brought about by possible modifications of schedule. The data are also utilized in
other places in the study, especially in developing
the computational models. A description of this survey is provided in Chapter 3.

The modifiability of work schedules was investigated by means of industry scheduling studies. Using
techniques drawn from economics and industrial engineering, studies were made of CBD industries to ascer-
tain the factors which govern their present scheduling, and whether or not their schedules could be
modified. Virtually every industry in the CBD was
subjected to an investigation of this kind. The results of this study provided an explicit test of the
first criterion, the modifiability of work schedules
in the CBD. The findings were also employed in applying the third criterion. Chapter 4 will describe
the industry scheduling studies and will present
their findings.

An intensive study was made of the response to
work staggering on the part of the people who work in

the CBD, and of other related matters. The sociological study is described in Chapter 5 and its principal findings are summarized there. This study furnishes a test of the second criterion, the acceptability of schedule change. It also provides important information utilized in connection with the
fourth criterion, tolerance and resistance to work
staggering. The other information collected in the
sociological study proved crucially important in the
development of computational models, as described in
Chapter 6.

A study of travel practices to and from work--
the transit study--was made as part of the sociological study. It is considered a separate research because it collected travel information which was sub-
sequently analyzed by separate procedures. The information obtained in the transit study contributed
to the application of the third criterion, the relief
of subway congestion. It was also useful in other
analyses.

In addition to these four field studies, there
were many other researches and analyses utilizing the
data produced by the four studies, the transit and
employment statistics and many other kinds of qualitative data. Insofar as the fifth criterion--dura-
bility--could be applied in advance of experience,
many of these other analyses contributed to it.
There were also many other specific and detailed
problems which arose continuously in the course of
the inquiry and which had to be resolved by a large
number of studies using primary and secondary source
data. Many of these are described in the ensuing
chapters and in their appendixes.

Summary

The study of feasibility required the six major
bodies of data just described, along with a vast
amount of other details culled from many sources.
They are the foundation upon which the whole inquiry
is based. Serious questions arose as to the quality
of these data. Obviously, since they were used, they
were judged adequate for the purposes at hand.

However, in each instance a great deal of attention
was given to the quality of the data, and the results are presented in evaluations which appear
throughout the ensuing chapters.

One further characteristic of the data needs to
be mentioned--their dates. The statistics employed
by the study apply to times ranging from September,
1958, to the time of writing. This raises the questions: Are the data outmoded? Do the differences
in their dates make them unsuitable, in combination,
for the study? These questions are both taken up in
appropriate places in the study wherever a body of
the data is presented, and in the evaluations of
Chapter 8. In general, the conclusion is reached
that the dates of the data, given the observed characteristics of the various statistics, do not significantly affect the results of the study. The
basis of this conclusion will be carefully deline-
ated in the course of the exposition.

CONCLUSION

The design of this study consists of the three
components just described: the problem of inquiry,
the theory and criteria of work staggering, and the
statistical and other data. They lay down the terms
of the problem and the methods by which it will be
attacked, and hopefully solved. The design as described really presents only the general framework
of the inquiry. As the study unfolds, it will have
to be elaborated to meet the particular problems
thrown up by the accumulation of results--a process
of refinement which continues to the end.

CHAPTER **2** HOW MUCH CONGESTION?

HOW MUCH RELIEF?

This study begins by examining subway traffic.
First, two traffic measures will be established.
One will be a measure of volume. It will provide
the study with statistics which will be used in all
computations involving subway traffic. The other
will be a standard of subway traffic. It will be
the criterion of traffic conditions, and ultimately
the test of work staggering. Thereafter, these
measures will provide answers to two questions:
When and where does subway congestion occur? How
much relief is required? Much of what follows in
this study depends on the results of this opening
inquiry.

This chapter has to deal with a large number
of topics. It will prove helpful to describe the
course it will take.

The chapter contains four sections. The first
two deal with measures and the second two with congestion and relief。 The first section will establish a measure of the volume of subway traffic. Its
main concerns are to define a suitable measurement
concept and then to evaluate the available body of
statistics. The second section will present and
justify the standard of subway traffic which this
study has adopted。

These two measures, once defined and quantified, lead directly to the next sections of the
chapter. The third section will evaluate the prevailing extent of subway congestion and of available
unused space. The final section will estimate the

number of people whose travel times would have to be
changed in order to eliminate congestion.

THE MEASURE OF SUBWAY TRAFFIC

This study requires a measure of subway traffic. The need will arise in many places, among
which three will stand out. Later in this chapter,
traffic statistics will be required in order to determine where and when congestion occurs. In Chapter 6, a computational model will be produced by relating work schedules to transit traffic. To test
the feasibility of work staggering, in Chapter 7,
forecasts of traffic will be required. Elsewhere
too, reference will be made to subway conditions--
past, present, and anticipated future.

This section will produce a body of statistics
which, despite certain shortcomings, will prove acceptable. The first part of this section will develop the measurement concept which meets the needs
of the study. The second part will present actual
statistics. In the final part they will be evaluated, adjusted, and made available for future use.

The Measure

The kind of measure which this study needs is
dictated by the uses to which it will be put. It
must measure the volume of subway traffic and must
fluctuate, immediately and accurately, by time and
place, with changes in traffic volume. Since work
staggering is concerned with congestion, the measure
must reflect the occurrence and location of congestion, as well as its relief. To reach a suitable
measurement concept, it will prove useful to review
briefly the nature of subway traffic, with particular reference to the New York subway system.

Subway traffic is a flow of people. In the New
York subway system there is a vast--almost uncount-
able--number of such flows. Traffic flows into each
station, usually in either of two directions and
through multiple entrances. It proceeds down

stairways to change booths, through turnstiles, then
through aisles and sometimes other stairways to platforms.   From platforms, the traffic moves into trains
--by division, line, express or local, and often by
routing or destination of the individual train.   The
traffic subdivides into flows out of the trains at
each destination station.   The flow process is then
reversed: from train to platform to aisles, stairways, exits, and then out of the station.   At any
instant--particularly during the rush hours, the
system contains innumerable flows, traveling in as
many different directions as possible, and composed
of constantly changing streams of people.

Traffic--flows of people--occurs throughout the
system, and congestion can take place wherever there
is traffic.   There can be congestion on the stairs
into the stations, at the change booths and turnstiles, in the aisles, platforms and in the trains.
It can occur at any station, and in any direction--
into or out of the station, or toward any other
destination station.

Not all of these flows--and their congestion--
are relevant to a work staggering program.   Some are
unaffected by work staggering and others are only
indirectly related to it.   The aspects of the traffic flow with which this study deals have two characteristics, and they reduce the measurement problem
to manageable size.

First, work staggering is concerned only with
the traffic which flows to Manhattan's CBD during
the morning rush hour, and from the CBD during the
late afternoon rush hour.   This excludes: all traffic traveling in the opposite direction at these
times; and much of the traffic which does not reach
the CBD during the rush hour.   Second, only one part
of the total traffic flow is directly related to
work staggering, the people riding in trains.   To
the extent that congestion elsewhere is caused by
work schedules--and not by inadequate facilities or
services--work staggering may alleviate other places
of congestion.   But the one which this study will

affect most directly and for which a measure is
needed is the traffic in trains.

A measurement concept and a body of statistics
now exist which measure the flow described by these
two characteristics: the numbers of people in
trains traveling to and from the CBD during rush
hours. It is called the cordon count and it is used
by the New York City Transit Authority. This measure will be described in the next section, after
which it will be evaluated from the viewpoint of its
appropriateness--as a measure--to this study.

The Cordon Count

The Transit Authority has established two cordons around the CBD. One cordon is for entering
trains and the other for trains leaving the CBD.
Each cordon contains twenty stations chosen by a
fixed rule. An entering cordon station is the last
one a train passes before reaching the CBD. Each
cordon station leaving the CBD is the last one
through which a departing train passes. Every
train, entering or leaving, crosses the cordon at
one of the cordon stations. Appendix A gives a complete list of all the cordon stations, by division
and line.

A cordon count is the number of people in
trains crossing the cordons.

The Transit Authority conducts a systemwide
cordon count each October, and frequently also in
March. A team of trained men called checkers is
sent to the cordon stations. Each checker, during
his tour of duty, observes every train and every car
departing from his station. On the basis of his observations, he estimates to the nearest ten the number of persons in each car, and he records these estimates. He also notes the number of persons seated,
the number standing, the time the train leaves, the
number of cars, and other relevant data.

The observations are made over a period of several weeks, but only on normal, working weekdays.

The observation sheets are edited in the Authority office and the data are then summarized for release. The cordon counts are issued by 20-minute interval totals over the 24-hour day for each of the twenty cordon stations entering and leaving the CBD.*

One aspect of the procedure requires special mention because it affects the quality of the cordon count statistics. The checkers never record more people in any car than its so-called capacity, regardless of the actual number in the car. This capacity is the number which the Transit Authority uses to schedule trains. The cordon count, even when it records only the capacity, serves the purpose for which it was made. This particular capacity--called schedule capacity in this study--is below the maximum number which a car can carry. (Appendix G presents the various capacities of each type of car now used in the system.) It thus follows that any car reported at capacity may actually have more than that number. All cars at or below the capacity level are supposed to be correctly estimated and recorded by the checkers. The practice of truncation--cutting off the estimates at the capacity number--will be examined later in the chapter.

The Cordon Counts as Measures

It is now appropriate to ask: Are the cordon counts suitable measures of traffic for the purposes of this study? In answering this question, it will be assumed that the defects resulting from truncation can be remedied by appropriate adjustment procedures. (Or, if they are not remediable, cordon counts can be made which are not truncated.) The question may then be restricted to the measurement concept of the cordon count.

----

*The Transit Authority placed the original observation sheets of the October, 1962, count at the disposal of this study. The additional detail was very useful in several crucial places.

As a measure, the cordon count intersects the
flow of traffic at a single point. It reports a
number which measures the cross-sectional magnitude
of the flow. A fundamental question arises about
the suitability of such a measurement to the data
requirements of this study. Does this single point
of intersection correspond to, or adequately represent, the volume of passengers in the train over the
rest of the line? Will the expansions and contrac-
tions in the volume of flow show up in equivalent
changes in the cordon count? If schedules are
changed, and if congestion as measured at cordon
stations is reduced, will it also be reduced elsewhere on the line?

The nature of this problem may be depicted more
clearly by visualizing the volume of passengers in a
train as it progresses from its origin terminal. At
its origin, the train is empty. At each station en
route it picks up and discharges passengers. Characteristically, during the peak periods, the trains
pick up more passengers than they discharge until
they reach the areas of employment. Thus, the number of people in the train, if counted as it leaves
each station, will increase to some maximum point,
after which it will decline.

Variations can be expected in this general pattern. Some trains fill very quickly at their origin
stations or shortly thereafter. This occurs when
the origin station connects with large sources of
passengers, such as bus lines, trains, and the like.
Some trains fill very gradually along their routes.
Some trains pass through more than one area of employment or other destination, and their volume will
expand and contract more than once over the line.
Local trains have a special pattern. They expand
until an express station is reached, after which
they may sharply contract.

The question raised above asks whether, by in-
tersecting the flow of passengers at any one point,
it is possible to obtain information on the rate of
flow elsewhere along the line. The answer depends

upon the nature of the flow of the traffic along the
routes of the various lines.

The nature of traffic flow is described in Appendix B. The findings there are based on a brief
study, but they contribute to answering the question
under consideration. There are two significant
characteristics of the flow which are relevant here.

First, there is a definite pattern of flow into
the CBD from each of the four origin areas: north,
northeast, east, and southeast. The trains fill
regularly and systematically and then they gradually
unload. The pattern of flow is one of expansion to
a maximum and then contraction. This regularity is
reinforced by its occurrence in each of the four
areas. There are differences among the areas in the
dimensions of their flows, but not in their shapes.

Because a pattern exists, it becomes possible
to measure the flow at any point and obtain information about the flow as a whole. All that is required is knowledge about the relative place of the
point of intersection in the entire pattern.

Second, in the flow pattern, the cordon stations occupy a special place. They are the maximum
stations of trains serving three of the areas. In
the fourth, the cordon station is 88 per cent of
the maximum. It is thus possible to measure the
flow at the cordon station and to make some inferences about the level of flow elsewhere along the
line.

As a measure, the cordon count is quite suitable to the purposes of this study. It measures
precisely the phenomenon with which work staggering
is concerned--the volume of traffic in the subway
cars. Although it measures the traffic at only one
point--the twenty cordon stations--the count at this
one point reflects, to a sufficiently known degree,
the state of traffic elsewhere along the line. If
changes in work schedule are capable of redistribut-
ing the flow--over time--of passengers into the subways, the cordon counts ought to be able to measure

the results both at the cordon stations and along
the lines their trains serve.

The Cordon Counts

An examination will now be made of the cordon
count statistics. The purposes of this examination
are to present the actual data, to identify the intervals of interest to the study, and to establish
the count which will serve as the basis for later
computations. The imperfection in the cordon counts
--noted in the preceding section--will not affect
the results of the ensuing inquiry.

The Periods of Interest

The cordon counts furnish numbers for the entire
twenty-four hours a day by 20-minute intervals.
There are thus two sets of seventy-two counts each.
Not all of them are of interest to the present study.
It is therefore convenient to reduce the number to
the periods which are relevant to the purposes of
this study.

Two such periods are required, one for the
morning, entering the CBD, and one for the evening,
leaving the CBD. These periods will be used for summarizing statistical data and for carrying on later
computations. They must include the morning and
evening peaks as well as additional intervals before
and after the peaks. For the purpose of determining
the periods of interest, the October, 1962, cordon
count will be used. Needless to point out, the results would not differ if any other recent count
were used in its stead.

Figure 2 shows the number of persons entering
the CBD through all subway cordon stations at 20-
minute intervals from 2:00 a.m. to 12:00 noon, as
reported in the October, 1962, cordon count. It
also shows the number coming from the Bronx and Manhattan combined, from Brooklyn, and from Queens.
Bronx and Manhattan are combined because the same
lines serve both these areas and they enter through

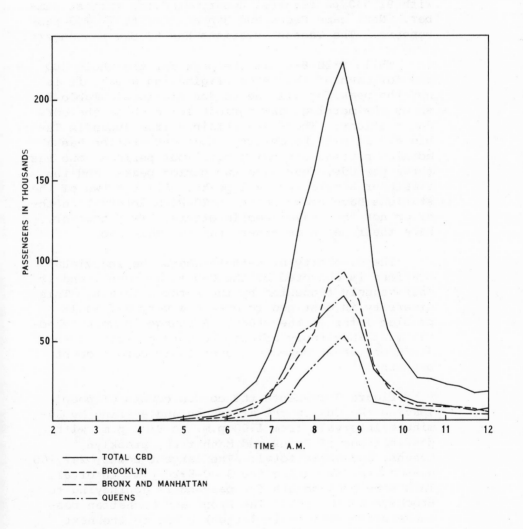

FIGURE 2

NUMBER OF PASSENGERS ENTERING THE CBD DURING
EACH 20-MINUTE INTERVAL FROM 2:00 A.M. TO NOON,
AS REPORTED IN THE OCTOBER, 1962, CORDON COUNT

the same cordon station. Some lines travel through
both Brooklyn and Queens. Their passengers are identified by the location of the cordon station.

The morning peak for the total system occurs
during 8:20-8:40 a.m. During this time 222,550 passengers were recorded for the whole CBD. Brooklyn,
with 91,940 passengers, contributed the largest number. Next came Bronx and Manhattan with 77,740 passengers. The Queens' stations had 52,820 passengers.

While 8:20-8:40 is the peak for the whole CBD
and for each of the three originating areas, it is
not the peak for all the cordon stations. Table 3
shows the morning peak periods for each of the cordon stations. These are obtained from Appendix Table 4. It will be observed that one station has a
morning plateau extending over four periods, one has
three periods, four have two period peaks, and the
remainder single interval peaks. All but two of the
stations have peaks in the 8:20-8:40 interval whether or not they have them in others. Two, however,
have their peaks in other than the main one.

The diversity of pattern among the individual
stations is obscured by the CBD total count, and is
only vaguely suggested by the borough totals. This
diversity is destined to create a very difficult
problem later in the study. A change in work schedule must inevitably affect the cordon stations in
different ways, depending upon their cordon count
patterns.

Figure 3 presents the cordon counts of people
leaving the CBD in the afternoon and evening by 20-
minute intervals from 1:00 p.m. to 9:00 p.m. with
destinations of Bronx and Manhattan, Brooklyn,
Queens, and their total. The largest count, 212,200
passengers, is during the 5:00-5:20 p.m. interval.
This same peak occurs for passengers journeying to
Brooklyn and Queens. The Bronx and Manhattan passengers register their largest count in the next
interval, 5:20-5:40 p.m.

TABLE 3

The Peak Intervals of Each Cordon Station, Entering the CBD

Stations	7:20 7:40	7:40 8:00	8:00 8:20	8:20 8:40	8:40 9:00
86th & Lexington (Express)	x	x	x	x	
68th & Lexington (Local)				x	
72nd & Broadway (Express)		x	x	x	
66th & Broadway (Local)			x	x	
125th & St. Nicholas (A,D)			x	x	
72nd & Central Park West (AA,BB,CC)				x	
Borough Hall (Lexington Ave. Express)				x	
Clark Street (7th Ave. Exp.)			x	x	
High Street (A,E)				x	
York Street (D)			x		
Court St. (Brighton, 4th Ave. Lcl.)				x	
Court St. (West End, Nassau)				x	
Bedford Ave. (14th St. Line)				x	
Manhattan Bridge (Brighton, W.E., S.B. Exp.)				x	
Manhattan Bridge (West End Special)				x	
Williamsburg Bridge (Jamaica-Myrtle)			x	x	
23rd & Ely (E,F)				x	
Vernon-Jackson (Flushing Line)					x
Queensboro Plaza (Brighton Lcl., W.E. Exp.)				x	
Queens Plaza (4th Ave. Local)				x	

FIGURE 3

NUMBER OF PASSENGERS LEAVING THE CBD DURING
EACH 20-MINUTE INTERVAL FROM 1:00 TO 9:00 P.M.,
AS REPORTED IN THE OCTOBER, 1962, CORDON COUNT

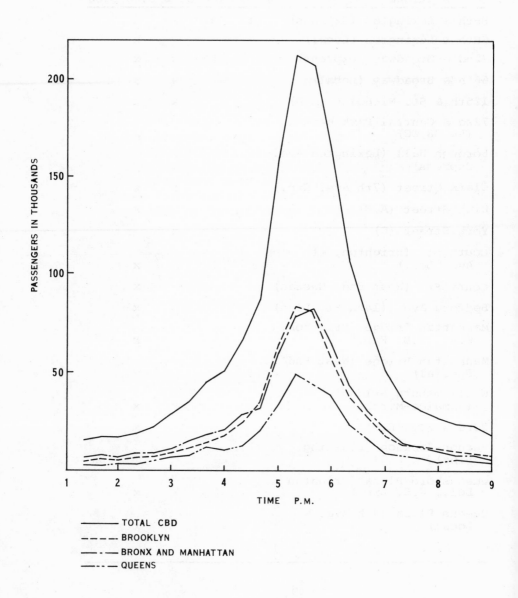

Any definition of the rush hour is inevitably
an arbitrary one. The rush depends not only upon
the number of passengers, but upon the capacity of
the system to transport them. It requires no further evidence to identify the morning and evening
peak intervals as "rush." The question arises, however, as to how far before and after these peaks the
"rush" extends. Neither numbers of passengers nor
percentage of daily total provide a satisfactory
device for reaching a suitable definition.

This study has its own special purposes and can
identify its periods of interest in accordance with
them. For the morning, the cordon count intervals
will extend from 6:20-10:00. This includes the
peak, six intervals earlier and four intervals later.
Within this range, there ought to be ample room for
any shifts of transit traffic as a result of work
schedule change. Most of the changes which may ultimately be tested will be reflected in the cordon
intervals included within this range.*

The evening range, for passengers leaving the
CBD, has been set by the same considerations at
3:20-7:00 p.m. This range also contains eleven
intervals, five before and five after the CBD peak
of 5:00-5:20 p.m.

The 1962 Count

The October, 1962, cordon count has been selected
for the various computations of this study. The
question arises as to the representative character
of the October, 1962, count as compared with the
counts of other years. The question will be answered by the ensuing examination of annual counts
during the period 1959-63.

The cordon counts, by borough and total, for
the a.m. and p.m. periods of interest, are presented

---

*This range of eleven intervals is also dic-
tated by the required dimensions of the later computation tables. See Appendix S.

in Tables 4 and 5. The data of these tables are
shown graphically on Figures 4 and 5.

The 1959-63 experience yields two significant
generalizations for the problem at hand. First it
shows that cordon counts were very stable over the
five-year period. The stability occurs in the total
as well as by borough, and it applies also to the
relative position of each borough to the total.
Some year-to-year variations are disclosed by the
figures; the evening count gives almost a cyclical
appearance. Nevertheless, taking both sets of data
together, the dominant effect is one of stability.

The second finding from these data is the relative position of the October, 1962, count. Although
the five-year period is judged stable, October, 1962,
was the highest year. In the mornings it was not
highest by much. In the evenings it was perceptibly
higher than 1960, the lowest year. For the purposes
of this study it is an advantage to use the maximum
year. The tests of feasibility will thus be made
against the greatest traffic volume of recent experience. Conclusions drawn from this extreme event
will assure a larger margin of safety in the final
results.

Conclusions

This presentation of the cordon count data produced two results which will be used throughout the
study. The periods of interest--incorporating the
rush hours and adjacent intervals--will be 6:20-
10:00 in the morning, and 3:20-7:00 in the evening.
The October, 1962, cordon count will be employed for
all the calculations involving subway traffic.

EVALUATION AND ADJUSTMENT
OF THE CORDON COUNTS

The cordon counts will now be critically examined. The purpose is to determine whether the data
are--or can be made--suitable to the needs of this
study. The needs will occur in three principal
places.

TABLE 4

October Cordon Counts, by Borough Origin and Total, Entering the CBD Between 6:20 and 10:00 A.M., 1959-63

Borough	1959	1960	1961	1962	1963
Bronx & Manhattan	472,000	457,880	477,590	459,920	464,410
Brooklyn	447,590	451,340	440,060	473,680	452,440
Queens	258,450	256,270	261,410	272,940	248,170
Total	1,178,040	1,165,490	1,179,060	1,206,540	1,165,020

TABLE 5

October Cordon Counts, by Borough Destination and Total, Leaving the CBD Between 3:20 and 7:00 P.M., 1959-63

Borough	1959	1960	1961	1962	1963
Bronx & Manhattan	479,940	429,710	463,000	485,850	452,750
Brooklyn	412,000	410,380	425,290	463,530	453,470
Queens	238,950	252,620	250,740	274,660	250,160
Total	1,130,890	1,092,710	1,139,030	1,224,040	1,156,380

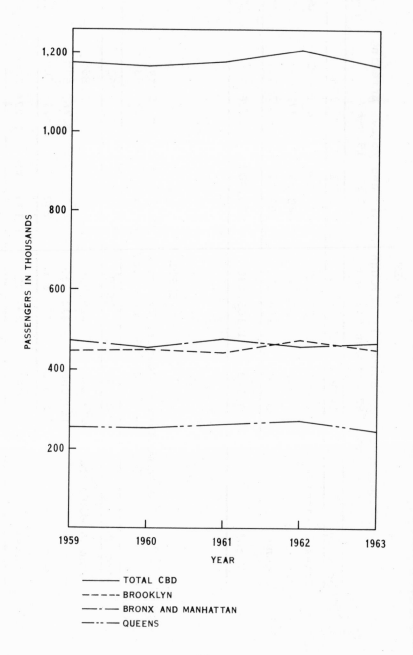

FIGURE 4
NUMBER OF PASSENGERS ENTERING THE CBD
BETWEEN 6:20 AND 10:00 A.M.,
AS REPORTED IN THE OCTOBER CORDON COUNTS,
1959 – 63

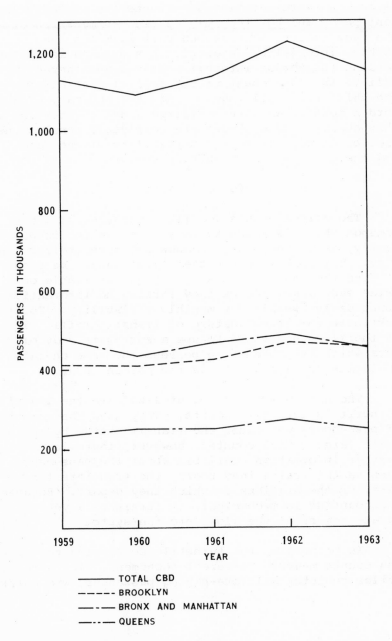

FIGURE 5

NUMBER OF PASSENGERS LEAVING THE CBD
BETWEEN 3:20 AND 7:00 P.M.,
AS REPORTED IN THE OCTOBER CORDON COUNTS,
1959-63

PASSENGERS IN THOUSANDS

YEAR

——— TOTAL CBD
----- BROOKLYN
—·—· BRONX AND MANHATTAN
—··— QUEENS

45

The ensuing examination divides into three
parts. The first will investigate the variability
of subway traffic. Its results will disclose how
traffic varies and, by implication, how stable it
is. These findings will be the basis for a judgment
as to how representative the counts are of the recent past, and how they may be used as measures of
the near future. The second part examines the
counts, interval by interval. Its purpose is to establish the cordon interval patterns and thereby to
relieve the 1962 count of any special aberrations.
The third part will inquire into the accuracy of the
cordon counts, an issue deferred since earlier in
this chapter. When these are completed, conclusions
will be offered as to the suitability of the data
and the adjustments which they require.

The Behavior of Transit Traffic

The cordon counts are fixed measures of a phenomenon which is known to vary. To use the counts
safely, it is necessary to know how much traffic can
vary. The cordon counts themselves cannot be used
to find this out. At best, they are available only
twice each year. Hence they furnish no information
about daily, weekly, or monthly variability. To investigate the "true" nature of transit traffic, it
is therefore necessary to use a surrogate body of
data which is presumed to possess the same characteristics of variability as the cordon count.

The data which will be utilized are the Transit
Authority's turnstile counts. They give the numbers
of passengers who enter the transit system by paying
their fares. Once counted, however, there is no
further information available about the passengers,
such as the trains they board, the transfers they
make, or the stations at which they depart. Because
the counting is mechanical, it furnishes a very accurate report of the flow into the system.

In principle, the turnstile counts and the cordon counts measure different phenomena. The turnstiles register all fare-paying passengers who enter

the system, both those traveling through the cordons
and others. The cordon counts measure only those
traveling to (or from) the CBD. Despite this difference, the turnstile counts are an acceptable substitute for the cordon counts in this analysis of
traffic. The primary problem here is to determine
the amount of variability in traffic, particularly
during the peak hours when people are going to and
from work. During these periods the working people
undoubtedly constitute the overwhelming number of
passengers in the system. On this presumption, the
variabilities in turnstile count are considered to
correspond to those of the cordon counts. For the
purposes at hand, the correspondence need not be
identical to be useful.

Long-Term Trends

The trend in turnstile counts, particularly
during the morning and evening rush hours, has ex-
hibited remarkable stability since 1954. Even before those years the peak hour counts, while declining, fell much less than the 24-hour turnstile count.
This stability is also present in the individual
hourly counts both morning and afternoon. This is
shown in Figure 6 for the October turnstile registrations from 1952-63 on a 24-hour basis, and for
both the morning and evening rush hour periods.

The long-term stability in turnstile counts
corresponds to the same kind of stability in the
cordon counts, as shown earlier in this chapter on
Figures 4 and 5.

For this study, it is valuable to discover that
the system has been in a stable period as far back
as ten years, even though no one can foresee whether
or not this long-term stability will continue into
the future. If such stability were not present in
the data--if there were a trend either upward or
downward, or if the year-to-year variations were
large instead of minute, or if some multiannual cyclical pattern were evident--it would be necessary
to make allowances for such potential changes when

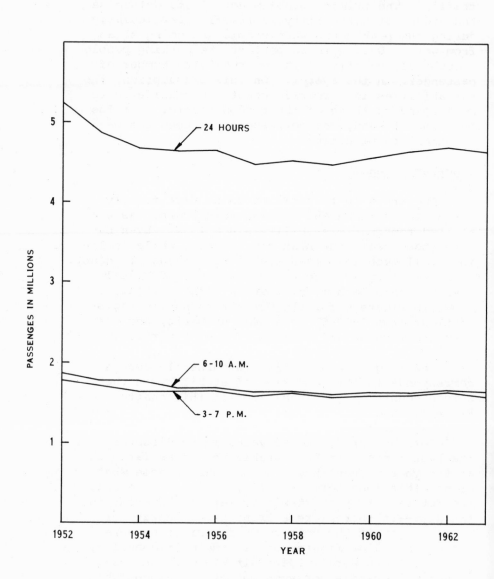

FIGURE 6
OCTOBER TURNSTILE REGISTRATIONS,
24 HOURS, 6:00-10:00 A.M., AND 3:00-7:00 P.M.,
1952-63

using the cordon counts for feasibility computations. However, no such allowances or adjustments seem required from the historical statistics.

Seasonal Variations

The cordon counts used in this study are taken annually in October. The question naturally arises: Where does October fit in the year's volume of traffic? Figure 7 presents the average monthly turnstile registrations for the period 1959-63.

The maximum month over the five-year period 1959-63 was March. October was the second highest. Figure 7 discloses that an important source of variation in turnstile registration is the seasonal pattern of traffic.

Neither the existence of a seasonal pattern nor October's particular place in it call for any adjustment in the cordon count data. However, in interpreting the results of later computations, it will be important to recall that October had 97 per cent of the maximum months' turnstile counts over the five-year period. The analysis of seasonal variations is based on the 24-hour turnstile count and not on the peak hour counts. It is not known whether the same fluctuations occur during the morning and afternoon peak periods. But since seasonal variations are known to exist in CBD industry, the peak periods may also show their effects.

Weekly Patterns

Although the cordon counts are taken throughout the normal work week, it is of interest to know whether there is a distinctive traffic pattern within the week. This subject was investigated using turnstile data from five CBD stations and from the Lexington Avenue line as a whole.

The significant findings from the analysis of weekly patterns are twofold. The first is that

FIGURE 7
MONTHLY AVERAGES OF TURNSTILE REGISTRATIONS,
1959 – 63

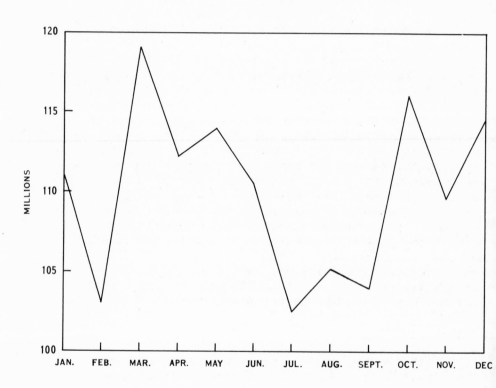

there is little if any variability on a daily basis. The day-to-day counts--when the effect of seasonal variation is removed--show surprisingly little difference. The second finding is that the intraweekly patterns vary station-by-station and for the line as a whole.

The weak pattern of intraweekly variability and diversity among stations permit this factor to be disregarded in the use of cordon count data.

Residual Variability

Thus far, the study of variability produced these results: Within recent years there has been no noticeable change in turnstile counts resulting from long trends or cyclical variations; there is a marked intra-annual pattern and very little intraweekly pattern. When the effects of these sources of variation are removed from the counts, how much additional variability still remains?

There are two parts to the answer to this question, as given in the analysis of turnstile statistics. The first part of the answer is: There is surprisingly little residual variability in the turnstile counts day-by-day, after the effects of the seasonal pattern are removed. The second part of the answer is that residual variability differs among the stations.

These findings do not require any adjustments in the cordon count data. However, in using the cordon counts, consideration must be given to the inherent variability in the flow of traffic. In the problem of this study, it is important to know how much higher the volume of traffic might rise, simply within the range of normal variation.

Transit Operations

The number of people passing through the cordon stations is inevitably affected by the availability of subway service. If the service is insufficient,

fewer people will turn up in the cordon counts than
ought to be there. It is therefore appropriate, in
this examination, to investigate the actual operations during the October, 1962, count.

For this examination, the subject of transit
operation divides conveniently into two topics: the
adequacy of service and the operating efficiency
during the counts. These are the main questions to
be answered: Are the historical data distorted by
inadequacies of service or operating efficiency? In
using the data must these operational factors be
taken into consideration?

The changes which the Transit Authority is
planning to introduce will affect the use and interpretation of the cordon count data when applied to
future conditions. These changes will also be investigated.

Schedule Adequacy

The adequacy of train schedules depends upon
the quantity of service in relation to demand--both
as a function of time. The demand for service consists of the number of people seeking transportation
at stated times. One measure of demand is the cordon count itself. It turns out that demand is an
exceedingly complicated factor to quantify, and will
be shown in Chapter 6 to be influenced significantly
by the supply of service. Here it is necessary to
assume that the cordon count reflects the demand for
service--an assumption which disposes of much of the
present problem.

The evidence does not reveal that the system
was inadequately scheduled, according to existing
standards. An analysis was made of the relationship
of schedule capacity* to the number of passengers

_____

*The term "capacity" as used here, refers to the
level which the Transit Authority uses for schedul-
ing--called, in this study, the schedule capacity.
See Appendix I for a fuller explanation.

reported in the cordon counts. The data show that
the number of passengers was usually well below the
schedule capacity except when the actual number of
trains exceeded the scheduled number. This happened
when the system was recovering from previous delays.
There were occasional intervals at some stations
where the schedule capacity was pretty substantially
utilized, but this may have been a special occurrence
during the October, 1962, count. There is no reason
to question the appropriateness of the count on the
grounds of inadequate train schedules.

Operating Efficiency

Any actual cordon count is inevitably affected
by the operating conditions which prevail while it
is being taken. An analysis was made of the operating efficiency which occurred during the October,
1962, count. It is reported in Appendix E. The
evidence discloses that the system ran behind schedule in most of the 20-minute intervals, both morning
and afternoon. However, during both periods the
system had pretty well recovered by the end of the
observed period. This was brought about by actual
operations exceeding the scheduled ones during the
last three intervals of the morning period and during the last interval of the afternoon period.

From this it follows that if the trains had
operated according to schedule, the cordon counts
would have been higher, perhaps not fully as high as
the difference between actual and total efficiency
but somewhat higher than they actually were. This
implies that people had to wait for trains or else
were delayed within trains which were late.

While it appears likely that cordon counts
would be higher if operating efficiency were higher,
there is no need to adjust the cordon counts to offset this factor. The departures from efficiency, as
disclosed by the October, 1962, count, were not substantial. Although all intervals were behind schedule, the lowest efficiency was 93 per cent in the
morning and 96 per cent in the afternoon. Most of

the intervals were higher than this level. Further,
there is no reason to expect that the system can
operate at 100 per cent efficiency at all intervals.
In any such intricate system, perfect operation
would be a most improbable event. The difference
between the actual efficiency and the optimum level
would thus be only a few percentage points and they
would probably not be reflected in an equal percentage increase in cordon counts. Hence, while operating efficiency may have influenced the October, 1962,
count, it was probably by a small and indeterminable
amount. Therefore, no adjustment will be made in
the October, 1962, count for this factor.

Planned Changes

An operating factor which must be considered in
using the 1962 cordon count is the proposed increase
in West Side IRT trains from nine cars on express
trains and eight on locals to ten cars on each,
planned for 1964-65.* The October, 1962, cordon
counts of the West Side IRT stations reflect the
prevailing undercapacity of the line then and are
not affected by the change. However, in our later
analysis of the prevailing amount of congestion,
station by station, and in the evaluation of alternative work schedules (in Chapter 7), we will have
to take into account these planned changes. No
doubt the 1962 count shows more congestion--and less
traffic--than will be the case with ten-car trains.

---

*Editor's Note: Although data on these changes
and on improvements in New York's transit system in
the mid-1960's are unavailable, this study's value
rests on its proposals and documentation. With its
heavy reliance on the 1962 findings, it is still the
only statistical compilation of work staggering and
its potential effects on the lives of the citizens
involved.

The Cordon Interval Patterns

A cordon interval pattern is the relative number of people, interval by interval, passing through a cordon station. The pattern can conveniently be expressed in percentages. Each interval will be a percentage of the total number passing through the station in the eleven intervals. The sequence of these percentages--a distribution totaling 100 per cent--is the cordon interval pattern of the station or system.

There are two problems which call attention to the cordon interval patterns. In selecting the October, 1962, cordon count, its particular set of patterns was also adopted, at least by implication. This ought to be looked into before the data are utilized elsewhere in the study. Secondly, during the October, 1962, count there were some operating difficulties which distorted the results. The cordon interval pattern of the particular station provides an acceptable method of adjusting the actual data.

The cordon interval pattern of any station is the consequence of the supply and demand for service. The pattern will show the effects of systematic as well as accidental variations in both factors. During the peak hours, the demand conditions are probably quite stable because they are governed by the highly stable requirements of work hours. The supply conditions, however, are subject to sudden shifts caused by delays and other operating difficulties during the actual time of the counts. Where these operating difficulties produce long interruptions in service or distortions of the schedule, the special problems mentioned above will arise.

In using the October, 1962, data, the conditions which prevailed during that count are introduced into the analysis. Whether or not this is desirable depends upon the particular problem in which the data are used. In some instances it will be essential to retain the specific characteristics of the

October, 1962, count. In others, they would prove a
distorting influence.

        To eliminate the effect of the October, 1962,
conditions--wherever this proves desirable--a five-
year cordon interval pattern was computed for each
cordon station. It is based on the average patterns
of each station for the years 1959-63. The data,
method, and results are given in Appendix E. The
cordon interval patterns can be used to compute modified cordon counts. By multiplying the total 11-
interval count of each station by the percentages of
the cordon interval pattern, the result will be a
modified cordon count. It will retain the total of
the particular count, but will redistribute the numbers according to the five yearly interval patterns.

        Such a modified cordon count has a valuable
property. It retains the desirable level of the October, 1962, count and it gives the individual intervals the generality of the five-year patterns.
It thus removes from the October, 1962, count the
effects of any special, perhaps erratic, factors
which may have distorted the counts.

        Two sets of cordon counts--both based on the
October, 1962, data--will now become available for
the several uses in this study. These two sets may
be used integrally or by mixing them on the basis of
some appropriate criterion. Mixed counts will consist of actual data for some stations and the modified data for others. The particular problem will
dictate the appropriate count in each case. Tables
of the adjusted cordon counts are given in Appendix
G.

                THE ACCURACY OF THE CORDON COUNTS

        This evaluation will now address its final--and
most serious--problem: Are the cordon counts accurate? Do they correctly measure the number of people
traveling through the cordons? These questions, no
longer postponable, will now be answered.

The conclusion will be reached, in the ensuing
analysis, that the cordon counts are probably not
accurate but that they are usable by this study.
The nature of their inaccuracy will be shown as systematic: They underestimate the numbers of subway
passengers. This underestimate is confined to about
four cordon intervals and will be partially corrected by a procedure to be presented below. But despite the correction, the resulting statistics will
remain too low and will create, on that account,
some difficult problems later in the study.

There are three grounds for calling into question the accuracy of the cordon counts. They are:
the relationship of the counts to employment statistics; the surprisingly limited amount of congestion
which they reveal; and several steps in the procedure
by which they are made. Each of these will now be
explained.

Cordon Counts and Employment

A comparison of the cordon counts and employment statistics disclose differences which indicate
that the cordon counts are too low. The results of
the comparison are only indicative, and not specific.
Neither the statistics nor the assumptions employed
in the computation which produced the comparison are
as strong as might be desired. But despite these
shortcomings, the analysis concludes unavoidably
that the cordon counts are lower than they ought to
be.

The October, 1962, counts report that 1,206,540
people crossed the cordons between 6:20 and 10:00
a.m. This was the highest number in the five-year
period, 1959-63. The lowest occurred in 1963 and was
1,165,020. Thus in using the October, 1962, statistics, the comparison will be as advantageous as possible to the cordon counts.

The cordon counts include all the passengers in
the train, not only those who work in the CBD. The
passengers consist of people traveling to the CBD
and elsewhere. They also have many different kinds
of destination. They are passengers going to work,

to school, to shop, to visit service establishments
and professional offices, and they are travelers
headed toward the transportation terminals of the
CBD.

Unquestionably, the people who work in the CBD
make up the largest proportion of the riders during
the rush hours, but their proportion is unknown. It
probably varies in the individual intervals, but
again by unknown amounts and by unknown directions
of change over time. If a guess were hazarded, it
would place the people who work in the CBD between
80 and 90 per cent of the total passengers during
the 6:20-10:00 a.m. period.

The available employment data produce an estimate that 1,150,000 people work in the CBD and cross
subway cordons to work between 6:20 and 10:00 a.m.
According to the employment statistics 2,046,400
people work in the CBD (in September, 1958). About
10 per cent have work schedules outside the main
portion of the normal weekday, leaving a total of
1,840,000. Of these, 67.11 per cent are estimated
to cross the subway cordons on their way to work,
reducing the total further to 1,236,000. An estimated 86,000 travel outside the eleven intervals
from 6:20-10:00 a.m., thus yielding a final estimate
of 1,150,000. (These statistics and computations
will be developed in Chapters 3 and 6.)

The estimated number of people who work in the
CBD and cross the subway cordons to work--1,150,000
--is 50,000 lower than the October, 1962, cordon
count and 15,000 lower than the October, 1963, count.
By these figures the passengers who did not work in
the CBD were 4.7 per cent or 1.3 per cent of the
1962 and 1963 counts. These percentages of other
riders are considered unreasonably low, especially
when the cordon counts include the late intervals
from 9:20 to 10:00 a.m. They are substantially below the 10 to 20 per cent of other riders suggested
above.

If the 10 to 20 per cent of other riders is
valid, then the October, 1962, cordon count contained

an error of between 71,000 and 231,000 passengers. Assuming that 1,150,000 work in the CBD and cross the cordons to work; and assuming that they represent 80 to 90 per cent of the total number of riders; the cordon count would then have to be 1,437,500 (at 80 per cent) or 1,277,777 (at 90 per cent). Subtracting 1,206,500 from each of these numbers gives the results of 231,000 or 71,277. The cordon counts would then underestimate the actual number of riders by 16.1 per cent (on the 80 per cent basis) or 5.6 per cent (on the 90 per cent basis). To correct the existing counts would require adjustment factors of either 19.2 per cent or 5.9 per cent.

These results suggest that the cordon counts understate the number of passengers by substantial amounts and percentages. Unfortunately, the results rest upon relatively elaborate computations using statistics not much stronger than the cordon counts themselves. They do, however, point decidedly to a downward bias on the part of the cordon count and this is accepted as a reasonable finding. They do not furnish a reliable amount of the underestimate, but it must lie between 5 and 15 per cent. The absence of such an amount makes it impossible to determine the degree of inaccuracy in the counts, and hence to correct them.

Congestion

The second basis for questioning the accuracy of the cordon counts comes from an analysis of the prevailing extent and intensity of congestion during the rush hours. This will be presented in detail later in the chapter. The analysis of congestion is made by straightforward arithmetic procedures. The conclusion that the results are surprisingly low is a judgment based upon qualitative rather than statistical materials. However, despite the tenuousness of the data, the conclusion becomes inescapable that the cordon counts do not register all the people who are riding in the subway, particularly during the peak of the congestion.

The Procedures

There are at least four elements in the cordon count procedure which call the results into question. Some of them may have minor effects on accuracy, but at least one is very serious. They will be briefly described here.

First, the cordon counts are judgments, not counts. The checkers do not--indeed could not possibly--count the number of people in the cars. They assume that all seats are filled (to capacity, according to standard capacity data), and they judge the number of standees. Many questions can be raised about the accuracy of such judgments, particularly when made of people in moving trains. Reportedly, check studies have been made and they are said to vindicate the claims of accuracy by the checkers. There is no further basis for accepting or rejecting the results of the procedure at this time. It is, however, a misnomer to call these results "counts."

Second, the checkers make their judgments to the nearest ten. This imparts an accuracy which is plus or minus five. Relatively, this is a very small deviation from an exact count. If all other aspects of the procedure were satisfactory, this one would occasion no concern.

Third, the observations of the checkers are subjected to an editing process in the offices of the Transit Authority. It is one of the factors which may affect the accuracy of the results. It is noted here primarily because it is part of the procedure, but it has not been evaluated.

Finally, the most serious problem arises from the practice of estimating the number of people no higher than the so-called capacity of the car.

Of these four sources of possible inaccuracy, only one--the capacity limit--can be subjected to further scrutiny. The others are merely noted for

the record. Since they cannot be evaluated, the
counts have to be accepted without assessing their
influence. This implies a judgment that they have
either little or offsetting effects on the resulting
statistics.

Truncation

The practice of not reporting more than a capacity number of passengers in any car produces
truncated statistics. The practice itself is not
necessarily impermissible, especially since the
Transit Authority makes the cordon counts primarily
for the purpose of scheduling. This is served by
discovering the number of cars filled to capacity--
which is the basis for rescheduling of trains. The
truncation practice, however, is not beyond criti-
cism when the resulting data are issued as cordon
counts purporting to represent the number of people
in the trains.

The practice of truncation produces underestimates of the number of people because the capacity
limits are lower than the maximum number of people
who can ride in the car. The Transit Authority estimates that its capacity figures are about 10 per
cent below the maximum carrying capacities of the
car. There is other evidence to suggest that they
are considerably more than 10 per cent below the
number of people who are actually in the cars during
the height of the rush. Accordingly, the use of
these capacities as the upper limit produces a serious underestimate.

The practice of truncation has two kinds of adverse effects on the resulting statistics. As just
described, it must understate the number of people
in trains, especially when the cars are at or above
their capacity. This will occur during the height
of the rush hour, particularly between 7:40 and 9:00
a.m. It is also possible that the practice of truncation introduces a generalized downward bias in the
counts. The habits of mind and the bench marks for
estimating may affect the observations of cars below
the capacity level. Obviously this cannot be proved

without actual studies. It is, however, a reasonable possibility and needs to be noted in evaluating
the implications of the truncation practice.

An attempt has been made, on the basis of very
appropriate but hardly sufficient evidence, to estimate the amount of inaccuracy caused by the practice
of truncation. Appendix G describes the data and
the method by which this was done. The Appendix
also develops a correction factor which is called
the truncation adjustment. It seeks to remedy the
underestimates of cars reported at the capacity level, but has no effect on the possible underestimates
of cars having fewer than a capacity number of passengers.

The analysis presented in Appendix G indicates
that the practice of truncation reduced the counts
by about 1 per cent during the period 6:20-10:00 a.m.
and about 1.6 per cent during the 7:40-9:00 a.m. period. The use of the truncation adjustment adds 1.3
per cent to the interval of 8:00-8:20, 2.4 per cent
to 8:20-8:40, and 1.1 per cent to 8:40-9:00. The
truncation adjustment provides an improvement in the
original data but it falls short of the amount of
correction suggested by the comparison with the employment statistics. Over-all, it adds about 12,000
people, which is less than the 71,000 to 231,000
which the preceding analysis suggested were missing.

The Net Effects

This brief analysis of the accuracy of the cordon counts reached the conclusion that the counts
understate the number of passengers in the trains,
but the amount is unknown--possibly between 5 and 15
per cent. It is also probable that the understatement is confined to the intervals from 7:40 to 9:00
a.m. If this is valid, then the cordon counts for
6:20 to 7:40 and for 9:00 to 10:00 may be considered
as usably accurate.

The truncation adjustment makes a partial correction in the underestimated intervals. However,

even with the adjustment the results are still lower
than they probably ought to be. The amount of additional correction which these intervals require cannot be estimated on the basis of available evidence.

Conclusions

The cordon count statistics, to be serviceable
for this study, must accurately measure the subway
passengers, be representative of current and recent
transit traffic, and be adaptable for use in projections of traffic over a moderate period in the future. The examination just concluded dealt with
many topics which pertain to these required characteristics. These findings may now be summarized
into adjustments and rules of use which, when applied, will produce data satisfying the needs of the
study.

Factors Without Effect

Three of the potential sources of variability
in traffic proved minimal and hence will not affect
the cordon count data. These are the long-term and
cyclical causes of variation, intraweekly patterns,
and operating efficiency. The data show that these
factors do not distort the cordon count statistics
which will be used here.

The absence, in recent years, of a long-term
trend or cyclical variation contributes to the representative character of the 1962 counts, both with
respect to recent experience as well as to expectations of the near future. Stability in these respects means the data do not have to be adjusted to
make them represent the counts expected within the
proximate future.

No adjustment will be made in the cordon counts
to offset the effects of operating performance. The
study of operating efficiency did not disclose that
the system deviates from its schedule to an unusual
degree. The use of data uncorrected for operating
efficiency imparts to them a realistic character and

enhances their representativeness both for past experience and for projection to the future.

Factors Affecting Use
and Interpretation

The examination produced certain kinds of variation in traffic which need to be taken into account
at appropriate places in the analysis, but do not require any adjustment in the actual cordon count statistics. These were the seasonal variations, the
random or inherent variability in the data, and the
planned changes on the West Side IRT.

The pattern of seasonal variation indicates
that October runs about 3 per cent below the peak
month. In October, 1962, it was 6 per cent below
the peak. The studies of inherent variation in
traffic showed that the number of passengers can
vary, after giving effect to seasonal variation--by
a few percentage points. In using the October, 1962,
cordon counts to represent future possibilities of
transit traffic both these factors will shed light
on the upper limit of possible cordon counts.

The planned changes in the West Side IRT cannot
be used to estimate the cordon counts. But they
will be applicable to evaluating congestion and to
assessing the effects of alternative work schedules.

Alternative Cordon Counts

As a result of the analysis, two alternative
sets of cordon counts were made available for purposes of this study. These are the actual October,
1962, counts and the modified counts incorporating
the cordon interval patterns of the station.

The actual counts will be suitable wherever the
problem under analysis requires the exact October,
1962, experience. This will be the case in quantifying the prevailing extent of congestion and in the
special criteria which will emerge for testing the
feasibility of alternative work schedules.

The modified counts based on the cordon interval patterns endow the data with a representativeness covering a period of years, in particular the
last five. By extrapolation, the patterns ought
also to be applicable to the near future, probably
more so than the actual counts of any given year.

These two sets of counts may be used alone or
in combination, depending on the needs of the particular problem.

Adjustments

The examination produced one required adjustment in the data, the truncation adjustment. Its
effect will be to improve the accuracy of the count.
It is probably not enough of an improvement, for
there still remains a perceptible understatement of
the number of people passing through the subway cordon. It cannot therefore be said that the resulting
adjusted cordon counts are accurate. They improve
the data in the correct direction, hopefully by
enough to suit the purposes of the study.

THE STANDARD OF SUBWAY TRAFFIC

The feasibility of work staggering depends,
above all, on its ability to reduce subway congestion during rush hour. But reduce by how much? And
to what level? Any rider knows when a subway car is
overcrowded. But when is it not overcrowded, but
merely crowded or even acceptably crowded? And
when, as the number of passengers diminishes, does
the ride begin to be comfortable, even pleasant?
These questions point to a major decision confront-
ing the study of work staggering: What standard of
subway traffic should be used as the criterion of
feasibility?

This study has adopted a standard of subway
traffic called the comfort level. It was formulated
and developed by the engineers of the Transit Authority. As a standard, it provides a numerical

answer to the questions raised above and will be
used throughout this study as a criterion of acceptable transit traffic. If instituted, the comfort
level will substantially improve riding and related
conditions, especially during the rush hours--but it
will not provide a seat for every rider. In this
section, the comfort level standard will be explained and its choice justified.

The Comfort Level

The comfort level is designed to provide riding
conditions with specific--and improved--characteris-
tics. At comfort level, every seat in the car is
occupied by a rider. There are also standees in the
car, but they are not crowded. Their conditions are
specified by two characteristics. Their bodily contacts with each other are minimal and they should
have sufficient space to hold small items and to
read a newspaper.

These are better conditions than the ones that
now prevail in the subway cars during the rush hours.
In particular, the standees will benefit from the
comfort level standard. If the characteristics of
low pressure contact and sufficient space to read
the newspaper are actually introduced, the standees'
crowdedness will disappear. The comfort level does
not provide any direct improvement in the riding
conditions of the seated passengers. But the reduction in the number of standees will certainly improve their riding comfort.

This concept of the comfort level is formulated
qualitatively, by verbal statements. To serve as a
standard it must be translated into numbers of people. The Transit Authority engineers converted the
concept of comfort level into numerical standards,
reporting as follows:

> Our studies of a reasonably comfort-
> able riding level were based upon
> dimensions of an average adult, taking
> into account many factors such as

bulkiness of outerwear, the crooked arm
position of the average passenger carrying a handbag, or folio, books, or
newspapers; the allowance of only a
minimum of body pressure between standing passengers; and the assumption that
50 to 60 per cent of the standing passengers read newspapers. From the
foregoing it was estimated that each
standing passenger occupies an ellip-
tical area 2 feet by $1\frac{1}{2}$ feet.

These criteria were applied to drawings of the
floor area of each type of car. Ellipses (scaled
from 2 X $1\frac{1}{2}$ feet) were drawn on the floor area, after allowing adequate space for seated passengers.
The number of ellipses was then counted. The resulting numbers, plus the number of seats in the
car, produced the comfort level of each type of car.
The comfort level capacities for the four principal
cars of the system are given in Table 6. Appendix H
gives capacity data for each type of car, by cordon
station and line.

TABLE 6

Capacities of Principal Types of Subway Cars

Division	Car Type	Per Car Capacities			
		Seats	Maximum	Schedule	Comfort
IRT	all	40	200	180	140
IND	all	60	250	220	170
BMT	R27 and up	50	280	250	180
	A,B,Bx	80	300	260	200

A brief review was made of these procedures and their resulting comfort level standards. It produced the following observations.

The allowed space of 2 X 1½ feet appears to be reasonable. This assessment is based on the anthropometric data given in the Handbook of Human Engineering. The body measurement data reported in the Handbook indicate that the 2 X 1½ ellipse ought to be adequate for an adult, under conditions of the normal subway ride.

On the other hand, questions may be raised about the application of this space to the cars and the resulting standards. These are briefly noted in Appendix H. The conclusion reached by this review is that the comfort level standard has been applied acceptably by the Transit Authority engineers, but with a slight bias toward maximum utilization of car space. A more liberal application would bring down the comfort level capacity by about 5 per cent. However, it will serve no purpose to deviate from the Authority's standards in this study and hence they will be observed in all subsequent computations and evaluations.

Why This Standard?

The choice of the comfort level was a balance between two opposing considerations: the quality of the ride and its cost. It was made by an evaluation of qualitative considerations, not by arithmetic computations of quality and cost. Such computations are not possible in the present state of knowledge of this subject. The factors which led to the choice can be readily explained.

The comfort level standard, if introduced, would provide a significant improvement in riding conditions. This will be immediately evident from the data of Table 6. The comfort level capacity averages approximately two thirds of the maximum capacity of the cars and three quarters of the

schedule capacity.* The effect of the comfort level
would be a reduction of 25 per cent or more in the
number of riders. This is a significant improvement
in conditions.

Actually, the 25 per cent reduction understates
the amount of improvement which the comfort level
would produce. The improvement in riding conditions
would take place primarily among the standees in the
cars. If the comfort level capacity is evaluated
for standees only, the amount of improvement is far
greater. The number of standees at comfort level is
only two thirds of the number at schedule capacity.
At maximum capacity--which is the one prevailing
during the rush hour--the number of standees would
be reduced to less than 60 per cent. Since the
crowded conditions are experienced primarily by the
standees, the amount of improvement shown by this
computation is more realistic than the one including
the seated passengers.

The use of a standard which requires standees
in the cars is bound to prove disappointing, at
least initially. The statistics of Table 6 tell why
every rider cannot be given a seat. If the standard
provided for no standees--all passengers seated--
the cars would carry only about a fifth of their
maximum capacity, or a fourth of their present
schedule capacity, or a third of their comfort level
capacity. These are the proportions of seating
space to the total carrying capacities of the car.
Additional seats might be installed in the cars
which would raise the percentages by only small
amounts. It will be self-evident that the cost of

----

*The maximum capacity is the number of people
which the Transit Authority experts believe to be
the upper limit of possible riders in a car. The
schedule capacity is the number by which the Transit
Authority now schedules its trains and which serves
as the maximum estimate of riders during the cordon
counts.

such a standard is prohibitive. But even if cost
were not a factor, it could not be introduced under
present conditions. The transit system simply does
not have sufficient facilities to transport the people who have to enter and leave the CBD within an
acceptable range of time if the train loads were reduced to a fifth, a fourth, or even a third of their
present capacity.

The comfort level standard goes a long way toward improving the quality of a subway ride. The
question arises: Can the ride be improved even further? Can the number of standees be reduced to an
even lower level? Actually the standard can be set
at any point, but the quality of the ride will not
necessarily be improved. Once the number of standees is reduced so that they have adequate room--
little or no contact; space to read a paper or hold
bundles, as the comfort level provides--further reductions in standard do not necessarily provide
equivalent improvements in riding conditions. Reducing the number of standees raises quality only so
long as conditions are crowded. As crowdedness diminishes, the rate of quality improvement also diminishes.

A quality criterion alone does not dictate how
far the number of standees in the cars should be reduced, but cost does. As the number of standees is
reduced, the cost of transportation may rise. It
rises because the system has to add trains, personnel, and other inputs to provide the needed transportation service. Reducing the number of standees
in the car cannot fail to increase the cost of operation except under very special conditions.

These special conditions can be found in a program of work staggering. There is a narrow ledge of
possibility that such a program can bring about the
introduction of comfort level conditions without imposing an equivalent cost increase on the system.
The Transit Authority has the facilities and equipment to provide comfort level transportation--if the
flow of passengers can be suitably modified. The

basis for this supposition will become evident later
in the present chapter.

It is by no means certain that work staggering
can modify the flow of passengers to suit the available facilities and operating requirements of the
system.   Indeed, it may meet the Transit Authority's
requirements only part way and thereafter may cause
some additional outlays for equipment or operations.
At this juncture, it is important only to point out
that the system has enough unused capacity immediately before and after the peak period to introduce
the comfort level standard. If this unused capacity
can be filled, an improvement in riding conditions
will be achieved without an equivalent cost increase
to the system or a higher fare to the rider.

The choice of the comfort level standard was
made long before the possibility of rescheduling
work and meeting the cost conditions of the transit
system was examined.   Therefore, there could be no
advance knowledge as to whether the realistic possibilities of work staggering would in fact require
any cost increase. The cost consequences will depend on the results of the feasibility tests to be
described later in this report. However, there was
enough advance indication that the present cost levels could be preserved to warrant the adoption of
the comfort level standard.

THE PREVAILING STATE OF SUBWAY CONGESTION

It is now possible to ask--and to answer--an
important question: When and where does subway congestion occur? The times and places of congestion
cannot be identified conclusively, for reasons which
will shortly appear. But a fairly clear picture of
conditions and possibilities will emerge from the
inquiry.

Subway congestion will be defined--and measured
--as the number of passengers, during any interval,
in excess of the comfort level. If the excess of
any interval turns out to be negative--that is,

fewer passengers than the comfort capacity--the interval will then be said to have unused, excess
space equivalent to the negative number of passengers. In the analysis of congestion, the amount of
available and unused capacity will be an interesting
by-product.

Two sets of data will be used in this analysis.
The first consists of the comfort level capacity of
each interval during the October, 1962, cordon count.
These are given in Appendix Tables 17, 18, 19, 20,
21, and 22. The second consists of the October,
1962, cordon counts as presented in Appendix Tables
13 and 15. The cordon count data are the actual October, 1962, statistics (adjusted for truncation)
rather than as modified by the cordon interval patterns. The actual are used so that the cordon
counts will be compatible with the comfort level capacity data. The latter are based upon the actual
number of cars per interval during the October, 1962,
count. There are no equivalent data which could be
used to evaluate cordon counts modified by the cordon interval patterns. Hence for reasons of consis-
tency it is necessary to use actual data for both
the cordon counts and comfort level capacity. The
comfort levels for all cordon stations in the area
served by the southeast trains are 88 per cent of
their totals.

The analysis of congestion--excess passengers
and excess space--will be made in three ways, each
corresponding to a particular interpretation of conditions or of the comfort level standard. The first
two ways evaluate the excess passengers and space
under actual operating conditions during the October,
1962, count. Both accept the actual operations as
given, but they differ in the way in which they apply the comfort level standard. The third evaluates
congestion on the basis of hypothetical capacity operations. Its results are reported below in the
section called the net excess. The alternative assumptions and criteria--and their consequences--will
reveal some of the reasons why the times and places
of congestion cannot be located exactly.

The data of the ensuing sections are taken from Appendix J which describes the procedure by which excess passengers and excess space were computed.

Actual Excess

During the October, 1962, cordon count, the passengers in the subways experienced certain actual conditions of congestion. These actual conditions can be measured by subtracting the actual comfort level capacities from the cordon counts. The results of this procedure will be historically realistic, and will disclose what the people actually experienced by way of congestion or excess space. On the other hand the ensuing analysis will not reveal whether or not the actual conditions were normal or avoidable or inherent in the system. This kind of appraisal of congestion will be made later.

Tables 7 and 8 present, respectively, the numbers of excess passengers entering and leaving the CBD. These tables contain the first estimates of the actual excess passengers under the conditions of scheduling and operations prevailing in October, 1962. They will be analyzed and refined in the ensuing analysis.

Table 7 shows that 14 of the entering stations had excess passengers during one or more intervals and that 6 stations had no excess passengers. The table also shows that the congested intervals in the morning occurred between 7:20 and 9:00 a.m. (omitting the exceptional case at 6:40). The most congested interval was 8:20-8:40 during which 13 of the 20 stations show excess passengers. The next most congested are the 8:00-8:20 and 8:40-9:00 a.m. intervals with 8 and 7 stations, respectively. 7:20-7:40 and 7:40-8:00 have 3 and 2 stations. Prior to 7:20 and after 9:00 a.m. congestion does not appear to have occurred.

The pattern in the afternoon is slightly different from the one in the morning. Fifteen of the leaving stations show excess passengers and 5 do

TABLE 7

Excess Passengers Entering the CBD, by Cordon Station and Interval, October, 1962

Stations	6:20 6:40	6:40 7:00	7:00 7:20	7:20 7:40	7:40 8:00	8:00 8:20	8:20 8:40	8:40 9:00	9:00 9:20	9:20 9:40
86 & Lexington				467		2,771	1,994	1,518		
68 & Lexington						1,328	2,005	770		
72 & Broadway				98	808	2,558	2,420	2,123		
66 & Broadway										
125 & St. Nicholas					1,638	3,414	6,362			
72 & Central Park West										
Borough Hall						2,648	2,256			
Clark St.						1,813	2,088			
High St.		130								
York St.							922			
Court St. (Btn., 4 Ave. Lcl.)							2,032	624		
Court St. (West End, Nassau)										
Bedford Ave.										
Manhattan Br. (Btn., WE, SB Exp.)						1,610	3,284	2,048		
Manhattan Br. (WE Special)							1,064			
Williamsburg Br. (Jam.-Myrt.)										
23 & Ely						3,133	4,831	3,555		
Vernon-Jackson							1,330	1,952		
Queensboro Plaza (Btn. Lcl., WE)				260						
Queens Plaza (4 Ave. Lcl.)							520			

TABLE 8

Excess Passengers Leaving the CBD, by Cordon Station and Interval, October, 1962

Stations	3:20 3:40	3:40 4:00	4:00 4:20	4:20 4:40	4:40 5:00	5:00 5:20	5:20 5:40	5:40 6:00	6:00 6:20
Grand Central (Lex. Ave. Exp.)					1,180	3,801	1,562		
59 & Lexington (Lex. Ave. Lcl.)					1,376	2,998	3,049	1,879	
Times Square (7 Ave. Exp.)					10	1,923	2,222	977	
59 & Broadway (Bway. Lcl.)						2,000		120	
59 & Broadway (A, D)					441	7,265	6,758		
59 & Broadway (AA, BB, CC)									
Bowling Green						2,688	2,746		
Wall & William					1,894	2,323	750		
Broadway-Nassau							1,102		
East Broadway									
Whitehall St.					1,650	129			
Broad St.					904	1,239	68		
1st Ave.							280		
Manhattan Br. (Btn.,SB,WE Exp.)						4,011	3,961	1,348	
Manhattan Br. (WE Special)									
Williamsburg Br. (Jam.-Myrt.)									
Lexington & 53					113	4,476	4,246	1,224	
Grand Central (Flushing)					1,283	3,434	1,462		
Lexington & 60 (Btn. Lcl., WE)									
Lexington & 60 (4th Ave. Lcl.)						220			

75

not, according to Table 8. All the congestion occurs between 4:40 and 6:00 p.m. The four intervals
of this period have 9, 12, 13, and 5 congested stations, respectively.

There are no distinguishing characteristics
which set the congested stations apart from the uncongested ones. The congested stations--both entering and leaving--have express and local trains.
Their trains serve all the areas--north, northeast,
east, and southeast. All divisions--IRT, IND, and
BMT contribute to the congestion.

The planned increases in train length on the
West Side IRT will reduce the congestion but will by
no means eliminate it altogether. The addition of
cars will inevitably reduce the number of excess
passengers. Some of the congested intervals, as
shown on Tables 7 and 8, will disappear entirely.
All the others will have fewer excess passengers
than at present. In only one case, however--59th
and Broadway, on the Broadway Local--will the congestion disappear altogether by the increase in
train size. All the other stations will still have
some congestion in one or more intervals.

The same computation--passengers minus comfort
level capacity--also yields negative quantities.
Wherever capacity is greater than the number of passengers, the difference measures the amount of
available but unused space in the trains. Tables 9
and 10 present respectively the amount of excess
space entering and leaving the CBD. On these tables
blank spaces mean that the intervals had excess passengers, not excess space. Small lines (-) in the
intervals signify that no passengers were reported.

These tables give the obverse case of the excess passenger table. Every station having entries
in each column is a station with no excess passengers. In the morning, from 6:20 to 7:20 and from
9:20 to 10:00 all the stations (but one) have available space. As the peak period approaches the number of intervals with unutilized space diminishes.
In the afternoon from 3:20 to 4:40 and from 6:00 to

TABLE 9

Excess Space (Equivalent to Passengers) Entering the CBD,
by Cordon Station and Interval, October, 1962

Stations	6:20 6:40	6:40 7:00	7:00 7:20	7:20 7:40	7:40 8:00	8:00 8:20	8:20 8:40	8:40 9:00	9:00 9:20	9:20 9:40
86 & Lexington	2,800	5,600	2,903		247				6,000	5,520
68 & Lexington	2,280	1,690	3,890	200	801				1,490	900
72 & Broadway	3,770	5,170	2,760						10	2,550
66 & Broadway	2,950	1,660	3,180	2,880	2,500	1,750	1,160	1,790	2,130	2,180
125 & St. Nicholas	4,090	4,260	4,170	2,720				2,921	10,000	5,550
72 & Central Park West	1,260	1,350	2,310	6,210	3,240	3,330	6,850	7,120	6,860	4,510
Borough Hall	2,586	1,786	3,370	1,522	502			2,806	6,924	7,546
Clark St.	2,446	2,256	2,955	783	872			2,454	2,613	4,343
High St.	820		250	1,760	181	3,850		2,719	6,210	3,680
York St.	637	1,284	2,786	2,990	2,300	1,000	1,000	3,750	3,824	3,098
Court St. (Btn.,4 Ave.Lcl.)	1,874	4,312	2,962	2,612	1,995	2,004			1,589	2,062
Court St. (West End,Nassau)	-	2,434	1,152	-	972	1,652	424	53	954	462
Bedford Ave.	1,420	1,370	380	490	1,370	850	500	2,550	3,020	2,260
Manhattan Br. (Btn.,WE,SB Exp.)	2,669	9,929	3,142	4,290	398				5,230	6,316
Manhattan Br. (WE Special)	-	-	-	-	437	47		30	-	-
Williamsburg Br.(Jam.-Myrt.)	3,910	3,450	3,630	1,127	1,540	390	1,206	3,726	5,450	2,210
23 & Ely	3,200	4,170	4,330	2,330	1,030				2,350	1,940
Vernon-Jackson	1,570	2,980	3,770	460	2,020	1,100			1,560	2,690
Queensboro Plaza(Btn.Lcl,WE)	3,670	3,830	390		880	1,400	3,070	2,690	4,920	7,060
Queens Plaza (4 Ave. Lcl.)	-	950	1,610	660	50	190		780	1,000	1,420

TABLE 10

Excess Space (Equivalent to Passengers) Leaving the CBD, by Cordon Station and Interval, October, 1962

Stations	3:20 3:40	3:40 4:00	4:00 4:20	4:20 4:40	4:40 5:00	5:00 5:20	5:20 5:40	5:40 6:00	6:00 6:20
Grand Central (Lex. Ave. Exp.)	1,830	2,180	2,850	384				930	5,320
59 & Lexington (Lex. Av. Lcl.)	2,810	1,220	2,470	2,170					720
Times Square (7 Ave. Exp.)	2,310	4,000	4,850	3,700					670
59 & Broadway (Bway.Lcl.)	3,430	3,390	2,860	4,500	3,400	420			2,190
59 & Broadway (A, D)	4,790	4,020	6,190	7,200				1,160	2,750
59 & Broadway (AA, BB, CC)	990	1,630	1,370	4,960	4,900	3,520	6,530	5,600	6,740
Bowling Green	5,622	5,582	4,240	6,036	958			224	2,240
Wall & William	3,894	5,912	5,192	3,058				1,383	1,025
Broadway-Nassau	1,200	2,190	1,120	2,250	4,463	127		2,980	5,530
East Broadway	3,268	3,088	3,784	2,518	4,310	2,054	976	1,374	4,240
Whitehall St.	2,678	2,182	2,092	92			673	603	5,050
Broad St.	886	1,762	1,252	636				1,568	1,622
1st Ave.	1,960	2,440	1,860	2,250	700	630		810	3,410
Manhattan Br. (Btn., SB, WE Exp.)	4,174	5,306	4,870	3,542	1,012				2,842
Manhattan Br. (WE Special)						481	350		
Williamsburg Br. (Jam.-Myrt.)	2,200	3,110	5,010	3,980	2,020	690	370	2,740	4,360
Lexington & 53	1,310	1,940	2,970	1,590					2,470
Grand Central (Flushing)	3,520	1,930	4,500	2,480				430	300
Lexington & 60 (Btn.Lcl., WE)	3,440	3,660	5,350	4,740	4,210	2,480	2,490	2,410	3,650
Lexington & 60 (4th Ave. Lcl.)	2,470	1,910	1,860	2,410	220		550	1,540	710

6:20 all the intervals have excess space. In the
four intervals of the peak most of the stations do
not have any excess space.

One main observation may be made about Tables
9 and 10. They show the scope which now exists for
rescheduling the passengers' travel time. In every
case, the numbers of excess passengers are fewer
than the numbers of excess spaces. It would thus be
possible--at least theoretically--to provide all
riders with comfort level transportation without
adding a single car to the capacity of the system.
Moreover, if some of the trains could be shifted
from the earlier and later intervals somewhat closer
to the present peak, it would not be necessary to
reschedule passengers by more than one or two intervals in order to achieve a comfort level. This is
the way work staggering might be instituted without
increasing costs.

The Net Excess

An objection can be raised against the preceding analysis. Not all the excess passengers, as
shown on Tables 7 and 9, signify subway congestion.
Some of the excess was caused by inadequate sched-
ules--either numbers of cars per train, trains per
interval, or both. Some was caused by operating delays; even a short back-up of trains will increase
the crowding during the rush hours. Some was caused
by insufficient facilities which are to be supplied
in the near future. By eliminating these sources of
excess passengers, an irreducible amount of congestion can be estimated--congestion arising from too
many passengers per interval, given the existing and
projected capacity of the system.

A computation of the net excess of passengers
entering the CBD during the morning rush hours is
presented in Appendix I. This computation differs
from the preceding ones in the three particulars
noted above. It corrects the cordon counts for operating delays. It employs a measure of maximum
comfort level capacity per 20-minute interval. And

it incorporates the planned changes in train size
and other operating facilities. It also retains the
adjustment for the southeast stations.

   In computing the net excess, at least two simplifying assumptions have been made. It is assumed
that the flow of passengers is unaffected by the
capacity scheduling during the intervals which need
it. Actually, with full capacity, people would
probably change their travel times. Moreover, the
computation assumes that full capacities can be
scheduled--and run--whenever the intervals require
them. These assumptions separate the computations
from reality, but not by enough to mar the resulting
estimates.

   Table 11 presents the estimates of net excess
passengers entering the CBD through each station.
It contrasts markedly with the preceding estimates.
Altogether, only nine stations of the twenty have
any net excess passengers. Of the nine, three have
negligible amounts, and one has few enough to disre-
gard--520 during a 20-minute interval. This leaves
five stations having appreciable congestion problems.

TABLE 11

Net Excess of Passengers Entering the CBD,
by Cordon Station

Station	7:40 8:00	8:00 8:20	8:20 8:40	8:40 9:00
68 & Lexington			2,005	770
125 & St. Nicholas	1,134	3,549	6,583	
High St.			2,622	
Court St. (Btn.,)				)
4 Ave. Lcl.))				)
Court St. (West End,)				) 8
Nassau))				)
Manhattan Br. (Btn.,				
WE, SB Exp.)		308	2,158	2,048
23 & Ely		3,399	4,567	1,855
Vernon-Jackson			70	
Queens Plaza (4 Ave.Lcl.)			520	

Altogether, only fifteen intervals are congested. Again, by reducing the minor cases, twelve congested intervals remain. They range from 7:40 to
9:00. The first interval has one station; the second, three stations; the third, five stations; and
the fourth, three stations.

It is also of interest to note that three stations have congestion in three of the intervals.
They are: 125th Street and St. Nicholas Avenue (the
IND A and D trains), the 23rd Street and Ely Avenue
station (IND E and F trains), and the BMT Brighton,
West End and Sea Beach Express trains counted at the
Manhattan Bridge. Only one station has two congested intervals: the IRT local stop at 68th Street and
Lexington Avenue. The remaining stations are congested in only one interval each, the third one--
8:20-8:40.

The subway congestion which, under the given
assumptions, is considered irreducible is portrayed
by Table 11. It occurs in four intervals but predominantly in 8:20-8:40, and it occurs principally
at four stations.

Assessment

Subway congestion was analyzed in the section
just concluded at two levels, each producing its own
statement of congested intervals and stations. The
minimal level--the net excess--identified six congested entering stations and thirteen intervals, lying between 7:40 and 9:00 a.m. (eliminating the negligible cases); and the middle level evaluated congestion on the basis of actual operations and capacities during October, 1962, applying the comfort
level on a 20-minute basis. It produced fourteen
congested entering stations and fifteen leaving
ones, occurring between 7:20 and 9:00 a.m. and from
4:40 to 6:00 p.m.

These findings must now be assessed from the
viewpoint of the whole study. Do the tables accurately portray the congestion? Do the stations,

intervals, and numbers of excess passengers reflect
the travel conditions in the system? The answer--as
will presently be shown--is that there was probably
more congestion than the tables reveal, but that it
cannot be specified any more precisely on the basis
of the available cordon counts.

In assessing these statistical results, the
first level--the actual operating conditions and the
20-minute interval comfort capacity--is the most
relevant of the two. The capacity schedule which
produced the net amount of excess passengers is not
applicable because it represents a hypothetical situation, whereas the ensuing analysis is concerned
with real conditions.

Those tables reveal a remarkable situation.
They show a surprisingly small amount of congestion
in the subway system during the rush hour. It is
small both in the degree (per cent) of congestion,
and in the number of congested stations and intervals.

The small amount of congestion shown by these
tables can be summarized in various ways. First,
the proportion of intervals showing any congestion
is low. Second, the low amount of congestion is
also disclosed by the percentages of excess passengers. Why, it may be asked, should they be considered low? Low in relation to what standard?

The evidence against which these numerical results are compared is twofold. There has been persistent clamor against subway congestion for a long
time, principally in the newspapers and journals of
this area. Admittedly this is a tenuous and insub-
stantial basis for judging the statistics. The
journalistic complaints about subway crowding are
not specific with respect to the location, extent,
or degree of congestion. Nevertheless, the sheer
persistence of complaints suggest a more widespread
and severe congestion than the statistics indicate.

A second basis for the judgment is more pertinent, and partly quantitative. It comes from

information collected by the sociological study of
the Staggered Working Hours Project. (For a description of this study see Chapter 5.) It reports
the views of subway riders about conditions in the
subway which do not correspond to the statistical
results.

The respondents of the survey were asked: "In
general how satisfied are you with the way you travel to and from work each day?" They were given a
choice of answers ranging from very dissatisfied to
very satisfied. The replies underscore the discrim-
inating response to the question. Sixty-five per
cent of the subway riders reported favorable feelings toward their mode of transport (very satisfied,
fairly satisfied, the way is all right). Only 34
per cent of the riders reported that they were dissatisfied or very dissatisfied with their subway
travel. A substantial degree of satisfaction with
the subway as a mode of transportation prevails
among the people who use it on their journey to
work.

When these same respondents were asked about
conditions on the subway during rush hours they provided quite a different kind of response. This time
only 31 per cent of the subway riders regarded the
conditions favorably. Their answers ranged from a
reaction of very good to so-so. Sixty-six per cent
of the riders considered the subway conditions during the rush hours as bad or very bad. When asked
what they considered bad about subway conditions,
the respondents replied overwhelmingly--crowding.

The significant finding is the 66 per cent who
consider the subway conditions bad during the rush
hours. This contrasts with only 36 per cent of the
passengers who, according to the cordon count statistics, travel under congested conditions. (This
36 per cent represents the total number of passengers traveling in each of the intervals shown on
Table 7 as a per cent of the total cordon count.
The intervals of Table 7 identify the stations and
times having excess passengers. The numbers used in

this computation of 36 per cent were then taken from the corresponding intervals of Appendix Table 13.) Almost twice as many people experience unfavorable conditions as the cordon counts indicate.

If this assessment is valid--if there is more congestion in the subways than the statistics reveal --there can be only one source to the discrepancies between the real conditions and those reported by the cordon counts. The counts must understate the number of people traveling through the cordon stations during the rush hour. The comfort level capacity data on which the calculations are based are taken from the actual observation of the numbers of cars passing through the stations during the count. It is most unlikely that any significant errors crept into the reporting of trains and cars. Accordingly, the comfort level data have to be accepted as accurate. If they are accurate then the cordon counts must be too low, because the number and per cents of excess passengers are reached by simple subtraction of capacity from counts.

Conclusions

The assessment of congestion produced a valuable if disappointing by-product. It reached the conclusion that the cordon counts, despite the truncation adjustment, still underestimate subway traffic. Hence, if the counts are used later in the study to test the effects of alternative work schedules upon subway traffic, they will produce distorted results--biased in the direction of showing relief of congestion when such relief may not really be available. It therefore becomes necessary to correct the counts again before they are used to test feasibility. This will be done on the basis of findings in Chapter 6.

What remains then of the analysis of congestion? Are these results invalid? Actually, the shortcomings of the cordon counts cause only minor damage to the findings of congestion.

Certainly the perimeter of subway congestion includes at least the stations and intervals revealed as congested by the excess passenger tables. The tables also show the peaks and other high places of excessive traffic. The shortcomings in the counts hide the marginally congested stations and dampen the full force of congestion in the others. But for many purposes, these unrevealed aspects of congestion are not particularly important. Where they are, a way has been found--as just noted--to bring them to light.

Actually, enough is revealed by analysis of congestion to suit the requirements of the study of work staggering. This will become evident as the inquiry proceeds.

THE RELIEF OF SUBWAY CONGESTION

The location and degree of subway congestion are now sufficiently known so that the needed amount of relief can be fruitfully investigated. The congestion statistics presented above will inevitably lead to underestimates of the required relief. However, by anticipating the reconstructed cordon counts developed in Chapter 6, and by applying the correction factors developed from them, the congestion statistics can be used to calculate the relief requirements.

By how much must the cordon counts be reduced in order to eliminate subway congestion? The answer is obvious: by amounts sufficient to remove excess passengers from all intervals of all stations. To discover these amounts, however, requires some reasoning and some computation.

Of the two measures of congestion presented above, the most appropriate one for the problem at hand is the net excess. This is the amount of excess reduced to a minimum by allowing for a maximum number of trains, higher operating efficiency, and the planned expansion of facilities. Congestion cannot be reduced below the amount of the net excess

by any other available measures. Hence, it represents the congestion to which the above question
refers.

The net excess of passengers, by station and
interval, is given on Table 11. To remove the excess from any single interval of any station--by any
general program such as work staggering--the entire
interval, including all stations, has to be reduced.
There is no general way to bring about a reduction
in the passengers of one station without reducing
the others. Hence, the obvious answer given above
must be amplified. To eliminate subway congestion,
each interval containing stations with excess passengers must be reduced by a total amount which,
when distributed to the individual stations according to their per cent of the total, will remove the
excess passengers from the congested ones.

The required amount of reduction for any interval can easily be calculated. For example, the 8:00-
8:20 interval shows three congested stations having
respectively 3,549, 308, and 3,399 excess passengers.
By how much must the total interval be reduced in
order to eliminate all these excesses? To determine
this amount, each of these excesses must be divided
by the percentage which its station has of the total
interval count. They are, respectively, 9.9 per
cent, 8.1 per cent, and 9.4 per cent. These percentages are obtained from Appendix Table 23. The
results of these divisions are: 35,776, 3,788, and
36,237. These numbers and the corresponding ones
for all the other excess passengers are presented in
Table 12.

To eliminate the excess passengers from the
8:00-8:20 interval, the maximum number of passengers
of the three must be removed from the CBD total for
the interval. By removing the maximum, 36,237, its
corresponding excess will be reduced to zero, and
the excesses of the other two stations will be
brought even lower than zero. If anything less than
the maximum is used, the maximum station will continue to have some excess passengers.

TABLE 12

Equivalent Net Excess Passengers
(Before Final Correction)

Station	7:40 8:00	8:00 8:20	8:20 8:40	8:40 9:00
68 & Lexington			32,235	12,392
125 & St. Nicholas	9,939	35,776	68,218	
High St.			32,172	
Manhattan Br. (Btn., WE, SB Exp.)		3,788	28,357	24,410
23 & Ely		36,237	44,600	16,315
Vernon-Jackson			7,000	
Queens Plaza (4 Ave. Lcl.)			18,571	

The procedure just illustrated produced the equivalent total CBD excess cordon counts shown on Table 12. In presenting these numbers, two important accompanying statements must be made. First, the use of Appendix Table 23 to convert the excess passengers to their equivalent totals assumes that the percentages of the table (based on 5-year averages) will continue to prevail after some general change affecting subway travel, such as work staggering. It is entirely possible that a change in work schedules will alter the percentages of the individual stations, but there is no basis at present for forecasting such alterations. Hence the prevailing pattern was used—with full awareness of its possible distortion—as the best available estimate of the probable pattern. Second, the equivalent total CBD excesses given in Table 12 are preliminary; they are as yet not increased by correction factors presented in Chapter 6.

Table 13 presents the maximums of each column
of Table 12. It also presents these maximums increased by the corrections developed in Chapter 6.

TABLE 13

Required Reductions in Total CBD Cordon Counts,
by Interval, Preliminary and Corrected

| | Required Reductions | |
Interval	Preliminary	Corrected
7:40-8:00	9,939	9,939
8:00-8:20	36,237	36,418
8:20-8:40	68,218	88,206
8:40-9:00	24,410	30,903

These are the amounts by which the cordon
counts must be reduced--under all the conditions so
far stated as to scheduling, operating efficiency,
and improvements in facilities, and according to the
reconstructed cordon counts developed in Chapter 6--
in order to reduce subway congestion and to provide
comfort level transportation. They will be used in
Chapter 7 as the basis of the criteria of feasibility of work staggering. Alternative CBD work schedules will be tested there to determine whether or
not they can remove these numbers of people from the
total CBD interval cordon counts.

CONCLUSIONS

This chapter had two goals. First, it had to
establish measures and measurements of subway traffic, both for its own use and for the rest of this
study. Second, it sought to identify the prevailing
location and degree of subway congestion and to

determine how much relief is needed. The results
may be succinctly summarized.

As a measure of subway traffic, the cordon
count is wholly acceptable, but the actual statistics are less than satisfactory as measurements.
They will have to be used by this study, but with
awareness of the nature and location of their shortcomings.

The comfort level is an acceptable standard of
traffic. Its numerical values are also satisfactory
but must be used with the knowledge of their special
characteristics--they are conservative and must be
interpreted accordingly.

Next, the measurements and standards of traffic
were put to work to locate and quantify subway congestion. The findings were considered usable but
too restricted in extent and intensity on account of
the limitations of the statistics. By employing a
correction device which becomes available after
Chapter 6, estimates were made of the amount of relief required in the total CBD cordon counts during
the four congested intervals.

There are serious inadequacies in the traffic
statistics, particularly for the purposes of this
study. They have been unhesitatingly exposed during
the course of the chapter. These shortcomings cannot fail to affect the strength of the results produced by the inquiry. Nevertheless, the data are
judged, after careful assessment, to be at least
minimally adequate for the uses to which they will
be put.

CHAPTER 3 CBD INDUSTRY AND WORK SCHEDULES

This study is built upon a foundation of industry and work schedule statistics. They are used in the design of researches, especially into the modifiability of schedules reported in Chapters 4 and 5. They are a crucial component in the relationship of transit traffic to work schedules, as analyzed in Chapter 6. In Chapter 7 they are the principal data employed in the computations of feasibility. These statistics--their strengths and frailties--must be made available, and this is the appropriate place to do it.

Two purposes give shape to the ensuing presentation. The first is to establish the actual statistics of industry, employment and schedules which are used throughout the rest of the study. This includes an explanation of the data and an appraisal of their validity. It will not be possible to present all of the statistics of industry, employment and work schedules used in the study. They are too numerous and the tables would overburden the text and appendixes. The statistics of the CBD as a whole will be given in the section to follow, and Appendix K contains the data of major industry divisions. This will suffice to establish the statistics, which is the first purpose of the presentation.

The second purpose is to provide substantive information about industry and scheduling in the CBD. From this information, interpreted qualitatively, conclusions will be drawn about the nature of work scheduling, the sources of congestion, and the appropriate industries to investigate for schedule modifiability.

90

There will be two sections to this chapter.
The first will describe the CBD as a whole. The
second section will consist of a comparative analysis of the major industry divisions and an appraisal
of the statistics.

THE CBD

This study perceives the vast complex of the
CBD from the simplifying perspective of work staggering. As a result, it can describe the CBD by concentrating on its principal characteristics: its industries, employment, location of employment, and work
schedules. These are the things which are relevant
to the study of work staggering.

The industries are aggregates of places of employment whose work schedules are the cause and remedy
of transit congestion, at least by the fundamental
assumption of work staggering. The numbers of people
scheduled in each industry are given by the employment statistics. The location of employment within
the CBD can be a significant factor because of the
time it takes to travel between cordon stations and
places of employment. Finally, the work schedules
disclose the times imposed by the industry upon their
people, and thereby upon the times they travel.
These characteristics furnish a picture of the CBD
as a collection of transit destinations and origins
which control, at least in part, the travel times of
the people who work in them.

The description will consist of three parts:
industry and employment, location, and work schedules.
In each, special attention will be given to the sta-
tistics--to their origin, reliability, and other pertinent characteristics. Each part will also explain
the significance of its subject to work staggering.
Thus, this presentation of the CBD will lay down a
pattern to be followed in Appendix K in describing
the major industry divisions.

Industry and Employment

This study views the CBD's industries in a very special way. It sees them as scheduling units--as entities which fix the times their people start and stop work. This has implications with respect to decision making about work schedules, timing, inter-industry relations, employee relations, and many other factors which will be expounded in Chapters 4 and 5. The study also sees industry and employment as units to be rescheduled. As such they must be divisible and combinable within constraints imposed by their functions and people. This special perspective will be felt at once, in describing industry and employment in the CBD. It will emerge with increasing clarity as the study proceeds.

The statistics of CBD industry and employment come from a tabulation prepared by the New York State Department of Labor and the New York City Department of City Planning. To use these statistics, the Staggered Working Hours Project had to modify them in various ways. The original statistics and the modifications will be described partly in the present section and partly in the one which follows.

The Division of Employment of the New York State Department of Labor maintains records of firms covered by unemployment insurance, including such data as the type of business and the number of employees. Most firms in the CBD are legally required to be covered by unemployment insurance. The principal exceptions were (at the time of the statistics) governmental and nonprofit organizations and firms with less than two employees. However, the exempted establishments could elect voluntarily to be covered by unemployment insurance and would therefore be included in the records.

The New York State Department of Labor (Division of Research) and the New York City Department of City Planning cooperated to produce a tabulation of covered employment for September, 1958. This tabulation gives statistics of employment by major industry

division, and by 2-, 3-, and 4-digit industry classification. These statistics are available both for
the CBD as a whole and for each of its census tracts.
These statistics are referred to throughout this
study as the Tabulation.

The New York City Department of City Planning
made supplementary surveys, attempting to fill in
some of the statistical lacunae. It made special estimates of selected noncovered and governmental employment. The final estimates still exclude the self-
employed, domestic workers, unpaid family workers,
and uniformed armed services personnel.

Table 14 presents the estimates of the numbers
of firms and employees by major industrial divisions
of Manhattan's CBD. The first two columns give the
Tabulation's original statistics of firms and employment. The third column contains the adjusted estimates of employment produced by the New York City Department of City Planning.

The total covered employment in the CBD, according to the Tabulation, amounted to 1,879,612 people
in September, 1958. The New York City Planning Department's adjusted total brings the employment to
2,046,400, an increase of 166,788. The table shows
where the principal increases were made. They are
primarily in services, transportation, communications, electric, gas, and sanitary services. All of
the other divisions show smaller increases.

An important general rule, in regard to these
differences in statistics, is followed throughout
this study. The New York City Department of City
Planning total of 2,046,400 is used as the total CBD
employment in all places where this statistic is required. It will be encountered repeatedly during
the course of this report. However, wherever the
study requires employment statistics by individual
industry (2-, 3-, or 4-digit levels) or by census
tract, the data of the Tabulation are used. They
are not adjusted by the increases of the New York
City Department of City Planning.

TABLE 14

Number of Firms and Employees in Manhattan's
Central Business District, by Major
Industrial Division, September, 1958

Division	Firms	Employment	Adjusted Employment*
Agriculture, forest- ry and fisheries	43	318	
Mining	77	1,884	1,900
Contract construction	1,830	35,358	44,700
Manufacturing	21,341	519,167	527,500
Transportation, com- munication, elec- tric, gas, and sanitary services	3,252	176,057	206,100
Wholesale trade	18,731	226,731	233,900
Retail trade	11,066	193,186	209,000
Finance, insurance and real estate	11,416	312,920	336,700
Services	18,061	275,229	355,500
Government	1,026	130,994	131,100
Nonclassified and other	1,594	7,768	
Total	88,437	1,879,612	2,046,400

*By the New York City Department of City Planning.

The use of these two data sources produces a
discrepancy in the statistics which remains unrecon-
ciled, and for several reasons. First, the Department of City Planning's estimates apply to major industry divisions as shown on Table 14, and not to
individual industries. To distribute the increases
to the component industries in some systematic,
arithmetic way would have satisfied the numerical
discrepancy, but would not necessarily have produced
more accurate results at the individual industry
level where the accuracy is needed. Next, the Tabulation's statistics are also available--and used--on
a geographical basis, by census tracts, and by industry within census tracts. These could not have been
corrected by the adjustment procedure. Accordingly,
some portion of the numerical discrepancy would
still have remained. Third, as it turned out, the
principal adjustments were made in places where the
study doesn't really require them. Hence, as a matter of expediency the damage resulting from the unre-
solved discrepancy is small. Finally, by using the
Tabulation's lower estimates rather than the higher
ones of the City Planning Department, the computations of feasibility are given a slightly conservative bias. In estimating the effects of changing
any industry's schedule, fewer persons are shifted
than if the City Planning Department's statistics
were used. The amount of difference is small, but
it places that much additional onus on the task of
demonstrating the feasibility of work staggering--a
desirable safety factor for the study as a whole.

The Modified Employment Statistics

The statistical requirements of this study in
respect to industry and employment evolved gradually,
as results of the research and analysis began to accumulate. Accordingly, the need to modify the Tabulation's industry and employment statistics continued
to develop--indeed to the very last stages of the
study. At this juncture, the nature of the difficulties with the tabulation will be reviewed. Some of
the modifications will be presented here. Others
will be given in appropriate places later in the report.

The principal problem encountered in using the
Tabulation arose from its industry classification.
The Tabulation classifies firms according to the
Standard Industrial Classification of the United
States Bureau of the Budget. For many purposes this
is an adequate classification system. However, for
the study of scheduling it often produces unsuitable
results, as the following examples disclose.

There is a general problem in industrial classification which is also felt in this study, sometimes
keenly. Under the Standard Industrial Classification
an establishment is classified "according to its
major activity." Where an establishment engages in
more than one activity--as frequently happens--a
choice has to be made in classifying it. If the activities are closely related, no great harm may result. But when they are quite different, one activity is lost. As an example, many firms in lower Manhattan classified as used machinery wholesalers engage in manufacturing, repair, and installation. An
even more acute example concerns a major CBD industry, textile converting. Firms engaged in converting
can be found classified as dry goods wholesalers, tex
tile manufacturers, and in some instances as business
credit institutions (on account of their factoring
activities). At the 4-digit level of classification,
this may not be a serious problem, if the activities
occur in different premises. But at the 2-digit and
major industry division levels, the value of the
classification diminishes steeply.

This general problem gives rise to a specific
one with which this study had to contend. Establishments are classified by the industry to which their
product or service belongs. But frequently the particular establishment is engaged in a specialized
company function which is itself another industry.
Examples are: the large industrial kitchen of a
restaurant chain which is classified as a restaurant;
or a garment factory located on the premises of the
company office of a retail chain and classified as a
retail store. Even more common is the case of office
establishments which are classified in the industry

of their company. This is typically the case in contract construction, building operation, stevedoring,
and some others.

    The classification system creates special prob-
lems by placing publishing offices among manufacturing industries; by grouping radio and television companies together with telephone and telegraph companies. At least insofar as scheduling is concerned,
publishing is quite different from manufacturing,
and radio and TV have little in common with telephone
and telegraph. None of these cases is an inaccurate
classification; they adhere to the rules of the system. But they produce combinations of establishments
which, from the viewpoint of work scheduling, are
quite dissimilar.

    The extreme case arises in connection with a
special type of establishment, the central administrative office. The CBD is an important national
and world center of company headquarters, or of company offices with special functions (in relation to
finance, advertising, engineering and design, and
the like), or of regional or district offices.
Their functions fall predominantly within the category of administration, although some may engage in
purchasing or wholesaling, but not as their major activity. These establishments are particularly difficult to classify industrially, because they usually
belong to companies with many industrial activities
and because they perform company functions, the same
as those of companies which locate them within the
premises of their principal operations. There are
many of these establishments in the CBD, and they
are classified by the Tabulation according to the
principal industry of their parent company. This
produces comical results. For example, the Tabulation reports that there are 102 firms with 5,740 employees in primary metal industries--but the CBD has
no blast furnaces, steel works, or foundries (of any
size). Similarly, there are supposed to be seven-
teen petroleum refining establishments with 7,428
employees in the CBD. Both are obviously company
offices. The offices and operating establishments

of these industries are entirely different from the
viewpoint of scheduling, but they are combined in
the statistics of the Tabulation.

Insofar as possible, adjustments had to be made
in the Tabulation to overcome the effects of the
classification. A special study was made of central
administrative offices and is reported in a technical paper of the Staggered Working Hours Project entitled, "Employment in Central Administrative Offices
in Manhattan's Central Business District." It furnishes estimates of employment in central administrative offices, and of the numbers by which the industry statistics should be reduced in order to yield
net employment in operating establishments. All of
the estimates are approximate. The only claim made
for them is that they produce final statistics which
are probably better--for the uses of this study--
than the original ones.

Other adjustments and corrections were also
made in the original data. Office industries were
separated from the operating industries, and were
classified accordingly. In some industries, both
kinds of establishment--office and operating--were
found classified together. Wherever possible, they
were separated into two categories and identified
appropriately. The original data were also adjusted
and corrected in other respects. They will be reported later in the chapter.

Table 15 summarizes the employment statistics
as modified by the Staggered Working Hours Project.
The table also repeats the statistics of the Tabulation and of the New York City Department of City
Planning.

The modifications introduced by the Staggered
Working Hours Project improve the original statistics, at least for the purposes of this study. They
should not be construed as final, complete, or even
better estimates of employment than those of the
Tabulation and the Department of City Planning. The
modifications were not made systematically and

TABLE 15

The September, 1958, Employment in Manhattan's Central Business District, by Major Industry Division, as Modified by the Staggered Working Hours Project

	Tabulation	City Planning Department	Total	Central Administrative Offices
Agriculture, forestry, and fisheries	318		318	
Mining	1,884	1,900		1,927
Contract construction	35,358	44,700	35,358	
Manufacturing	519,167	527,500	365,000	97,282
Transportation, communication, electric, gas, and sanitary services	176,057	206,100	160,489	
Wholesale trade	226,731	233,900	226,731	13,755
Retail trade	193,186	209,000	193,186	22,152
Finance, insurance, and real estate	312,920	336,700	378,290	
Services	275,229	355,500	275,229	5,083
Government	130,994	131,100	125,876	
Nonclassified and other	7,768			
Central administrative offices			140,199	140,199
Undistributed			145,724	
Total	1,879,612	2,046,400	2,046,400	

consistently in all industry categories, but only
where the Project required them for its studies of
scheduling and rescheduling. The significance and
limitations of these modifications will become evident as they are described more fully.

The Findings

Table 15 establishes the statistics of industry
employed in the study.

The best available estimate of the number of
people who work in the CBD is 2,046,400. It is the
number produced by the New York City Department of
Planning and is shown as the total of the second column of Table 15. It is retained throughout the study
despite the adjustments and corrections of the component data. All subsequent computations requiring
the total CBD employment use this number.

The statistics of the major industry divisions
as modified by the Staggered Working Hours Project
are given in the third and fourth columns of Table
15. These data follow closely the original statistics furnished by the Tabulation. The differences
will be explained in the descriptions of the industry divisions in Appendix K.

The largest industry division of the CBD, according to the Tabulation and the City Planning Department, is manufacturing. Even after removing an
estimated 97,282 people in central administrative
offices, it has 437,486 employees. However, the
Staggered Working Hours Project reduced this number
to 365,000 by excluding some of the office industries.
After this modification the finance, insurance, and
real estate division with its 378,290 people becomes
the largest of the CBD divisions, accounting for almost 19 per cent of the total. Services follow with
275,229 employees. Wholesale and retail trades are
next in size with 11 and 10 per cent of the total
respectively. Transportation, communications, and public utilities have 8 per cent of the total; central

administrative offices have 7 per cent; and government 6 per cent. Contract construction, the smallest group, has relatively few employees in the CBD.

The statistics of Table 15 summarize industry
and employment by major industry divisions. They
are aggregate statistics composed of the data of
three levels of subdivision--the so-called 2-, 3-,
and 4-digit levels. The more refined statistics are
available to this study for purposes of analysis and
computation. (See Appendix K.)

The CBD is an area of very heterogeneous employment. It contains a large amount of manual, physical,
production or blue-collar employment. These are to
be found in contract construction, manufacturing,
transportation, services, government, and to some extent, even in wholesale trades. It also has very
large amounts of white-collar employment in office
establishments, trade, the financial industries, services, government, and in professional establishments. It has not been possible to reduce these occupational categories to specific quantitative estimates. To some extent, establishments and industry groups have been identified with respect to their
predominant occupation. These will turn out to be
important in scheduling and rescheduling, and will
be explained in appropriate places. However, the estimates are made only for the industries in which
this study is particularly interested. They are not
to be construed as descriptive of the CBD as a whole.

The Location of Employment

The location of employment within the CBD is an
important factor in transit traffic. Travel time to
the various cordon stations varies significantly
from different places in the CBD. It is accordingly
of interest to examine the distribution of employment over the area. This will establish the prevailing pattern of location for use later in the study.

The CBD is divided up by the Bureau of the Census into so-called census tracts. There are 127

tracts in the CBD, and locations may be seen in Figure 8. The statistics of employment in the census tracts used in this section are furnished by the City Planning Department, and contain its adjustments.

Every one of the census tracts in the CBD has some reported employment. The tract with the largest employment is 7, situated down in the financial district, with an estimated 135,100 employees. The smallest is census tract 24 which is to be found along the East River running a short distance below 14th Street, and having a reported 100 employees. One tract has over 100,000 employees. Nine have between 50,000 and 100,000; fifteen have between 25,000 and 50,000; twenty-seven have between 10,000 and 25,000; and the rest have less than 10,000.

Figure 8 shows the distribution of employment by census tract in the CBD. The numbers in the upper left-hand corner of the tracts are the census tract numbers. The numbers in circles give the per cent of total CBD employment to be found in each of the tracts. Only 1 per cent and greater are shown on the figure.

The figure reveals the principal areas of employment in the CBD. The densest area runs lengthwise through the center of the CBD. North of 14th Street most of the employment is to be found between 8th and 3rd Avenues, with a tapering off to the west and east of these two boundaries. Below 14th Street the major concentration falls below Canal Street and extends across in the lower portion of the CBD. Some areas are relatively free of employment. With minor exceptions, the area to the east of 3rd Avenue and extending to the east of the Bowery have few employees. The west side tracts, west of 10th Avenue, are also sparsely populated with places of employment, at least relative to the central portion.

The very tip of the CBD has the heaviest concentration of employment. Census tract 7, with 7 per cent of the CBD, is the densest and it is surrounded by census tracts 9, 13, and 17, with 4, 3, and 3 per

FIGURE 8

PER CENTS OF TOTAL EMPLOYMENT, BY CENSUS TRACT

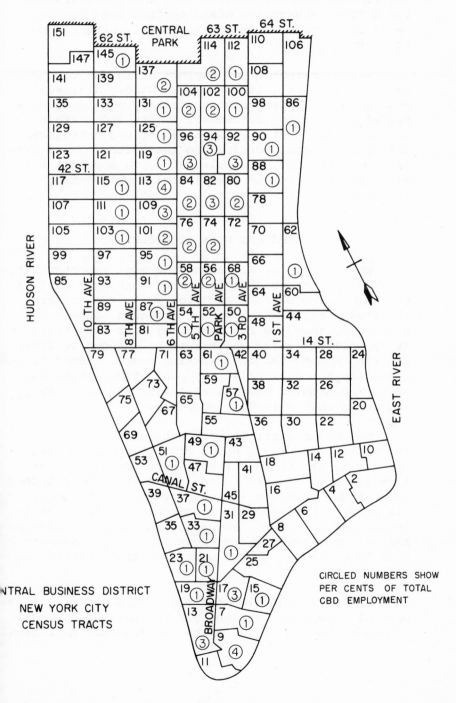

CIRCLED NUMBERS SHOW
PER CENTS OF TOTAL
CBD EMPLOYMENT

NTRAL BUSINESS DISTRICT
NEW YORK CITY
CENSUS TRACTS

cent respectively. As a whole, they have 17 per cent
the highest concentration in the CBD. The area between Times Square and Grand Central also has a
heavy concentration which abates only slightly to
the north and south.

The distribution of employment in the CBD may
be summarized as follows: It is widely diffused
over the area, with greatest density running longi-
tudinally through the center. There are, within
this over-all pattern, two areas of concentration:
the upper central portion and the bottom. This general pattern will be supplemented, in Appendix K,
with maps showing the location of employment by
major industry division.

THE CBD WORK SCHEDULE

Work schedules are among the most important statistics in the study of staggered working hours. As
the times people start and stop work, they control
the travel times which produce transit congestion.
Above all, they are the target of work staggering.
It is work schedules which must be changed in order
to bring about staggered working hours. Hence to investigate the feasibility of staggering, statistics
of work schedules must be available--as accurately
and in as much detail as possible.

To obtain suitable work schedule statistics,
the Staggered Working Hours Project conducted its
own survey of CBD industry. There are other statistics relating to work schedules in the CBD, but they
are not adequate for the purposes of this study.
Its needs impose special requirements with respect
to the definition of the data, the format of presentation, and industry breakdown. These requirements
will be clarified in the course of this chapter and
elsewhere.

The work schedule of the CBD as a whole will be
presented in this section. It conveys the over-all
schedule pattern of the area. In Appendix K, schedul

will be presented for the major industry divisions.
But before turning to the statistics, the meaning of
the term "work schedule" as used in this study will
be explained.

The Meaning of "Work Schedules"

There are two reasons for defining the term
"work schedule" at the outset. First, in this study
it applies to a large and crucial body of statistics.
This is all the more necessary because the term is a
commonplace one, with various possible definitions.
Second, within this definition--and the procedures
governed by it--there are some assumptions and policy decisions about work staggering and its investigation. The definition provides an opportunity to
clarify some of the theoretical aspects of the subject.

A work schedule consists of the times a person
starts and stops work. Most jobs have more than one
starting and stopping time during a single day, such
as for lunch or other breaks in the routine. For
the purpose of this study, the only times of direct
interest are the ones related to the person's travel
times. They are ordinarily the first start and the
last stop times of the day.*

---

*The other scheduled times are not irrelevant
to the study, especially the lunch hour. One of the
possible ways a firm or industry might adapt to work
staggering is by shortening the lunch hour or modifying its other scheduled breaks. Despite their relevance, these other times were excluded from the definition of work schedule used in the survey. They
would have increased the complexity and the cost of
the survey. They would also have added some insolu-
ble problems to the study--how to forecast changes
in these time breaks as a consequence of work staggering. The statistics of present practices and the
forecast of changes in them were replaced by an
assumption--that the present gross working day will
persist, at least in the main. See Chapter 4 for a
discussion of this point.

From this general definition, two possible concepts of work schedules follow. One concept is the
"real" or "actual" schedule. It consists of the
times a person actually starts and stops work, not
when he is supposed to. It thus takes into account
early or late starting and stopping. In particular,
it reflects lateness and overtime, two conditions
known to exist in the CBD. Many studies of work
schedules utilize this definition, especially those
which ask people when they started work today. This
definition has two desirable properties. It asks
for an actual behavior and it reflects the schedule
practices which really govern transit traffic, because they correspond to people's actual behavior in
respect to work times.

The other concept is the authorized or official
schedule. It consists of the times that the person
is supposed, by the terms of his employment, to
start and stop work. It excludes all temporary or
unauthorized changes in starting and stopping times,
especially lateness and overtime.

Of the two concepts, the one used throughout
this study is the authorized, not the actual schedule.
All of the statistics of this chapter--which will
also be used in later computations--specify the times
people are authorized to start and stop work. They
do not include any modifications of these times,
even authorized ones if they are only temporary.
They certainly do not include any informal changes
of schedule, such as through lateness or early departure. This is a basic definition of the work
schedule statistics of this study and it is used
without exception. The reasons for adopting the
authorized rather than the actual schedule are of interest, particularly as the data are to be used for
transit analyses.

The choice was dictated by several considerations. First, it was found that the authorized
schedules were more easily obtainable than the actual ones. The authorized schedules are established
and known and can be obtained and verified with ease.

The place of employment can provide a single, reliable informant for all the people who work in it. On the other hand, the place of employment is not a reliable informant with respect to actual schedules, certainly not on a widespread basis. Firms either do not know or are unwilling to disclose the extent of lateness among their employees. Thus the authorized schedules proved more readily and reliably collectible than the actual ones. Second, the authorized schedules are the ones to be modified by work staggering. The actual schedules cannot be the basis of research or of a work staggering program. Places of employment will be asked to change their official times. Hence they are the ones which must be the foundation for the study of the feasibility of work staggering.

As a consequence the work schedule statistics produced by the survey cannot be directly connected to travel times and transit traffic. A conceptual and quantitative gap exists between the work schedule statistics and the transit statistics. Accordingly a bridge is required to connect the two. It will be presented in Chapter 6. An adjustment procedure is developed there which provides a systematic way of converting the authorized schedules into actual ones. In this way the limitations imposed by the choice of the authorized rather than the real schedules are overcome, thereby permitting the study to use the better definition for the survey of work schedules.

There is another element in the definition which arises from the theory of work staggering adopted by this study. A work schedule consists of both the start and stop times, not either one singly. The schedule unit is the combination of times. If, through work staggering, schedules are modified, both start and stop times--not just one of them-- will be changed. This study assumes--at least as a working hypothesis--that the start and stop times will be changed by the same amounts. To apply this assumption it is necessary to have schedule data consisting of combined start and stop times. Many of the studies of CBD schedules furnish statistics

separately for start and stop times. They could not
be used in the computations of schedule change. The
work schedule tables of this study--and all the computations using them--are based upon the combined
times as the work schedule unit.

Thus far, work schedule has been defined with
respect to a single individual. It can now be extended to aggregates. The work schedule of a place
of employment consists of each pair of start and
stop times and the numbers of employees assigned to
them. It is produced by adding up all of the people
who have the same schedule. A firm may thus have--
and typically has--more than one work schedule.
Every different pair of start and stop times authorized by the place of employment is a separate schedule. The schedule of an industry is the sum of the
schedules of its component firms. Similarly the
schedules of other aggregates in this study will consist of totals formed in the same manner. Among the
various aggregates in this study are firms, industry
subdivisions, industries, major industry divisions,
and the CBD as a whole. There are also schedules
for special parts of industries such as offices, and
of separate functions of industries, such as departments of commercial banks.

The tables of work schedules which will be presented in this chapter and Appendix K adhere to the
definition just developed. The times which they
specify are the regular and authorized first start
and last stop times. The data are available for the
entire week, but the tables will only contain the
morning and afternoon periods of the transit rush
hours, and only the Monday through Friday schedules.

The CBD Schedule

The CBD work schedule is the composite of the
schedules of its industries. It is formed by adding
the schedules of each major industry division.
These, in turn, are the sum of the schedule of their
component industries. The source of the CBD schedule is thus the individual industry schedules.

The CBD work schedule is presented in Tables 16 and 17. Table 16 gives the schedule in numbers of people, and Table 17 in per cents. The per cents shown in Table 17 were obtained through the survey of schedules conducted by the Staggered Working Hours Project. These per cents were turned into the numbers of Table 16 by distributing the total CBD employment--as obtained from the New York City Department of City Planning--to the various cells of the table.

The Format

The form of the schedule tables is designed for the use of this study, and will be briefly explained. Each row (horizontal line) of the table refers to a specified starting time, ranging from 7:30 to 9:30 a.m. Similarly, each column is a stopping time, as specified at its heading. The range is from 3:30 to 6:00 p.m. The morning and late afternoon ranges cover the times required for the study and computations. (See Appendix S.) Thus, the right-hand column states the total number of people authorized to start work at each starting time. The bottom row of the table gives the number of people authorized to stop work at each stopping time. The individual cells in the body of the table contain the numbers of people authorized to start and stop at the indicated joint times.

The usefulness of this format will become fully evident when schedule change is under consideration. A change is registered by shifting the numbers of any cell along its own diagonal line--upper left to lower right--in either direction, depending on whether the shift is to an earlier or later time. The number, once shifted, requires that the corresponding row and column totals also be changed. This way of recording a change corresponds to the actual process in industry, and can be visualized from the format of the table. It also is easily programmed for processing by computer.

TABLE 16

Selected Scheduled Starting-Stopping Times of Work, Regular Weekdays: Estimated Numbers of Employees of Manhattan's Central Business District

Start \ Stop	3:30	3:45	4:00	4:15	4:30	4:45	5:00	5:15	5:30	5:45	6:00	Other	Total
7:30	2,155	29	1,381	66	2,601							2,636	8,868
7:45	129	54	30	1,077	528	163						323	2,304
8:00	17,749	5,842	45,970	2,082	49,953	13,237	51,588					19,379	205,800
8:15			2,568	1,857	2,881	9,322	8,837					5,433	30,898
8:30			3,151	17,434	106,963	30,835	71,815	25,662	25,176			5,643	286,679
8:45				252	23,982	116,782	67,029	7,983	8,095	467		282	224,872
9:00					15,500	46,033	552,551	27,959	115,273	477	33,431	17,355	808,579
9:15						780	266	22,165	22,666	23,590	695	14,577	84,739
9:30							1,242	213	29,872	60	5,743	6,798	43,928
Other	12,835	3,200	19,544	600	5,392	242	7,810	2,232	6,745	423	23,406	267,304	349,733
Total	32,868	9,125	72,644	23,368	207,800	217,394	761,138	86,214	207,827	25,017	63,275	339,730	2,046,400

110

TABLE 17

Selected Scheduled Starting-Stopping Times of Work, Regular Weekdays:
Estimated Per Cents of Employees of Manhattan's
Central Business District

Start \ Stop	3:30	3:45	4:00	4:15	4:30	4:45	5:00	5:15	5:30	5:45	6:00	Other	Total
7:30	.1		.1		.1							.1	.4
7:45				.1									.1
8:00	.9	.3	2.3	.1	2.4	.7	2.5					.9	10.1
8:15			.1	.1	.1	.5	.4					.3	1.5
8:30			.1	.9	5.2	1.5	3.5	1.3	1.2			.3	14.0
8:45					1.2	5.7	3.3	.4	.4				11.0
9:00					.7	2.3	27.0	1.4	5.6		1.6	.9	39.5
9:15								1.1	1.1	1.2		.7	4.1
9:30							.1		1.5		.3	.3	2.2
Other	.6	.2	1.0		.3		.4	.1	.3		1.1	13.1	17.1
Total	1.6	.5	3.6	1.1	10.2	10.6	37.2	4.2	10.2	1.2	3.1	16.6	100.0

The Over-all Pattern

The tables disclose that the predominant starting time in the CBD is 9:00 a.m., when 39.5 per cent
of the people are scheduled to start work. Three
other starting times have significant numbers and
per cents of people, though not nearly as many as
9:00 a.m. At 8:30 14.0 per cent start work, at 8:45
11.0 per cent start work, and at 8:00 a.m. 10.1 per
cent start work. Outside this range the numbers and
per cents are relatively small.

The predominant stopping time is 5:00 p.m.,
with 37.2 per cent of the people scheduled to stop
work then. There are also three other time periods
which have significant numbers. At 4:30 10.2 per
cent stop work, at 4:45 10.6 per cent stop work, and
at 5:30 10.2 per cent stop work. Again, the other
time periods have relatively few numbers or per
cents of people.

The table cells also give the combined starting
and stopping times. 9:00 a.m. to 5:00 p.m., with
27.0 per cent, is the predominant work schedule.
There are no other schedules with anything like this
proportion of the people. The next largest is 9:00
to 5:30 with 5.6 per cent of the CBD, immediately
followed by 8:30 to 4:30 with 5.2 per cent. The
rest are in smaller percentages scattered around the
main time, primarily starting earlier than nine, but
stopping both earlier and later than five.

The tables also have rows and columns called
"other." They contain two kinds of schedules.
First, the largest proportion consists of people
whose schedules fall outside the range given by the
table. They start before 7:30 or after 9:30; or
stop before 3:30 or after 6:00; or both. The second
group included in the "other" category are people
for whom work schedules were reported as "unspecified" or "irregular." These are people who have no
definite starting or stopping time, or whose starting or stopping times may vary day by day. They include some owner-executives, professionals, and

others with similarly unscheduled occupations. Some
of these people actually start or stop within the
range of times of the table, but their number is unknown. It is not considered large enough to affect
the statistics significantly.

<u>Findings</u>

      The tables show, for the total CBD, at what
starting and stopping times people are now concentrated. But they do not tell whether the schedules
are congested at any of these times. This will require the results of computations which will not become available until Chapter 7. In advance of those
results, however, some general observations may be
made about schedule congestion. As a matter of fact,
this had to be done in carrying out the inquiry.
Many research decisions involving congestion had to
be made on the basis of the schedule data alone, before the relationship between schedules and transit
traffic was established quantitatively.

      Starting and stopping times can be called con-
gested only in a derivative sense--by the way they
affect the flow of transit traffic. If the prevailing CBD schedule produces transit congestion, the
times with the highest concentrations of people are
the ones most likely responsible for it. These, according to Tables 16 and 17, are 9:00 a.m. and 5:00
p.m. The shape of the cordon counts--with their
gradual rise and decline around the peaks--points to
the adjacent schedule times as also contributing to
congestion. The CBD work schedule shows substantial
concentrations around the peak times: at 8:30 and
8:45 in the morning and at 4:30 and 4:45 in the late
afternoon. The morning schedule times follow the
traffic peak, the late afternoon ones precede it.
Thus, transit congestion may be traceable to two
periods--8:30 to 9:00 a.m. and 4:30 to 5:00 p.m.

      Further, if stop time congestion occurs during
the 4:30 to 5:00 period, then 5:30 may also be a
critical time--at, or near an excessive number of
people. It has 10.2 per cent of the CBD, which is

the same as 4:30, and almost as many as the 10.6 per
cent at 4:45. But since it stands one half-hour
away from 5:00, with only 4.2 per cent scheduled at
5:15--as contrasted with the 10.6 per cent at 4:45--
the 5:30 time may not actually add to transit congestion. The 8:00 a.m. starting time has very similar
features, and it too may have about as many people
as it can hold.

If existing work schedules produce transit congestion, then the times with excessive numbers of
people are 8:30 to 9:00 a.m., and possibly also 8:00;
and 4:30 to 5:00 p.m., and possibly also 5:30.

This result, however circumspect, figures importantly in the study. These are the times which
are examined whenever an industry's contribution to
transit congestion is assessed. They are thus
treated as congested times for the purpose of lo-
cating the responsible industries. They are also
used in connection with the studies of schedule modifiability. Industries are sought which can modify
their schedules away from 9:00 a.m. and 5:00 p.m.,
and from the other times in the congested period, if
possible.*

----

*These congested times cannot be applied rigor-
ously in the search for industries capable of modifying their schedules. It is advantageous to find industries which can shift away from the peak times,
even though they may remain within the congested
period. Other industries, capable of shifting out
of the period, may make room for them. Also, the
gross working day creates effects in the stopping
times which, while not satisfactory, cannot be excluded by rule. For example, a firm with an 8:30 to
5:00 schedule might be able to shift one half-hour
earlier, to an 8:00 to 4:30 schedule. This will improve morning conditions more than late afternoon
ones. Even though its stopping time remains within
the congested period, the change may prove advantageous for the CBD as a whole. The congested times
are used as general guideposts in the studies of
schedule modifiability, not as fixed norms.

SUMMARY

The description of the CBD as a whole produced
several things of value for this study. It defined
the major bodies of statistics: employment and work
schedules. It also furnished substantive information concerning industry, employment, the location
of employment, and work schedules. The same
statistics for the major industry divisions are given
in Appendix K.

The next section will present a comparative
analysis of the industry divisions. The chapter
will conclude with the evaluation of the statistics.

A COMPARATIVE ANALYSIS OF THE
MAJOR INDUSTRY DIVISIONS

The statistics of employment and work schedules
were presented in the preceding section for the CBD
as a whole, which is a geographic aggregate. Its employment and work schedules cover all places of employment within its boundaries. The second type of
aggregate, presented in Appendix K, includes the industry divisions and their components, the industries
and places of employment. They are the ones whose
decisions generate the employment and work schedules--
and schedule changes, if staggering is introduced--
which are then included in the CBD's geographic
totals.

The difference between these two kinds of aggregate has a bearing upon the subject of this study.
The work schedules and their possible modifications
will be made by places of employment and industries.
But their significant consequences, insofar as transit is concerned, will accumulate geographically, by
areas within the CBD and its totality. Industry and
area are components of the system which controls, at
least in part, the quantity and timing of the traffic
flow into and out of the CBD.

It now becomes possible to examine aspects of

the system which are made visible by the location
and work schedule statistics. By combining the
location statistics of the major industry divisions,
the industrial mix of the CBD shows up geographically. A comparative analysis of work schedules will
disclose the relative contributions of each division
to the total CBD pattern. The two parts of this section will present the analyses of location and work
schedules. Each will yield findings which shape the
course of the study.

The Location of Employment

Appendix K shows the location of seven of the
major industry divisions, each one individually.
The seven include all the large divisions except the
central administrative offices, for which location
data are not available. It is now of interest to
see how they are located in relation to one another.

Later in this study, the work schedules of the
CBD will be experimentally modified. The modifications will be made by industries and groups of industries. The location of the industries whose schedules are modified can affect the flow of people into
and out of the transit systems. The reason for looking into the comparative location of the major industry divisions arises from this possibility, as will
be more fully explained below.

Figure 9 provides a picture of comparative location by industry division. The letters inscribed in
the census tracts identify major industry divisions
according to the following code:

M = Manufacturing
T = Transportation, communication,and public
    utilities
W = Wholesale trades
R = Retail trades
F = Finance, insurance, and real estate
S = Service
G = Government

FIGURE 9
COMPARATIVE LOCATION OF EMPLOYMENT, BY INDUSTRY DIVISION

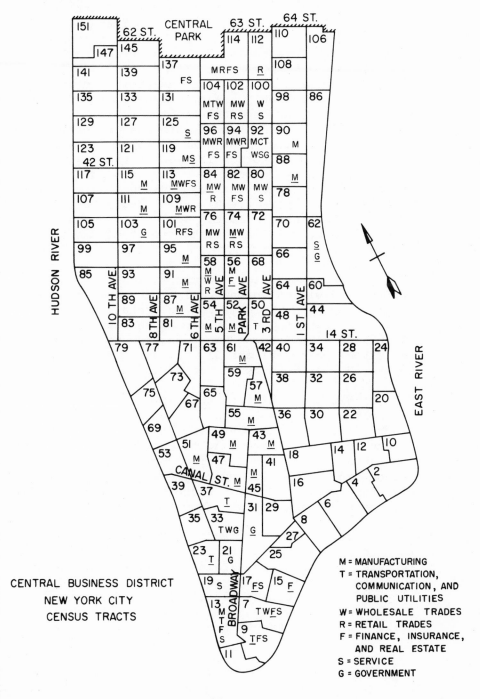

CENTRAL BUSINESS DISTRICT
NEW YORK CITY
CENSUS TRACTS

M = MANUFACTURING
T = TRANSPORTATION,
    COMMUNICATION, AND
    PUBLIC UTILITIES
W = WHOLESALE TRADES
R = RETAIL TRADES
F = FINANCE, INSURANCE,
    AND REAL ESTATE
S = SERVICE
G = GOVERNMENT

This figure was drawn by inscribing the code letter
of each industry having 5,000 or more employees in
the census tracts. Thus, for example, in tract 137,
directly below Central Park, the two letters F and S
signify that the finance and service divisions each
have 5,000 or more employees in the tract.

To interpret Figure 9, it is useful to locate
the tracts having only a single code letter. These
occur uniformly at the edges of the central concentration. Most of the tracts with single letters are
manufacturing areas. They are found on the western
side of the concentration from 42nd Street down. As
14th Street is approached they turn toward the center and then proceed southward through the center to
Canal Street. There are also two manufacturing
tracts on the eastern edge. None of the other divisions has nearly as many tracts to itself as manufacturing.

The transportation, communications, and public
utilities division turns up alone in three tracts,
50, 37, and 23. There is but one retailing tract,
112. There are two widely separated service tracts,
19 and 125. Government has two adjacent tracts at
the Civic Center, 21 and 31. Finance has a single
tract, 15, on the edge of the financial district.

Within the center of the CBD, in the main areas
of employment concentration as depicted earlier on
Figure 8, the tracts have many large industries. It
is particularly interesting to observe that the combinations vary a good deal from one another. There
are no single patterns which prevail within the sections and neighborhoods. There are constantly shifting industry combinations from tract to tract.

Figure 9 also conveys an additional item of information. In many of the tracts one of the code
letters is underlined. This signifies that the underlined industry has 40 per cent or more of the employment in the census tract. This information
shows which industries dominate the tracts numeri-
cally--and which tracts are not dominated. From

this perspective there are a few salient observations.

Manufacturing dominates the largest number of tracts. But these are on the outer edges of the main employment areas, and between the two main centers--above 14th Street and the financial district. Finance dominates four tracts. Three are in the financial district and the other is tract 56 above 23rd Street between Park and 5th Avenues. The service industries are dominant in two tracts in the north of the CBD and they share tract 62 with government. Government also dominates tract 31 at the Civic Center and tract 103. The transportation, communications, and public utilities division is dominant in the very large census tract 9 at the tip of the CBD, in census tract 23 on the lower west side and census tract 37 below Canal Street west of Broadway. Significantly the wholesale and retail trades which together comprise almost a fourth of the CBD employment are represented only in tract 112, where retailing has the principal amount of employment.

A problem will arise later in this study to which this analysis of location provides an answer. If the work schedules of a given industry are changed, how will its particular location affect the flow of people to and from the transit systems? This problem will prove inaccessible on a detailed quantitative basis. It will not be possible to compute the changes on a census tract (or larger area, short of the total CBD) basis, and then translate these changes to their consequences upon traffic flow. It will therefore be necessary to fall back upon the general pattern of industry location as developed in this section.

The important observation produced by Figure 9 is this: The divisions are widely dispersed over the CBD and they tend to be well mixed within the densest census tracts. From this statement, a valuable consequence follows. If the schedule of a particular industry were modified--uniformly and

totally--its geographic effect would be spread widely
over the CBD. Moreover, in the areas of largest con-
centration--where schedule and transit congestion
are the most acute--a schedule change of a single industry will not modify the whole neighborhood's
schedule uniformly, even where one industry is dominant. The combination of industries is an assurance
that the change by any one will affect only part of
an area's employment--which is precisely the kind of
rescheduling sought by work staggering.

It would be far better if the problem could be
answered with specific quantities. In the absence
of sufficiently detailed statistics, the best available answer is the one just given. It is a judgment
made from the prevailing pattern of location by the
CBD industries as analyzed in this section.

The Major Industry Divisions' Work
Schedules: A Comparative Analysis

Three findings of interest will accrue from a
comparison of the major industry divisions' work
schedules. The scheduling patterns of the individual
divisions, as compared with the total CBD, will become evident. A comparison weighted by the size of
the divisions will show their relative contribution
to the prevailing CBD schedule, especially to the
times which were found to have too many people. By
looking at the total pattern--schedule times of the
CBD and each of its divisions--the possible alternative times for scheduling will begin to appear.
These findings will emerge from the ensuing analysis.

Table 18 presents the schedules of the total
CBD and of each industry division. The percentages
of the table are taken directly from the final rows
and column of the full work schedules. For present
purposes only the total amounts for each starting
and stopping time are needed, not the combined pairs
of times. The table affords a comparison of scheduling patterns of each division with the CBD as a
whole.

TABLE 18

Per Cents* of People of the CBD and Major Industry Divisions Scheduled
to Start and Stop Work During Peak Periods

	CBD	Contract Construction	Manufacturing	Central Administrative Offices	Transportation	Communications and Public Util.	Wholesale Trades	Retail Trades	Finance & Insurance	Real Estate	Services	Governments
Start Time												
7:30	.4	1.2	.5	.1	.7	.2		1.7		1.0	.2	.5
7:45	.1		.2			.2				0.1		.7
8:00	10.1	25.0	17.0	1.5	28.7	8.9	4.3	6.8	.9	7.2	6.1	11.3
8:15	1.5		5.6	.5	.1	.2	.3	.1	.1	.6	.3	1.8
8:30	14.0	8.2	29.9	3.5	2.1	23.0	13.1	4.0	12.9	6.5	6.2	20.3
8:45	11.0	1.1	5.1	15.8	3.9	5.3	18.4	1.6	23.1	1.7	13.9	9.1
9:00	39.5	53.4	29.3	71.3	44.7	35.6	51.5	17.2	52.6	31.9	38.3	27.8
9:15	4.1	.1	1.0	2.5	.1	2.6	1.4	26.2	1.3	3.6	5.2	.7
9:30	2.2	4.3	1.6	2.0	.4	5.3	.6	2.0	1.0	2.9	6.3	.5
Stop Time												
3:30	1.6	1.2	1.0		.3	.3	.2	4.3	.1	.7	1.4	.5
3:45	.5		1.7		.1				.4			.1
4:00	3.6	1.6	3.6	.8	16.0	2.2	1.3	1.7	2.0	4.4	3.6	5.0
4:15	1.1	.6	4.7			.1			.1	.1	.1	.6
4:30	10.2	12.0	21.7	6.3	1.1	4.5	3.0	3.3	18.4	3.2	2.1	11.0
4:45	10.6	1.0	9.4	19.2	.2	13.8	11.1	1.0	19.9	3.8	11.7	8.3
5:00	37.2	48.5	33.9	56.9	48.0	32.6	46.3	8.6	49.4	27.2	30.4	40.9
5:15	4.2	11.8	4.6	8.8	5.1	20.5	3.2	1.3	.2	3.5	5.1	2.4
5:30	10.2	9.1	8.0	4.9	5.3	5.8	23.0	14.9	1.1	8.8	20.9	1.2
5:45	1.2				.1	.3	.1	12.8		.4	.1	.1
6:00	3.1	3.2	2.5	.6	5.9	5.0	2.0	11.6	.2	3.5	3.4	1.2

*Each aggregate's own total is 100.0 per cent.

For the total CBD, excessive numbers of people were attributed, earlier in this chapter, to the 8:30 to 9:00 a.m. period, with 8:00 a.m. just below the borderline of excess. A total of 64.5 per cent of the CBD's employment is scheduled to start between 8:30 and 9:00 a.m., and an additional 10.1 per cent at 8:00 a.m.

Table 18 discloses that all divisions but one exceed the CBD percentage at one, two, or all of the 8:30 to 9:00 a.m. starting times. The divisions differ in their distributions of employment at the three times. Some are heavily concentrated at 9:00 a.m., others at 8:45 a.m., others at 8:30 a.m.--and some at more than one of these times. The only exception to this starting time pattern is the retail trades.

It is of interest to examine the 8:00 a.m. starting time as part of the scheduling pattern. Some of the industries now make considerable use of this time. The contract construction division (employees reporting to sites), the manufacturing division, transportation, and government schedule more than the CBD average at 8:00 a.m., and some of them significantly more. On the other hand, central administrative offices, wholesale trades, and finance make almost no use of the 8:00 time.

Two other starting times will prove particularly important later in the study. They are 7:30 and 9:30, which now lie entirely outside the congested or near-congested intervals. None of the divisions makes any significant use of the 7:30 time at the present. Only three divisions schedule 1 per cent or more of their employees at this time. They are the construction trades, the retail trades, and the building service segment of real estate. It is clearly not the prevalent pattern to start work at 7:30 in any of the major industry divisions. There is relatively greater use of the 9:30 starting time. The service industries, communications, and the contract construction divisions have sizable percentages at 9:30. Real estate, the retail trades, the central

administrative offices, and manufacturing and finance
also make use of 9:30. It is, however, an underutilized time at present.

Stop time schedules are concentrated over the
hour period of 4:30 to 5:30 for the CBD as a whole.
Here again, only the retail trades depart from this
general practice. The rest of the industries schedule their employees within this period, concentrating
in one or more of the specific times. The stop time
patterns follow as a consequence of the starting
times. They are modified only by the differences in
the gross working day. The patterns which occur in
the morning are recapitulated in the late afternoon,
with only minor modifications.

The observations produced by Table 18 apply to
the schedule patterns of each individual industry.
They emphasize the present practices in schedules as
related to the over-all composite CBD schedule. It
is next of interest to compare the industry divisions' schedules weighted by their relative number
of employees. This gives a picture of each industry's specific contribution to the total CBD pattern.

Table 19 presents the schedules of the total
CBD and the industry divisions, all as a percentage
of the total CBD employment.

The table tells how much each industry contributes to the CBD total. The divisions which make up
most of the 39.5 per cent at 9:00 a.m.--the highest
concentration of employees starting work--are the
following: finance and insurance (8.0 per cent),
manufacturing (6.5 per cent), wholesale trades (5.8
per cent), central administrative offices and services (5.3 per cent each). These five divisions contribute 30.9 of the total 39.5 per cent.

The CBD total of 64.5 per cent for the three
starting times of 8:30, 8:45, and 9:00 a.m. come
mostly from the following divisions: manufacturing
(14.2 per cent), finance (13.5 per cent), wholesale
trades (9.4 per cent), services (8.1 per cent),

TABLE 19

Per Cents of CBD Employees Starting and Stopping Work During
Rush Hours, by Major Industry Divisions

	CBD	Contract Construction	Manufacturing	Central Administrative Offices	Transportation	Communications and Public Util.	Wholesale Trades	Retail Trades	Finance & Insurance	Real Estate	Services	Governments
Start Time												
7:30	.4	–	.1	–	–	–	–	.2	–	–	–	–
7:45	.1	–	–	–	–	–	–	–	–	–	–	–
8:00	10.1	1.3	3.8	.1	1.5	.3	.5	.6	.1	.3	.8	.7
8:15	1.5		1.2							–	–	.1
8:30	14.0	.1	6.6	.3	.1	.7	1.5	.4	2.0	.3	.9	1.3
8:45	11.0	–	1.1	1.2	.2	.2	2.1	.1	3.5	.1	1.9	.6
9:00	39.5	.4	6.5	5.3	2.4	1.1	5.8	1.6	8.0	1.4	5.3	1.7
9:15	4.1	–	.2	.2	–	.1	.2	2.4	.2	.2	.7	–
9:30	2.2	–	.4	.1	–	.2	–	.2	.2	.1	.9	–
Stop Time												
3:30	1.6	.7	.2	–	–	–	–	.4	–	–	.2	–
3:45	.5	–	.4	–	–	–	–	–	.1	–	–	–
4:00	3.6	.2	.8	.1	.8	.1	.1	.2	.3	.2	.5	.3
4:15	1.1	–	1.1	–	–	–	–	–	–	–	–	–
4:30	10.2	.1	4.8	.5	.1	.1	.3	.3	2.8	.1	.3	.7
4:45	10.6	–	2.1	1.4	–	.4	1.3	.1	3.0	.2	1.6	.5
5:00	37.2	.4	7.6	4.2	2.5	1.0	5.2	.8	7.5	1.2	4.2	2.5
5:15	4.2	.1	1.0	.7	.3	.6	.4	.1	–	.2	.7	.2
5:30	10.2	.1	1.8	.4	.3	.2	2.6	1.3	.2	.4	2.9	.1
5:45	1.2	–	–	–	–	–	1.2	–	–	–	–	–
6:00	3.1	–	.5	–	.3	.2	.2	1.1	.1	.2	.5	–

central administrative offices (6.8 per cent), government (3.6 per cent). These six divisions contribute 55.6 per cent out of the total 64.5 per cent.

The sources of the congestion in the late afternoon, in the stop times from 4:30 to 5:30, are the
same as the starting times. They may be read directly from Table 19.

Findings

This analysis of work schedules yields three
useful findings.

First, it shows that all industry divisions but
the retail trades schedule most of their people during the heaviest starting and stopping times.

Second, the principal contributors to the total
CBD pattern are the industry divisions identified
above, and exposed by Table 19.

Third, the available times for rescheduling
people to start work occur before 8:00 a.m. and after 9:00 a.m. 8:15 a.m. is the one time within the
principal scheduling period which remains underutilized. Thus, if rescheduling is confined to the
hour and half-hour (as this study finds it must),
then the only available alternative starting times
within the prevailing customary work day of the CBD
are 7:30 and 9:30 a.m.

EVALUATION

The statistics of employment and work schedules
which this study uses have now been presented, at
least in summary and representative form. They will
appear many times in the chapters which follow. They
are utilized to develop computational models. They
are also used in the computations of schedule change
and feasibility. Their importance to the entire
study can hardly be overstated. It is now appropriate to ask how good they are.

The statistics presented in this chapter are regarded as adequate for the problems of the study.
Wherever the original data were found unsuitable,
every effort was made to correct them and to make
them usable. In the case of the employment statistics, the Tabulation was adjusted in the many ways
described in this chapter. The warning has already
been given that the modifications do not produce a
corrected body of statistics of the CBD for general
use. All of the modifications are confined to the
particular industries and aggregates which figured
in the study of work staggering. This is the only
end use in which they claim to be valid.

Two general questions furnish the agenda of
this evaluation. The first pertains to the accuracy
of the statistics. Do they reliably reflect the magnitudes of employment and the work schedules prevailing at the time they were gathered? The second question concerns the utilization of the statistics for
testing the feasibility of work staggering--events
projected into the proximate future. They are thus
treated as forecasts of employment and work schedules in the CBD for the time staggered working hours
might be instituted. The question arises: Is it
safe to use them this way?

Each of the main bodies of statistics--employ-
ment and work schedules--will be examined in the two
sections which follow.

The Employment Statistics

The employment statistics divide into two groups
on the basis of their responsible sources. The first
is the 2,046,400 estimate of total CBD employment
produced by the New York City Department of City
Planning. The second consists of the estimates by
industry and by census tract, prepared by the New
York State Department of Labor with the collaboration of the New York City Department of City Planning
and further modified by the Staggered Working Hours
Project.

In response to the first question of this evalu-
ation--how accurate are the statistics?--several observations may be made. As measures of employment
in the CBD, the statistics understate the actual September, 1958, numbers. This comes about because they
omit certain categories of employment which were not
compulsorily covered by unemployment insurance at
that time. The 2,046,400 estimate has been partly
adjusted for the exemptions, but not the industry
statistics. Both sets of employment statistics are
thus underestimates, the total less so than the component industries. The amounts in both cases are
believed small enough to be tolerated by this study.
As will shortly be explained, the underestimate is
less damaging than it might seem.

The acceptability of the employment statistics
as a whole rests upon three considerations. First
and foremost, there is confidence in the qualifications of the two governmental agencies responsible
for them. Second, wherever the actual data can be
checked by reference to previous and later statistics of employment from these and other sources,
they exhibit sufficient regularity to justify using
them. Finally, nothing has been discovered during
the course of this study's detailed use of the data
which raises a question as to their general validity.
Some doubtful statistics were uncovered, but they
are attributable systematically to the special
source of the statistics and they by no means impeach the rest of the data. Accordingly, within the
limitations already described, the employment statistics are accepted as satisfactory measures for the
period of September, 1958.

The second question of the evaluation concerns
the use of these statistics as forecasts for the
initial period of work staggering.

The passage of time since September, 1958, can
affect the usefulness of the employment statistics
in two ways. The total employment in the CBD might
have changed to a larger or smaller amount. Or, the
employment of any industry might have changed relative

to the others. Thus, changes in the total or the industry mix of employment are the sources of possible
distortion in using the September, 1958, statistics
as representative of the later period.

The evidence is quite reassuring for the suitability of the total employment statistics to the
later period. Table 20 gives the total covered employment in Manhattan during the month of September
from 1958 through 1964. This is the closest approxi-
mation to the CBD for which statistics are available.
The CBD has about 98 per cent of Manhattan's covered
employment and about 90 per cent of its total employment. The statistics of Table 20 are shown graphically in Figure 10.

TABLE 20

Covered Employment in Manhattan During the
Month of September, 1958 to 1964

Year	Employment (000)
1958	1,913
1959	1,915
1960	1,922
1961	1,904
1962	1,903
1963	1,873
1964	1,865

From the point of view of this study the change
in employment between 1958 and 1964 is considered
negligible. Even if the trend persists through the
next few years it will not adversely affect the use

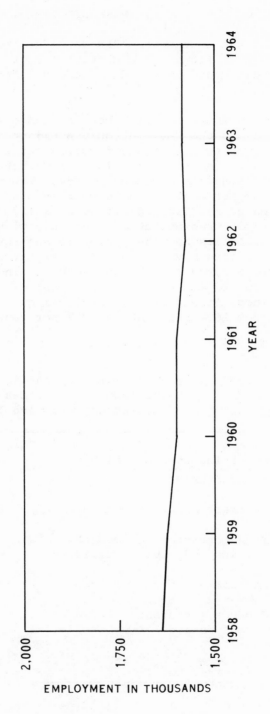

FIGURE 10

COVERED EMPLOYMENT IN MANHATTAN
DURING SEPTEMBER, 1958–64

of the September, 1958,data for the computations of
feasibility. As a matter of fact, the existence of
this trend is an added safety factor for the results
of the study.

There has also been a change in the industry
mix in the CBD, but only a slight one. Table 21
gives the per cent of employment in the principal
major industry divisions of Manhattan in September,
1958,and in September, 1964. The table shows that
the per cent of employment in manufacturing and finance has dropped slightly, while contract construction, transportation, communications, and public
utilities and the wholesale and retail trades and
services have risen. The largest change downward is
registered by the manufacturing industry, which fell
from 28.8 per cent to 25.6 per cent. The largest
increase was in the service industries, which rose
from 16.4 per cent to 18.7 per cent.

TABLE 21

Per Cent of Employment in Selected
Major Industries in Manhattan,
September, 1958 and 1964

Major Industry Division	Per Cent of Employment	
	1958	1964
Manufacturing	28.8	25.6
Contract construction	2.2	3.2
Transportation, communica- tions and public utilities	9.9	10.1
Wholesale and retail trade	24.6	24.8
Finance, insurance, and real estate	17.5	17.2
Service	16.4	18.7

Since 1958 there has been a very slight decline
in the total Manhattan employment. It rose slightly
from 1958 through 1960 and then a modest decline set
in which has persisted. On an annual basis the employment of 1963 and 1964 are the same, suggesting
that the decline was arrested in the last year of
the data.

These are very small changes in industry mix
over the six-year period. Some of the differences
may in fact arise from changes in insurance coverage
and possibly from data collection and processing procedures, and others from possible cyclical variations
in employment. Even if the changes stand as shown on
the table, they are not large enough to make any difference to the results of this study.

Accordingly, the employment statistics, as modified by the Staggered Working Hours Project, are considered adequate to the purposes of the study. The
underestimate in the 1958 statistics tends to be offset by the slight over-all decline in actual employment since then. If there is still a residual underestimate in the statistics when applied to the forecasting period, it redounds to the greater safety of
the final conclusions. The computations of feasibility will utilize lower, rather than higher statistics
of employment. By the computation procedure (see
Chapters 6 and 7), this will produce higher forecasts
of cordon counts resulting from work staggering than
would occur if the underestimates were corrected.
The bias toward higher forecasted cordon counts
adds to the burden of achieving or producing comfort
level conditions, during the peak periods. In this
way, the underestimates of employment are an added
safety factor for the conclusions of the study.

The Work Schedule Statistics

The work schedule statistics are entirely the
responsibility of the Staggered Working Hours Project.
The survey was made along with the studies of industry scheduling and modifiability. They thus cover
part of 1961 and 1962. Since the work schedule

statistics are the result of its own undertaking,
this study finds them entirely satisfactory to its
purposes. They are regarded as accurately representing the state of scheduling during late 1961 and
early 1962.

Again the question arises as to whether the
work schedules can be used as representing the
(future) time to which the feasibility computations
apply. Accepting the data for the time of the survey, three things can have happened to make the
schedules unrepresentative of the period in question.
There may have been modifications in work schedules
by individual companies and industries. The breaks
in the work day may have been changed, either lengthened or shortened by changes in lunch hour, coffee
breaks, and the like. Or the work day itself may
have been changed, probably shortened in the intervening period.

Surprisingly, changes in schedule occurring
since the date of the survey will have no effect on
the computations of feasibility. These computations
take the situation quantified by the employment and
work schedule statistics and modify it in certain
systematic ways. The feasible work staggering plans
specify schedules to be adapted by industries. The
computations and results are not in any way affected
by schedule changes in the intervening period.

Changes in the length of the lunch hour and
other breaks during the day, or shortening the hours
of work will have similar results upon work schedules.
They reduce the length of the gross working day
either by a later starting time or an earlier stopping time. There is no information available on
changes in the lunch hour and other breaks. The
statistics of average hours worked per week indicate
that the work week has remained fairly stable, despite the dramatic reduction in hours by the Elec-
trical Workers. The possible distortions in schedule arising from these two sources is considered
minimal, at least for the study. There is no evidence that the gross working day has been subjected

to any systematic reductions within the past few
years.

Accordingly, the work schedule statistics are
considered satisfactory for the computations in
which they are used.

Conclusion

A judgment was reached--on the bases reported
in the foregoing evaluation--that the employment and
work schedule statistics can be employed in this
study to produce adequate answers to the question of
the feasibility of work staggering. There are still
some shortcomings in the statistics, but they are
considered tolerable. The use of the 1958 statistics to represent conditions several years later is
fraught with the usual hazards of forecasting. For
the reasons already stated, the risks and potential
damage do not seem excessive.

CHAPTER **4** THE MODIFIABILITY OF
WORK SCHEDULES--
FUNCTIONAL CAPABILITY

Work staggering will require places of employment
to change the times their people start and stop work.
Just how many places and people will have to change,
and by how much time, remains to be determined. But
it will have to be enough to alter the flow of people
into and out of the CBD during the rush hours. Otherwise, work staggering is not feasible.

Can the places of employment in the CBD--the offices, factories, stores, banks, government agencies,
institutions, and the rest--change their work schedules?

Many can. This was established by studies of
scheduling in the CBD and of the people who work
there. This chapter and the next will furnish the
actual numbers and explain how they were obtained.
The method ought to be as interesting as the results.
But more important, the numbers won't really be comprehensible unless they are accompanied by definitions of terms and explanations as to how they were
produced. Whether, on the basis of these results,
enough people's schedules can be changed cannot be
shown until later. Hence, the goal in these two
chapters is to show the outer limits of change--the
largest numbers of employees and the largest amounts
of possible change. Hopefully, this will give enough
leeway to test the feasibility of staggering.

To test feasibility--and to implement a work
staggering program--the information about schedule
modifiability has to be plain and specific. It must
apply to recognizable units of employment that make

sense from the viewpoint of changing schedules.
(All people who live in certain boroughs, or who
work in odd-numbered buildings or on even-numbered
floors, or whose last names begin with any of the
first thirteen letters of the alphabet--these are
all identifiable units of employment, but they make
no sense at all for purposes of rescheduling work.)
The information must specify, for each unit, the
number of its employees, their present work schedules, and all the possible alternative schedules it
can adopt--within the range suitable for the CBD.

The information, specified in this degree of
detail, must have one other quality if it is to be
relied upon for reaching decisions about the feasibility of work staggering. It must not only tell
what firms can do. It must also forecast what they
probably will do, if asked to change their schedules. It must forecast the probable future compliance, on the part of places of employment--
entirely on a voluntary basis--with the changes they
are supposedly capable of making.

Needless to say, this kind of information does
not exist, apart from the report of this chapter and
the next. The need created a difficult problem: How
was the information to be obtained? The problem was
practical and theoretical--both closely interrelated,
as it turned out. It will be worthwhile to explain
the problem before presenting the solution.

Two million people work in the CBD. They work
in over 50,000 places of employment--the exact number
is unknown because the one-man enterprises are hard
to locate and count. To determine the schedule modifiability of each establishment--even to communicate
with each one--would be an insurmountable task, or at
least outside the limits of any justifiable use of
resources. Purely as a practical matter, some way
had to be found to reduce the number of places of
employment from which the needed information could
be obtained.

On the theoretical side, a different sort of
complexity arose. How was modifiability to be

determined? One obvious procedure was to ask the
places of employment whether or not they could change
schedules. This procedure, for several reasons,
proved unsuitable, even neglecting the practical matter of how to reach all--or enough--places. First,
it was considered doubtful that firms would know
whether or not they could change schedules. (At the
very least, before answering the question, they would
have to solve the very problem which is now the subject of discussion.) It was certain they would not
know their capability under conditions of a general,
but unspecified, schedule change in the CBD. Next,
it would not be possible to evaluate such information even if it were forthcoming. Whether a firm
said yes or no, on one could know whether the informant was expressing his personal interest in
schedule change or his firm's genuine capability.
Such responses were considered entirely too insub-
stantial a base for the purposes of the inquiry.
Finally, this kind of information, even if reliable,
would not conform to the specifications of the feasibility tests.

A theory of work scheduling had to be formulated
in order to overcome these problems--indeed, to answer the ultimate question before the inquiry: Can
work schedules be modified? A theory provides a
model of decision making about work schedules and
suggests how to investigate it. The model (a set of
abstract statements) tells how work schedules are
determined and changed: the procedures used, the
criteria governing decisions, the calculus employed
in making decisions, who the decision makers are,
and any other relevant factors. These are the things
which have to be investigated in any inquiry. In
turn, they disclose the kinds of techniques which must
be used in order to get the information which the
model requires.

For this purpose, a theory was developed which
required two kinds of investigation, using two research disciplines. One part, to be presented in
this chapter, is an adaptation of economics, consisting of the so-called functional determinants of scheduling. The other part is a sociological by-product,

and is called the personnel constraints on scheduling. It will be described in the next chapter.
Each part utilizes the research techniques of its
discipline, and produces the needed quantitative
results. The theory coordinates the findings of
both parts and produces a unified set of conclusions:
the extent of schedule modifiability in the CBD.

The conclusions are summarized in two tables.
Appendix Table 64, given in Appendix L, lists
every industry in the CBD and shows the schedule
changes it is capable of making--on functional
grounds only. Standing alone, this table must not
be interpreted as the complete or realistic capability of the CBD industries and it makes no such
claim. It has real meaning only within the theory
and computational procedures of this inquiry. To
attain a realistic estimate of modifiability, Appendix Table 64 must be adjusted by the second summary
table, Table 29, which gives the personnel constraints on modifiability. Table 29 must be applied
to the materials of Appendix Table 64 by a procedure
which is explained in Chapter 5. This yields the
final estimates of modifiability, and provides the
required information, according to specifications,
for testing the feasibility of work staggering.

One final word has to be said about the estimates of modifiability. They are forecasts, not
prophecies or decrees. The modifiability of work
schedules, even for this moment in time, cannot be
determined with precision, by means of exact readings
and numerical computations. It would be still more
difficult to project modifiability into the future
and to say something about compliance. In the final
analysis, the estimates of possible and probable
changes in schedule are judgments about future behaviors. They are carefully made, hopefully without
logical flaw, and based on evidence produced by
disciplined research--but still judgments.

To say that the estimates contain elements of
judgment--along with the research findings and the
reasoning derived from a theoretical model of work
scheduling--does not detract from their usefulness,

nor even from their reliability. At stake are the
extent and quality of judgment, not the fact itself.
If work staggering is instituted, some places of employment will prove capable of modifying their schedules and will comply. One man's guess about this is
not as good as another's. It will require some explanation of the theory of modifiability and of the
studies to show why.

SCHEDULE MODIFIABILITY

An account will now be given of the way the
estimates of schedule modifiability were made. It
will briefly answer two questions: What do the
estimates mean? And, how were they produced?

The course of the account will be guided by
Appendix Table 64 and Table 29, which contain the
summary findings about modifiability. There are
three concepts employed in these tables which require explanation. They are: schedule determinants,
units of employment and alternative start times.
These have to be defined if the tables are to be
understood; but to define them will require an explanation of how and why they were formulated, and
where the information came from. Thus, to report
the extent of schedule modifiability in the CBD, a
brief description of the theory which produced the
inquiry is required.

The Determinants of Work Schedules

For reasons already reported, the procedure of
asking places of employment whether they can change
their work schedules was not used. In its place, an
approach was worked out which avoids the pitfalls of
direct questioning, as well as others. Instead of
asking informants their opinions about modifiability,
this approach searches for the factors which govern
schedules. Once discovered, the determinants are
analyzed to find out if they permit or prevent schedule change. In effect, the study does what every
place of employment would have to do for itself--but
which, for reasons shortly to appear, it could

at best do only partially, if at all. According to
this method, schedules are judged modifiable to the
extent that their determinants do not obstruct
changes.

Work schedules have many different kinds of
specific determinants. In any place of employment,
one or more things will stand out as the controlling
factors in its schedule. In general, however, it is
convenient to group the determinants into two principal classes: functional determinants and personnel
determinants. The many specific ones fit adequately
into these two general classes.

Functional Determinants

A place of employment's work schedules may be
dictated by its operating needs and activities. This
happens whenever its people must have direct personal
relations with people who work in other places of
employment in order to fulfill their occupational
duties. Such relations can take place only if the
schedules of the two overlap at the times when their
relations must occur. These occupational needs and
activities make up the functional determinants of
work schedules.

Work schedules fix the times during which people
are present at work and available for performing their
occupational duties. Their duties may include relations with people of other firms. On both sides of
the relationship, the occupations can be at any level
of the organization, from relatively routine jobs to
the principal positions of the enterprise. The relationships with other firms include: buying and
selling, receiving and delivering information, documentation, materials, supplies products, and services,
and others. They may be face-to-face or telephone
contacts. They can occur at either establishment, or
elsewhere. They may happen at any time of the working
day. They involve sellers, buyers, bankers, experts
and consultants, government officials, labor representatives, service companies--indeed, the whole industrial catalogue.

The relationships which can affect--and deter-
mine--work schedules are those which must occur regularly and systematically during the beginning and
end of the normal working day. In general, schedules
overlap during the main part of the working day.
But during the opening and closing hours, differences
in schedule can interfere with the interfirm, interoccupational relations simply because one of the
parties may not be open for business. Even at these
times, not all relationships are significant to
schedules--only those which occur regularly and systematically, and which must happen if either side is
to perform its work. Sometimes emergency relations
may influence schedules, but only if they are important enough to outweigh other considerations. In
general, the recurrent ones which have to take place
during the early and late part of the day are the
functional determinants of work schedules.

Personnel Determinants

If ever a schedule change is proposed for the
CBD, places of employment may be expected to be particularly sensitive to its personnel implications.
These consist, in the first instance, of the response
of their own people--employers, executives, and employees. Their preferences, likes, dislikes, interests, and needs in respect to schedules will affect
many decisions as to the modifiability of schedules.
All places of employment will also be acutely interested in the effect of any proposed schedule change
upon their continuing accessibility to the local
labor market. In this case, the influence comes from
prospective employees, and it reflects their desires
as to work schedules. The social, cultural, and general community practices with respect to work time
fall into this class of schedule determinants.

An indirect influence on schedule modifiability
may arise from people whose schedules are not changed,
or who do not work in the CBD, or who do not work at
all. This influence can be transmitted via the employees, by affecting their preferences or attitudes
to schedule change. Or it can reach the CBD by means
of city or community institutions--political, social,

civic, recreational, or other. These indirect influences are not strictly personnel determinants, but
they will be given serious attention as a significant factor affecting the feasibility of staggering.

Regulations

The work schedules in some establishments may
also be fixed by regulations. These can be found in
union contracts, trade or area agreements, or by
legislation or ordinance, and may operate to allow
or prevent schedule change.

As determinants of schedules, regulations are
not of fundamental interest to this inquiry. Governmental regulations are not expected to interfere with
work staggering, if the city decides to introduce it.
Hence, if there are any such restrictions on schedules, they may be considered as neutral in their ultimate effects on schedule change. On the other hand,
regulations arising from private sources may prove
significant. In this inquiry, however, they are taken
care of by the study and evaluation of the other two
determinants. The underlying reason is that such
regulations, if motivated by the needs of employees
or constituents, will be examined in a more fundamental way by the other research methods. Accordingly,
these regulatory determinants will receive no further
attention as such.

The Theory

These determinants are derived from the disciplines which deal with decision making in places of
employment. As such they possess certain advantages
which would be lacking if they were nothing more than
ad hoc theorizing about the nature of scheduling.
Their relationship to the relevant disciplines makes
it possible to connect them up with models of decision
making. In turn, this gives the determinants meaning,
worth and weighting which the corresponding variables
possess in the original conceptual models. It also
makes it possible to investigate them by the methodologies from which they are drawn. Some of this theoretical structure will now be briefly described.

An appropriate starting place for formulating a theory of scheduling is the individual place of employment. It is evident, from general knowledge, that the place of employment decides its own work schedules within whatever legal, organizational, and market restrictions apply. The internal decision making process has many variants including unilateral determination by the employer, collective bargaining, and in some cases unilateral determination by a union. None of these variants, not even the last, affects the statement that the individual place of employment is the ultimate decision maker over its own schedules, and is therefore the appropriate unit at which to begin the analysis.

The question which needs to be raised is: What governs its decisions as to work schedule? The search for an answer leads directly to the available theories about places of employment and their motivations and processes of decision making. These theories are provided by various disciplines. Among them are economics and some of the noneconomic social sciences.

Work Schedules and the Economics of the Firm

As an economic entity, a firm is assumed to choose a work schedule--from among all available alternative schedules--which will maximize its net income. If the effect of alternative schedules upon net income is not clear--or not relevant, as in the case of institutions, administrative offices, and the like--a place of employment can use, as its economic criterion of schedules, the minimization of costs or maximization of revenues. There is reason to believe that all places of employment have alternative choices as to schedules, whether or not they actually pay attention to them. Theoretically, the range of choice is very large, perhaps infinite; but even within the customary working day, there are many alternatives. A review of actual work schedules confirms the variety of possibilities to be found even within a single industry.

It is pertinent then to ask: Why do different
work schedules have different effects upon net income, costs,and revenues? How does the timing of
work introduce such variability?

Work schedules may produce such different effects because they either facilitate or encumber the
relations between a firm and its suppliers and customers. If a firm's schedule differs from the
schedules of its suppliers and customers, there will
be times during which essential business relations
cannot be carried out--because one or the other is
not open for operations. These times, under prevailing conditions, will be confined to the begin-
nings or endings of the working day; during the main
portion of the customary day schedules overlap substantially. When these relations, essential to the
firm, its supplier or its customers, are obstructed,
many different kinds of operating effects may be
felt: losses in sales, failure to receive or deliver materials, supplies, or services. Schedules
that allow essential relations to occur can reduce
such losses.

Some additional cost variability may arise when
an established schedule is to be modified. A firm
may lose some of its employees who cannot accommodate
themselves to the new schedule. This entails a
temporary loss because of the training and skill which
must be replaced. (It may also provide benefits in
the form of a superior replacement.) The new schedule may also modify the firm's access to employees in
the local labor market. This can reduce or enhance
its supply. It may require a premium wage or the
removal of a previous premium. It may also provide
access to more or less productive people. Some of
these changes in the firm's economy are short-run;
others, however, may become permanent factors in the
cost and revenue structure of the firm.

These cost variations are traceable to specific
causes. A firm may have to add to its purchases of
goods, supplies, services, facilities, or people in
order to overcome the incompatability in schedules.
Or the price of such things may vary over the time

of the day. The economic effects of schedules can
thus be transmitted by price or quantity to the individual place of employment.

To complicate matters, it is likely that no
schedule will bring all costs to a minimum and raise
all revenues to a maximum. One schedule as compared
with another may raise some costs and lower others,
and raise or lower revenues from some outputs as
against others. A firm's economic choice among
alternative schedules must therefore weight a large
number of effects and find the optimum among them.
Such a procedure will lead, at least theoretically,
to an economic decision among the alternatives.

The activities which are affected by work schedules are those which occur in or through interoccupational relationships that take place regularly and systematically at the beginning or the end of the day.
They are readily accessible to empirical study because the scope of such study is comfortably restricted to only a few of the total interoccupational relations; and of these, to only the salient ones.
Once these relationships are discovered for a given
firm or industry, they can be subjected to a limited
but sufficient economic evaluation. For any given
relationship, it is usually not difficult to determine
how a change in work schedule will affect it--whether
it will impede, facilitate, or have no effect on it.
This is equivalent to determining the direction of
economic effect which changes in schedule will impose.
The effects cannot be quantified or weighted, and
hence the divergent effects of a particular schedule
upon different interoccupational relations cannot be
evaluated exactly. However, enough is known about
the nature of these relations to be able to determine
the principal consequences and to evaluate them in a
qualitative way.

By transforming the cost and revenue categories
to interoccupational relations, the economic criteria
of scheduling can be made applicable to empirical
study. The precision of cost and revenue functions
has to be abandoned, but applicable categories are

obtained and the results can still be evaluated from
an economic point of view.

Thus, from the viewpoint of economics, work
schedules are an organizational variable affecting
the incomes of places of employment. The schedule
determinants, both functional and personnel, act as
determinants precisely because they raise or lower
costs and revenue. The economic model of scheduling
makes it possible to evaluate the determinants and
to infer whether they facilitate or impede schedule
change.

Noneconomic Disciplines

A place of employment is not only a system of
economic inputs and outputs. It is a collection of
people brought together and organized for the purpose
of performing assigned occupational tasks. The place
of employment can thus be viewed as a social organization whose members, both individually and as groups,
are entities distinct and apart from the place of
employment. They may share some common interests with
it, but even their economic motivations must be
treated as separate from the economic interests of
their place of employment.

As systems of social organization, places of
employment are subjects of study by various noneconomic disciplines. These include sociology, social psychology, psychology, and to some extent anthropology
and political science. Economics deals with input-
output relationships of the enterprise and attributes
to them a motivating influence on its decision makers.
These other disciplines deal with social relations and
processes among the people of the enterprise and emphasize the social factors in decision making. They
concern themselves with decisions and decision making
as a consequence of the systems of organization and
interaction prevailing in the place of employment.

A change in work schedule is an organizational
change. People will respond to it, according to the
noneconomic disciplines, out of the decision processes of their formal and informal groupings. There is

by now a substantial literature in this field contributed by many of the disciplines just named. The
people's probable response can be discovered by an inquiry utilizing the research methodologies of the
appropriated disciplines.

     To determine the modifiability of work schedules,
it thus becomes essential to find out how people will
respond to a change. This means knowing more than
merely attitudes and opinions. It involves a deeper
searching into people's relationships to work schedules, to their motivations and determinants of behavior with reference to a possible change. The
probable response needs to be known not only for the
CBD work force as a whole but also for significant
identifiable segments of it.

     A sociological study was designed and carried out
among people who work in the CBD. A full report of
this study is issued separately. Chapter 5 will be
centrally concerned with this study and with its
findings, particularly those which are relevant to
schedule modifiability in places of employment.

Conclusions

     To test the feasibility of work staggering, this
study requires forecasts of the modifiability of work
schedules in the CBD. Modifiability means the ability
of places of employment and people to absorb changes
in their schedules. The forecasting aspect transfers
the capability of changing schedules to some future
time. In so doing, it transforms the notion of
ability to change from a concept of what is possible
into a notion of compliance. It thus becomes a forecast of what people and places of employment can and
will do, if schedule change is proposed.

     To produce the required information, it was
necessary to make use of whatever knowledge and technology are available relative to the subject of inquiry. The disciplines most pertinent to it are economics and the noneconomic disciplines dealing with
decision making in the place of employment. They
contribute bodies of theory, knowledge, and

methodology out of which to formulate the concepts
and procedures for making the necessary forecasts.

Economics provides a model of decision making
from which the capability of the enterprise may be
assessed--and forecasted. Its cost and revenue
functions supply the theoretical elements of its
decisions about schedules. The behavior of these
functions will be approximated by discovering the
scheduling determinants. Both the functional and the
personnel determinants produce economic effects upon
the place of employment.

The noneconomic disciplines produce forecasts
of people's probable responses to schedule change.
These forecasts grow out of theories of organizational behavior and decision making, as applied to
findings concerning the population under inquiry.
The two determinants do not uniquely derive from the
two sets of disciplines. Each of the determinants is
related to both bodies of theory. The functional
determinants are economic because they are impersonal,
because they are evaluated by their economic effects,
and because they are investigated by an applied economic methodology. However, the personnel determinants are also economic because they necessarily affect the costs of the individual firm. They are
separated, however, from the functional determinants
because they pertain to the people within the enterprise, because they correspond more closely to the
categories of the noneconomic theories, and because
they are discoverable by sociological techniques.
Also, certain aspects of the functional determinants
will turn up among the personnel determinants. It
was thus never intended to separate the schedule
determinants into unique derivations of one or the
other of the two sets of theory.

The determinants provide the means for assessing
the modifiability of schedules. They can be readily
interpreted as the relevant variables of theoretical
models of decision making produced by economics and
the noneconomic disciplines. This makes it possible
to conduct research studies, to collect information,

to analyze it, and to produce forecasts of capability
and probable behavior. The forecasts will be statements of future events, made within limits of proba-
bility, and conditional upon whatever restrictions the
empirical findings dictate. It is most unlikely that
any more definitive formulations of future events can
be made. Tentative though they will inevitably appear, the results will provide a useful basis for the
feasibility computations.

UNITS OF EMPLOYMENT

The units of employment to which functional capability is attributed on Appendix Table 64 are
various kinds of industrial aggregates. Most com-
monly they are industries, but not always at the
same level of aggregation. The list includes 4-, 3-,
and 2-digit groups and major divisions. To conserve space, the rule of using the largest possible
aggregate was followed. There are also multiple-
industry groups, of which the most important are the
"other" manufacturing industries. It embraces all
manufacturing except apparel and part of printing.
There are some industry-wide, internal company functions which are separated out for purposes of this
study. These include the company offices of real
estate operators, contract construction and stevedoring companies, and a number of functions of commercial
banks. Lastly, there are the central administrative
offices of multiestablishment companies, which cut
across many industries.

It was stated earlier that the decision making
unit in respect to scheduling is the place of employment. The structure of Appendix Table 64 indicates
that the findings of modifiability apply to units
comprising multiple places of employment. It is further noted that the studies of functional modifiability were conducted on the basis of aggregates, primarily industries, not individual establishments.
If decisions are individual, what is the justification for studies of scheduling by aggregates?

The economic analysis of scheduling by the firm, as briefly summarized above, justifies the studies on the basis of aggregates. The firm may be the ultimate decision maker over its own work schedule. But the economic analysis discloses that significant factors governing the firm's decision are external to it. They are the cost and quantity conditions which are determined in the markets of the goods and services which the firm seeks to buy or sell. The firm, in fixing its schedule, has to adapt itself to the market conditions which it cannot, by its own actions, affect in any significant way, unless it is an exceedingly large buyer or seller of a particular commodity or service.

The markets in which the cost and quantity conditions are determined consist of the buyers and sellers of the various products and services. There are many such markets and hence many aggregates. Any given firm belongs to a number of such aggregates-- to as many as the number of things it buys and sells. Represented in these many aggregates are many different work schedules--indeed, as much variety in schedules as the CBD might have.

Among the many aggregates to which a firm might belong, there can be one which is more stable in composition than any other. It is composed of the firms which produce the same or similar products: its competition or its industry. As competitors, the firms of an industry sell in the same or similar markets. Because products are similar, an industry also exhibits much similarity in the products and services which its firms buy. Hence, the firms of an industry are subject to similar schedule determinants.

The economic analysis of work scheduling thus leads, in the manner briefly sketched, to the result that an industry--or possibly multiples of industries-- share many common determinants of work schedules and, if they are large enough in any given market, can even influence the schedules of other firms and industries. There are many intervening steps omitted in this analysis but the general line of reasoning ought now to be evident.

Two important conclusions governing modifiability of schedules and its investigation are drawn. First, the unit of investigation for the discovery of determinants of work schedules ought to be aggregates, not individual firms. While the firm may be the ultimate decision maker over its own schedule, the principal conditions that govern its decisions are external. Therefore, from the perspective of the individual firm, the basic determinants of its schedule may not actually be perceptible. They come most clearly into view when examined on the broad basis of buying or selling aggregates.

Second, schedule modifiability from an economic viewpoint appears to lie outside the capability of firms acting alone, except in the case of individual firms which may, by virtue of their size, dominate either their input or output markets. This follows from the assumption that the individual firm adapts to the market conditions affecting the flows of its inputs and outputs. A single firm changing its schedule might worsen its economic position without having any noticeable effect on its market. However, an aggregate consisting of all the buyers or all the sellers of a given product can alter the economic determinants of their scheduling. The individual firm will be unable to perceive possible alternative work schedules because its influence upon conditions of input and output markets is insignificant. However, as part of an industry change, it can conceivably improve its situation. But this perspective lies outside the range of vision of the individual place of employment.

With respect to the units of employment which appear on Appendix Table 64, two things now need to be explained.

First, although the table uses aggregates, it is understood that the units which are considered functionally capable of modifying schedules are the individual establishments. Aggregates are used in the table because it is convenient to group the establishments and because this kind of grouping suits the subject of scheduling. But this does not imply that the aggregates have any kind of real organizational existence, nor that they have any authority over scheduling. In all cases, it is the establishments belonging to the industrial aggregates which are considered functionally capable of modifying schedules, wherever the table attributes such capability to the aggregate.

Second, within the aggregates, not all the establishments are necessarily capable of modifying schedules, even though it will be computationally convenient to assume that they are. A more careful statement would be: In general, the establishments within an aggregate may be considered capable of modifying schedules; exceptions consist of firms whose particular circumstances may produce special schedule determinants. Functional capability applies to establishments which share the common, characteristic, and general determinants of scheduling, as they may be found in the typical firm of the industry. It will be assumed, in the initial computational steps, that all establishments within an industry share the industry's capability, even though this assumption is known to be invalid. The assumption will be removed however on the basis of some of the next chapter's findings.

ALTERNATIVE START TIMES

The ability of firms to modify their schedules, on functional or other grounds, has to be assessed with respect to specific alternatives. The number of possible alternative schedules is theoretically very large, perhaps infinite. Schedules can be fixed at any length and can be given many different internal configurations; also they can be placed, permanently or varyingly, anywhere within the twenty-four hours of the day. This range of possible alternatives is not really available, however tempting it might be to explore the modifiability of schedules from the broad perspective of a drastic revision of the prevailing pattern of work day and work week. Neither the problem at hand nor, as it turned out, the tolerability of the people to schedule change, allow for such

a wide range of choice. In this study of modifiability, the practicable schedule alternatives acquired
a distinct range and form.

On Appendix Table 64, a unit of employment is
shown to be capable of modifying its work schedule
by noting that it can start work at 7:30, 8:00, 8:30,
or 9:30 a.m. This way of formulating the alternatives embodies many decisions about the redesign of
schedules for the CBD. The principal ones are: the
retention of the gross working day; the uniform
starting time; and the specific start times. Each
will now be explained.

The Gross Working Day

In any assessment of modifiability of schedules,
it proved essential to preserve, for purposes of
analysis and computation, the prevailing gross working day. The gross working day is defined as the
length of time between regular starting and stopping
times. Thus, a 9:00 a.m. to 5:00 p.m. schedule has
an 8-hour gross working day, while a 9:00 a.m. to
5:30 p.m. has 8 1/2 hours. In preserving the gross
working day, it is implied that all prevailing scheduling conditions are maintained: actual working hours
length of lunch hour, number and length of breaks
within the work day, and other similar scheduling arrangements.

The retention of the gross working day, as a
basis for this study, is both a convenience and a
necessity. It is convenient because it simplifies
the analysis of change and the computation of their
effects. In this connection, the format of the work
schedules, as shown in Chapter 2, has special significance. All changes in work schedules are expressed
by shifting the numbers along their respective diagonal lines, from upper left to lower right. Each
diagonal preserves the gross working day of all
people contained in it. If a number were shifted
either to the right or the left--that is, to another
diagonal--its gross working day would be increased
(to the right) or decreased (to the left). It is

thus simple and systematic, from the viewpoint of
computation, to preserve the gross working day.

It is moreover an inescapable requirement. The
gross working day is fixed either unilaterally by
the employer or by collective bargaining. It can be
changed, and places of employment occasionally do so.
However, it is beyond the capability of this study
to anticipate the nature or extent of any changes in the
gross working day. Hence, necessity dictates the
making of an important assumption: The present gross
working day will continue to prevail.

This however is only an assumption, and not a
particularly strong one. There is reason to believe
that the gross working day will change. In part,
this change is being caused by changes in the length
of the working day and week. The tendency to reduce
the daily and weekly work hours is continuing, although irregularly with respect to industry and form
of reduction. The changes already observed have
unusual and irregular characteristics. Some shorten
the work day and some, via overtime, preserve the
original actual start and stop times. Some preserve
the original gross working day for four days of the
week and reduce it on the fifth, usually Friday.
Changes are encountered from time to time in length
of lunch hour and other internal breaks during the
day. It may even be anticipated that a change in
work schedule, originating as part of a work staggering program, will induce modifications in the gross
working day as well. All these considerations add
up to a virtual certainty that the gross working day
is changing, and will continue to change, perhaps
even at an accelerated rate. Nothing can be done
about incorporating these realistic anticipations
into this study, and so the assumption that the gross
working day will continue has to be retained.

The assumption proves less damaging than the
explanation might suggest. The changes in question
are occurring slowly, and some do not affect the
gross working day or are offset by other changes.
Within the short run--certainly within the time hori-
zon for evaluating the effects of a program of work

staggering--the assumption that the present gross
working day will continue does not produce any noticeable distortions in the final conclusions as to
feasibility.

Uniform Starting Time

The work schedules which are considered as possible alternatives are designated by starting times.
Thus, a schedule may be called 8:00 a.m., and this
name signifies a schedule having many specific characteristics, including certain rules of computation.
The full significance of these alternatives will now
be clarified.

Schedule modifiability, indicated by a starting
time, applies to units of employment. It specifies
that the establishments are capable, on functional
grounds, of adopting the particular time as a uniform
starting time.

In applying the new starting times, the following
rules are employed.

1) If the uniform starting time is earlier than
9:00 a.m., all employees who now start at, or later
than, the alternative time are shifted to it. Those
starting earlier than the time are not changed.

2) If the uniform starting time is after 9:00
a.m., all employees who now start at 8:30 or later
are shifted to the new starting time. Those who now
start earlier than 8:30 are not changed.

The procedure for applying these rules will be
illustrated by the schedules of wholesale trades.
Appendix Table 64 shows that the wholesale trades are
functionally able to adopt starting times of 8:00,
8:30, and 9:30. Table 22 presents the present work
schedule of the wholesale trades. Table 23 shows
the schedule which would prevail if an 8:30 starting
time were adopted. All employees who now start at
9:30, 9:15, 9:00, or at 8:45 are shifted to 8:30,
along their respective diagonals.

TABLE 22

Numbers of People in the Wholesale Trades Starting and
Stopping Work at Various Times

Start Time	Stop Time												
	3:30	3:45	4:00	4:15	4:30	4:45	5:00	5:15	5:30	5:45	6:00	Other	Total
7:30	0	0	3	0	9	0	0	0	0	0	0	20	32
7:45	0	0	0	0	0	0	0	0	0	0	0	20	20
8:00	0	0	519	0	2,792	0	6,025	0	0	0	0	416	9,752
8:15	0	0	0	0	0	243	420	0	0	0	0	4	667
8:30	0	0	0	20	3,302	13,239	9,948	239	2,377	0	0	507	29,632
8:45	0	0	0	0	32	10,494	30,000	267	773	0	0	43	41,609
9:00	0	0	0	0	493	1,055	58,067	3,273	48,233	181	3,645	1,756	116,703
9:15	0	0	0	0	0	0	0	3,098	121	0	0	24	3,243
9:30	0	0	0	0	0	0	229	126	338	20	480	227	1,420
Other	493	0	2,494	0	126	131	303	265	298	0	521	19,022	23,653
Total	493	0	3,016	20	6,754	25,162	104,992	7,268	52,140	201	4,646	22,039	226,731

TABLE 23

Number of People in the Wholesale Trades Starting and Stopping Work
at Various Times Under an 8:30 Start Time

Start Time	Stop Time												
	3:30	3:45	4:00	4:15	4:30	4:45	5:00	5:15	5:30	5:45	6:00	Other	Total
7:30	0	0	3	0	9	0	0	0	0	0	0	20	32
7:45	0	0	0	0	0	0	0	0	0	0	0	20	20
8:00	0	0	519	0	2,792	0	6,025	0	0	0	0	416	9,752
8:15	0	0	0	0	0	243	420	0	0	0	0	4	667
8:30	0	0	722	1,233	75,299	46,653	58,928	1,193	6,022	0	0	2,557	192,607
8:45	0	0	0	0	0	0	0	0	0	0	0	0	0
9:00	0	0	0	0	0	0	0	0	0	0	0	0	0
9:15	0	0	0	0	0	0	0	0	0	0	0	0	0
9:30	0	0	0	0	0	0	0	0	0	0	0	0	0
Other	493	0	2,494	0	126	131	303	265	298	0	521	19,022	23,653
Total	493	0	3,738	1,233	78,226	47,027	65,676	1,458	6,320	0	521	22,039	226,731

In this procedure, the gross working day is preserved by moving the numbers of employees along their diagonals on the work schedule tables. This automatically changes the stop times. Thus, the uniform starting time contains both the designation of an alternative schedule, and a procedure for putting it into effect.

To each element in the procedure there are important substantive implications.

The most fundamental issue is the use of a uniform starting time for an industry as the means for applying an alternative work schedule. As the procedure shows, the rest of the application of the alternative follows logically and consistently (within the fixed limits) from the decision to utilize a uniform starting time. It is therefore essential that the justification and significance of this decision be given first.

Actually, there are only two bases on which alternative work schedules can be projected, given the studies of modifiability and their results. These studies were focused upon a single ultimate question: Can an industry, on functional grounds, modify its schedules, and if yes, by how much and in which directions? If yes, the answer could be applied either by projecting a uniform amount of change, or by a uniform starting time for the aggregate.

Projecting a uniform amount of change means that all employees are shifted to an earlier or later schedule by a fixed amount. Thus, if a given industry were shown capable, on functional grounds, of changing its schedule by as much as an hour, an alternative possibility of one half hour could be evaluated by changing schedules, along each diagonal, by one half-hour, first in one direction and then in the other. By this procedure, the present over-all pattern of scheduling would continue in effect, including the varied fixed amount, along its diagonals, in one direction or the other.

The uniform starting time, as described above, would shift all employees to a specified starting time. To attain such a schedule, people would be shifted by varying amounts of time.

These are the only two possible bases for projecting alternative schedules. They might be combined in various ways, thereby allowing a certain amount of uniform change and a certain amount of uniform starting time. While this is an elegant possibility, there is no way of determining, in any substantively rational way, just how it might be applied. The two basic methods used independently remain the only ones for which there might be any justification. They are equally convenient to use computationally. The choice of the uniform starting time rests primarily upon its greater reasonableness.

The uniform amount of change has one conceptual advantage over the uniform starting time basis. It preserves the internal schedule patterns of firms and industries. This maintains any existing functional relationship of schedules within firms, and to some extent among industries. Moreover, it does not introduce a scheduling principle now lacking in most industries--a uniform starting time. Nevertheless, despite this advantage and its implications, the other method remains preferable.

There are two fundamental grounds for the choice of the uniform starting time over the uniform amount of change. These are the uniform starting time's greater ease of communicability and comprehensibility, and its greater likelihood of corresponding to what might actually take place.

One of the important problems associated with implementing a program of work staggering is communicating the system of work schedules to places of employment and having it become imbedded in the mores of the CBD. In this form, the problem is a remote one, and perhaps ought not to interfere in the computation of feasibility. Nevertheless, it cannot really be avoided. Feasibility implies, among many other things, that a particular program of staggering

is realizable from as many points of view as can be
conceived and investigated. There are many choices
to be made as to the form of alternatives and ultimate patterns of scheduling in the CBD. Communicability to the community and comprehensibility of a
schedule program affect feasibility in a fundamental
way. Wherever these criteria can help resolve a
choice, they certainly ought to be brought to bear.
In this connection, the choice between uniform
starting time and uniform amount of change is decisively resolved by these criteria in favor of the
uniform starting time.

Why? Because it is believed that the communi-
ty--its industries, its employers, and its employees--
will perceive more clearly the message that a given
starting time is projected for particular industries
than that these same industries ought to start by a
given amount of time earlier or later than they now
do. The clarity will be greater, whether or not
they choose to adopt the projected schedule. Moreover, the uniform starting time offers the community
a distinct and permanent pattern to which it can, if
it chooses, adhere in the future. Employees, firms,
and industries--both present and prospective--will
know that a particular industry has a given schedule
in the CBD, the exceptions thereto notwithstanding.

Within this same reasoning, the introduction of
uniform starting times, despite their departure from
prevailing practice, may also be justified. This
justification turns on a question of how the equita-
bility of the projected changes will strike the com-
munity--the firms, industries, and employees. The
uniform starting time states far more clearly than
the uniform amount of change just what might be expected of an industry and its employees. The sheer
uniformity of the ultimate schedule carries within
itself a greater measure of apparent equality of
treatment than the uniform amount of change. Moreover, observing or disregarding the projected starting time will stand out, both to the firms and individuals and to the rest of the community, as a
clearer and starker act. Compliance will therefore

be induced, and noncompliance will either have acceptable and rational grounds or gradually wither
away. Despite the novelty, in many cases, of a uniform starting time for an industry, it will convey
a greater sense of significant and enduring schedule change than the alternatives based on uniform
amount of change.

The uniform starting time is used as a logical
and computationally convenient starting point. This
assumption will later be relaxed in a rational and
systematic way, in order to bring the ultimate estimates into increasingly greater correspondence with
anticipated reality.

The second reason for choosing the uniform
starting time as the basis for alternative work
schedules is that it is the more likely of the two
bases to turn out as projected. If each method
could be experimentally implemented, the resulting
work schedule--in reality, not hypothetically--would
correspond more closely to the one projected by the
uniform starting time than by the uniform amount of
change. The grounds for this belief can readily be
stated.

All the reasons of communicability and comprehensibility, with their implications and resultant
consequences, as described above, will undoubtedly
operate in favor of the uniform starting time. But
beyond these considerations, others, probably more
fundamental, will become effective. The uniform
starting time will require less schedule change of
people to achieve a satisfactory redistribution in
the CBD than the uniform amount of change. Resistance ought therefore to be less and compliance greater with the uniform start time. Further, the uniform
amount of change basis supposes that the prevailing
schedule patterns, within firms and industries, will
continue in effect after a schedule change--that is,
that the patterns are functional and are dictated by
the necessities of operation. This supposition is
highly doubtful. If the present patterns are not
genuinely functional, a general schedule change will
provide the occasion for other changes in schedule.

Indeed, such further changes will probably tend in the direction of uniformity of schedule, in particular toward uniform start times. Hence, for these reasons, it was concluded that projections of work schedules based upon uniform amounts of change would, if implemented, correspond less to actuality than projections based upon the uniform starting time.

Once the choice is made between these two bases, the rest of the procedure follows with ease. Given a starting time, projections are made by shifting the numbers of employees along the work schedule diagonals to the alternative starting schedule. A difference in procedure is introduced for alternatives before and after 9:00 a.m. Under starting times earlier than 9:00 a.m., all employees who start at or later than the new times are shifted to it; those earlier remain unchanged. New starting times after 9:00 a.m. are tested by shifting employees who now start at 8:30 a.m. or later to it, while those starting earlier than 8:30 a.m. are maintained at their present schedules.

These limits were introduced in order to avoid or reduce the use of 8:30, 8:45, and 9:00 a.m., the most congested times at present and the principal sources of the transit difficulties. Hence, the decision to avoid these times by the indicated computation procedures was based, not on scheduling considerations, but on desired transit effects. The question which this procedure raises is: Will firms be able to change their schedules in this way? Again, the best available answer is that they ought to be able to come very close to the kinds of rearrangements embodied in the procedure. For one thing, the sheer information that the 8:30 to 9:00 a.m. times need to be avoided in rescheduling will supply the CBD firms with important guidance they have so far not had. There are many indications that they will make use of this information in rescheduling--and thereby conform to the changes contained in the computational procedure.

Start Times

Four alternative work schedules, each designated by a start time, are projected in this study. They are: 7:30, 8:00, 8:30, and 9:30 a.m. All assessments of modifiability of schedules are made with respect to these four alternatives. Each implies, as described above, all the other changes, including a corresponding stopping time as governed by the prevailing gross working day. These particular times and their implications will now be explained and justified.

Actually, there are two main decisions embodied in these four times: their range, from 7:30 to 9:30, and the half-hour intervals between them. The specific alternatives are the result of these two prior decisions.

The decision to fix half-hour intervals between scheduled starting times stems from several factors. First, it was decided that any starting times projected by this study would have to be on standard quarter-hour times, and on on lesser subdivisions. The possibilities would therefore be on the hour, quarter past, half past, or quarter to the hour. Smaller intervals were ruled out because (1) the predominant practice by far in the CBD is to utilize these quarter-hourly times, and (2) none of the data or computations of this study would justify the use of smaller intervals. Hence to try to establish schedules at ten- or even five-minute intervals would be uncharacteristic of the CBD, essentially a clumsy and unaccustomed procedure, and would introduce degrees of detail into the system which neither the data nor the actual behaviors would justify. Hence, the quarter-hour intervals were adopted.

Next, it was determined that the intervals needed for rescheduling were actually a half hour in length, rather than the quarter hour, and these times were fixed on the hour and half hour. For this, there were two reasons. First, the combination of CBD geography and transportation time dictated the half-hour interval. It so happens that the travel times

between the main employment centers in the northern
and southern portions of the CBD are approximately
15 minutes, give or take a few minutes on the different lines. Hence, if work schedules were fixed at
15-minute intervals, the waves of traffic would
simply converge at the northern and southern stations at approximately the same times. The only way
to avoid this is to separate starting times by half-
hour intervals. Second, in many of the large firms
and large buildings, the internal transportation
system requires staggering within companies. The
half-hour interval provides ample room for such
staggering without disturbing the general scheduling
pattern. It thus relieves this study of considering
the feasibility of internal staggering, while at the
same time making suitable allowance for its occurrence on an individual company basis.

The decision to delimit the range of alternatives to 7:30 to 9:30 arises from two considerations.
First, this appears to be a sufficient spread of
time over which to distribute the people who work in
the CBD so as to relieve schedule congestion, and
ultimately transit congestion. The estimated per cents
of people starting work in this period under present
schedules is as follows:

Time	Per Cent
7:30	.4
7:45	.1
8:00	10.1
8:15	1.5
8:30	14.0
8:45	11.0
9:00	39.5
9:15	4.1
9:30	2.2
Total	82.9

Thus, a total of 82.9 per cent of the work force
starts between 7:30 and 9:30, with the principal concentrations occurring at 9:00, 8:30, 8:45 and 8:00.
Within this period there are five half-hour times. If
the 82.9 per cent were equally divided among the five,

there would be 16.6 per cent in each. This optimal
distribution would certainly provide all the decon-
gestion required in scheduling and in transit. Actually, the distribution would not have to be equal to
achieve the required improvement. It is thus sufficient to find that within these five intervals there
is enough room to achieve the desired scheduling and
transit relief.

Second, the evidence is convincing that the
working population of the CBD would find a greater
range of starting times intolerable. This will be
demonstrated fully in the next chapter. It will also turn out that the addition of the personnel constraints to the findings of functional feasibility
will make work schedule changes greater than one hour
virtually a nullity. This too will emerge from the
findings of the next chapter. Hence, the restriction
of the range of alternatives to the two hours, 7:30
to 9:30, is about as far as the working population--
employees, executives, owners, professionals, and
the rest--can be distributed.

FUNCTIONAL CAPABILITY OF SCHEDULE CHANGE

The modifiability of CBD work schedules, on
functional grounds alone, is shown on Appendix Table
64. The units of employment listed on the table are
industries, groups of industries, and special subdivisions of industries. Modifiability is shown by
indicating the alternative starting times which the
units of employment are considered capable of adopting. The table is the end result of studies of work
scheduling, and it contains all the alternatives of
rescheduling for purposes of work staggering which
are considered possible for the CBD.

It is highly unlikely that Appendix Table 64,
standing alone, would be adequately understood. It
contains many terms, specifications of numbers, and
theoretical notions about the modifiability of schedules whose definitions or significance will not be
sufficiently evident from the captions. Therefore,
in the interest of presenting the table, it was

necessary to explain its structure and content in the preceding section.

In this section, the way the table was constructed will be described. Thereafter, the principal findings about the modifiability will be submitted.

The Construction of Appendix Table 64

Appendix Table 64 is the end product of studies of work scheduling in CBD industries. The studies provided information about functional determinants of scheduling. On the basis of this information, assessments were made as to the industries' capability of modifying schedules. Appendix Table 64 specifies, for each industry, the conclusions which were reached by this procedure.

The Studies

There were two kinds of studies. First, there were intensive investigations of scheduling determinants, conducted in representative firms of the principal industries in the CBD. These investigations were supplemented by the existing literature on industrial organization which sheds light on many aspects of scheduling and its functional determinants. Most of these studies culminated in written reports, of which there are eighteen. Each report covers more than a single industry. The Notes and Explanations of Appendix Table 64 list the eighteen reports, and the body of the table specifies, for each industry, the report from which its conclusions are drawn. There were also investigations in some of the other industries which were not, for various reasons, issued as written reports.

These industry studies deal only with the functional determinants of work scheduling. They explicitly exclude all consideration of personal factors, such as the preferences of employees, employers—and especially of informants—and access to local labor markets. They follow the conceptual lines described in the theoretical section of this chapter.

Second, the work schedule surveys noted in Chapter 3 collected information about scheduling practices and determinants. These surveys touched almost every industry in the CBD; those omitted were either too small to consider, or else could not be located. The information obtained from the surveys which contributed to the construction of Appendix Table 64 included occupational data and interindustry relations.

The studies furnished not only the bases for assessments of modifiability in the industries they covered, but yielded general conclusions about scheduling and modification of schedules. These were used to assess modifiability in some industries which were not intensively studied. It was possible to extend the findings of the studies because information about occupations and interindustry relations of these unstudied industries were available from the schedule surveys. The industries which were assessed in this way will be evident on Appendix Table 64. They are the ones for which alternative schedules are specified, but which have no reference to any industry study.

The industry studies appear in Appendix M of this report.

The industry studies were designed to discover the functional determinants of work scheduling, and to evaluate, as objectively as possible, the possibilities of schedule change. The studies were not made in order to show that any industry can--or cannot modify its work schedule. The responsibility carried by the results--to predetermine the possibility of significant changes in the economic life of the community and in the working and personal lives of its members--imposed stern requirements of care, caution, and objectivity. If allowance is made for the pioneering nature of the work, the results may be presented and used as acceptable approximations of the functional capability of schedule change in the CBD.

Findings

The findings of functional capability are given fully in Appendix Table 64. They are the detailed results of the studies and the assessments based on them. The purpose here is to summarize and clarify the information presented starkly on the table. The presentation will be divided into four sections: (1) general findings as to functional determinants and modifiability; (2) the industries capable of modifying schedules; (3) the industries considered incapable of modifying schedules; and (4) special industries.

Functional Determinants and Modifiability

The studies of scheduling produced findings about functional determinants and modifiability which yield to some degree of generalization. The material of the table will emerge with greater clarity against a background of these general observations. The question to which the assessments of modifiability had to answer will place these generalizations in their proper framework. It was: Can starting and stopping times be shifted by moderate amounts (say one fourth to one hour) without hurting operations? The contemplated schedule changes are thus not large, and affect only the beginning and end of the normal workday.

Functional relations divide, as a matter of convenience, into two main kinds: relations with suppliers and relations with recipients of the firm's output--customers, clients, passengers, and the like. Every place of employment has both kinds of relationships, one kind for the inputs it consumes, the other for the product it produces. This division is useful because the two kinds of relationships differ in their influence on work schedules.

In general, relationships with suppliers did not prove a significant determinant of work schedules, nor an obstacle to changing them. Suppliers include all persons furnishing the place of employment with its input. These include raw materials, operating supplies, services of all kinds, and the like. Obviously

there are exceptions to this generalization. Where
a single supplier dominates a market or where suppliers of an important product (credit, judicial decisions) fix a common schedule, other firms and industries may find it convenient to adapt themselves to
it. The exceptions notwithstanding, suppliers tend
to fix their schedules to suit the convenience of
their customers.

One input which may be a deterrent to schedule
change turned up in the studies. It is the owner-
executive-manager group. These occupations characteristically work longer hours than the rest. Any
schedule change tending to reduce their hours would
be welcome. It is, however, possible that schedule
changes might lengthen the work day of executives.
They would resist such changes and their influence
would be felt in the firm's decision on work schedules. This factor is partly a personnel determinant
and partly a functional one. Its functionality consists in the limits to which executives' workdays
can be lengthened, regardless of their willingness
to accept longer hours.

On the other hand, relations with customers can
be effective determinants of work schedules. Places
of employment are sensitive, in fixing their schedules, to the needs and conveniences of their customers. Moreover, their capacity to modify schedules
depends upon the nature of their relations with
customers during the beginning and end of the day.

The influence of customers upon vendors'
schedules can be refined somewhat further by reference to the customer's location and to his position
in the distribution channel. Local customers exert
greater influence on vendors' schedules than out-of-
town customers. (Local means the metropolitan area.)
Local supplier-customer relations often exist in order to satisfy a critical time requirement in the
production flow. This may be illustrated by the
local food, printing, machinery, machinery maintenance, and many other industries. These industries

are largely dependent upon local customers, and are
sensitive to their time demands in fixing schedules.

On the other hand, schedule interdependence is
minimal in relations with out-of-town customers.
Both supplier and customer will undoubtedly want to
keep shipping time as short as economically possible,
but this will generally not determine the CBD seller's daily starting and stopping time. The influence of the transportation companies may be felt in
some cases, but the CBD producers have schedule
alternatives even in relation to this critical function.

The CBD has still one other spatial relationship
with customers--a hybrid local and out-of-town one.
The CBD is a major wholesaling center. Its wholesaling activities, incidentally, are far larger than
those represented by firms classified as wholesale.
Relations between wholesale function and customer
can occur locally--on producer's premises, or at
agents, brokers, or wholesalers--or outside the city,
by salesmen or agents. The customer may be a local
user, or may want the product shipped out of the area.
There are thus three significant combinations in the
locations of the shipping-destination relationship:
local - local, local - out-of-town, out-of-town - out-
of-town.

The impact of these relationships upon the suppliers' schedules may be generalized, again with
proper recognition of exceptions. Whenever the trans-
action--sales solicitation, negotiation, etc.--occurs
locally, the vendor will inevitably try to meet the
customer's schedule convenience. This is by no means
an iron-clad determinism, if for no other reason than
that a firm's customers do not necessarily all have
the same schedules, and hence do not affect the supplier's schedule in a consistent way. Another important local variant in this respect pertains to
industries having selling "seasons." During such
periods--which usually are short--normal schedules
are abandoned, and the out-of-town buyer's convenience
is pre-eminent. These, however, are special circumstances

and have little effect on the scheduling of the firms
during the rest of the year. When the transaction
occurs out-of-town, the customer's schedule is not a
determining one on CBD schedules. The effect of shipping destinations is the same as described above.

The influence of customers upon the vendor's
schedule stands out far more sharply when the customers are identified by their position in the channel of distribution. In this regard, a significant
polarity may be seen between producers and ultimate
consumer. The closer a firm or industry stands to
the ultimate consumer as customer, the more the customer governs the firm's or industry's schedule.

In the CBD, the final customers are the shoppers,
employees, visitors, clients, and others who come
there to buy goods or services. The most persistent
conclusion in the studies of scheduling determinants
is that industries whose customers are individual
consumers cannot modify their schedules in disregard
of the flow of their customers. These consumer
establishments depend upon being accessible to consumers for their business success. The times at
which they are open are therefore top-level decisions
of the individual place of employment. The local
consumer will continue to play a dominating role in
the schedules of these types of establishments. If
work schedules are modified, it may be expected that
these dependent industries will follow suit to some
degree.

This influence of final consumers upon their
suppliers--retail and service establishments--may be
transmitted by these industries to their suppliers,
depending upon the product or service. The variations in the way the consumers' influence may be felt
can be explained by another general factor in scheduling which was uncovered by the studies, and which
will be briefly noted here. Industries differ widely in the effect of time and timing upon their operations. Needless to state, all industries find time
a valuable resource which has to be conserved and
used economically. To some, however, time or timing
is far higher in value, and they are willing to spend

large amounts to conserve it. Further to this, the
kinds of time and its location within the day, week,
month, or year, or even longer periods will be of
critical and varying significance to industries. To
the apparel industry, style is a valuable resource
whose duration may be measured in weeks or months.
To the newspaper industry, the similar element of
novelty and distinctiveness is valuable only for
very short periods, perhaps hours. The food industries have daily, multiple-day, or weekly cycles
governed by consumer needs and the perishability of
their products, while the clothing industry operates
within seasons. The "money" industries have a daily
cycle for completing much of their work. The service
industries are unmistakably dominated by the wishes
of their clienteles. The sense of time and timing
emerge as characteristic qualities of industries.

These differing kinds of time-scarcity have quite
different effects upon work scheduling. Many of them,
even where time is an utterly critical factor, have
no effect at all upon schedules. Only when the
criticality is brief--within the daily cycle; and only of short duration--does it influence schedules.
The timing of newspapers, radio and television operations, entertainment, local passenger transit, and
the like are examples of industries having such time
characteristics. In these industries, to miss by
very short periods of time is to miss altogether.
They are particularly sensitive to daily work schedules.

The influence of final consumers upon earlier
parts of the distribution channel, insofar as scheduling is concerned, is governed by these considerations of time and timing to which the anterior industries are exposed.

One final word remains to be said about the general findings as to functional determinants of work
schedules and modifiability. In the course of the
studies it became increasingly evident that functional considerations are by no means inflexible and
fully deterministic of work schedules. Existing
industry schedules disclose a considerable amount of

variety. When these varieties are examined against
functional determinants, it is easily seen that functional requirements allow latitude in fixing schedules. The extent of the latitude varies among firms
and industries, but the notion that a firm or industry has a particular schedule because it could not
otherwise conduct its operations is distinctly not
supported by the findings of the study.

The Modifiable Industries

The capability of industries to modify schedules is shown on Appendix Table 64 by the entries
marked "yes." These entries fix the alternatives
which will be tested by subsequent computation. It
will be noted that many CBD industries are considered
capable of changing schedules without impairing their
operations.

Table 24 provides a summary of Appendix Table
64 in respect to the industries capable of modifying
their schedules. It divides the industries into two
main groups on the basis of the operating character
of the establishments: factories and office. For
each starting time, it shows whether all ("yes") or a
part ("some") of an aggregate is capable of adopting
each alternative starting time, according to the
entries on Appendix Table 64. The blank spaces must
not be interpreted as functional incapability. They
ought only be considered as not reported. In general
the functional capability of manufacturing was not
assessed for 9:30, nor of offices for 7:30.

The Nonmodifiable Industries

The studies revealed that certain industries
ought to be considered functionally incapable of
modifying their schedules, insofar as this inquiry
into feasibility is concerned. More exactly, there
are industries which cannot be regarded as capable,
independently of other schedule shifts, of modifying
their own schedules. On the other hand, it is probable that changes in the work schedules of the CBD wil
cause some of these industries to change. However,
the direction and amount of such modification cannot
be estimated at this time.

TABLE 24

Summary of Functional Capabilities
of Schedule Change

	7:30	8:00	8:30	9:30
FACTORY TYPE ESTABLISHMENTS				
Manufacturing				
Apparel	some	yes	some	
Other	yes	yes	yes	
Service	yes	yes	yes	some
Trucking and warehousing	yes	yes		
OFFICE ESTABLISHMENTS				
Administrative		some	some	some
Business professions		some	some	yes
Commercial		yes	yes	yes
Banks, finance, and insurance		some	some	some
Government (selected agencies)		yes	yes	yes

The industries which are excluded from the modifiable ones are shown on Table 25. They divide into
two groups: the security and commodity exchanges,
and all the others. Although numerically small, the
exchanges exert important influence on the schedules
of other industries and limit some of their ability
to reschedule. The reason the exchanges are excluded
is that they cannot modify their schedules without
producing consequences which ramify over wide distances and many industries. These consequences operate in opposite ways so that the present exchange schedule occupies a kind of equilibrium from which it will
not easily be moved. Furthermore, if the exchanges

were shifted to an earlier opening they would throw
more people into the morning congestion than are now
there.

TABLE 25

The Nonmodifiable Industries

SIC	Industry	Employees
41	Local and suburban transit	20,957
445	Local water transportation	2,950
52-59	Retail trades	191,285
6031	Mutual savings banks	3,362
6051	Establishments performing functions closely related to banking	6,452
6121	Savings and loan associations	735
6141	Personal credit institutions	3,793
6231	Security and commodity exchanges	3,650
651	Real estate--building operation only	36,892
70	Hotels, tourist courts, and motels	34,535
72 (Ex 721)	Personal services	11,436
75	Automobile repair, services, and garages	4,954
76	Miscellaneous repair services	2,451
783	Motion picture theaters	5,164
79	Amusement and recreation services except motion pictures	13,590
80	Medical and other health services	5,226
82	Educational services	2,557

The other industries have one common feature
which places them outside the modifiable group. They
are all dependent, for their economic performance,
upon the flow of private individuals, whether as

retail customers, clients, passengers, depositors or
borrowers. To establishments in these industries,
work schedules define their hours of exposure to
the business upon which their success or failure
depends.

The large establishments in this group treat
their hours of operation as a major business decision and devote important resources to determining
it properly. Many of the smaller establishments
are owner operated and are scheduled to suit the
owner's needs and judgment. To both large and small,
scheduling means situating the hours of operation
within the day so as to obtain optimum exposure to
the flow of customers. This inquiry cannot presume
to produce a judgment which is better than the ones
reached by the people in the industry, much less to
have them accept it. Accordingly, these industries
are regarded as outside the group which can be
treated as having modifiable schedules--on functional
grounds.

By the same considerations, it follows that this
group of industries may change their schedules if a
general revision takes place in the CBD. The local
transit systems will discover a shift in demand for
travel. The establishments which serve people before
and after work and during lunch hours will similarly
find their customers arriving at new times. They may
therefore have to modify their schedules.

However, even if these industries follow the
general CBD change, their impact upon transit will
probably not be important enough to cause concern.
They are even now scheduled outside the peak periods,
for the most part. It is therefore likely that they
will maintain a similar relationship to the schedules
of the other industries, after a general schedule change.

Special Industries

Brief mention will be made of two other groups
of industries not included in those already considered.
One group consists of less than 24,000 employees, an
insignificant number. These belong to industries

which were not studied for possible schedule change,
because they were simply too small to search out or
investigate, or because they are already scheduled
outside the rush hour. The other, to the contrary,
consists of industries having one or a few large
firms. These are shown on Table 26.

TABLE 26

Special Industries

SIC	Industry	Employees
481	Telephone communication	30,560
482	Telegraph communication	8,575
49	Electric, gas, and sanitary services	11,499

These industries are reserved for separate consideration of rescheduling, after the pattern for the
CBD has been set and on the basis of what may then be
needed.

INDUSTRY GROUPS AND THEIR
SCHEDULE ALTERNATIVES

Eighty-three CBD industries are capable, according to Appendix Table 64, of modifying their present
work schedules. These industries have 1,420,132
people, or 69 per cent of the total CBD employment.
Each of the 83 industries has from one to three possible alternative schedules (specified by starting
times: 7:30, 8:00, 8:30, and 9:30). These industries and their alternatives furnish the bases--
indeed the outermost limits--of work staggering in
the CBD.

It is necessary--both to formulate work staggering plans and to test their feasibility--to combin

these individual industries into suitable groups and
to develop alternative schedules for the groups. The
reasons are worth noting. First, schedules are aggregate or multi-industry practices and changing them
requires the collaboration of industry groups. It
was pointed out that work schedules, while a decision of each firm individually, are actually governed
by determinants which are predominantly external to
the firm and often to industries.

Next, grouping is also essential from the viewpoint of implementation, a possibility which must be
kept constantly in mind. If a work staggering program is to be comprehensible--a prerequisite to
implementation--it must be as clear and simple as
possible. There must be pattern and clarity to the
schedules of the 83 modifiable industries. This
means, among other things, that the 83 must be reduced to some smaller number of larger units if possible. Hence in contemplating the redesign of CBD
schedules, the grouping of industries serves the
ultimate goal of implementing a feasible work staggering plan.

These are the principal reasons for grouping
the industries, but one other needs to be mentioned.
If the industries are not grouped, the number of possible alternative ways of rescheduling them is astro-
nomically large. Eleven of the industries have one
alternative schedule, twenty have two, and fifty-two
have three. To each of these, one more must be
added--the alternative of no change at all. With
this number of industries and their alternatives, the
number of possible combinations is: $(2)^{11}$ x $(3)^{20}$ x
$(4)^{52}$. This is a wholly impracticable number of
alternatives to calculate, even on the best of comput-
ers.

Accordingly, the 83 modifiable industries were
combined into seven industry groups. They are: the
production industries, the administrative offices, the
business professions and services, the wholesale
trades, the financial industries, the insurance carriers, and the government agencies. These group titles
are mostly the customary ones, and they embrace the
industries usually classified in them. However, they

have a special meaning in this study which has to be
recognized and observed. The groups do not necessarily include all the industries which might be
classified within them on the basis of their titles.
They include only the ones listed among the 83 modifiable industries. There are other industries in
the CBD which would belong within one or another of
the groups, but they must not be included in them
unless they are specified as such in the course of
this chapter. The danger in adding to the list is
that it will inflate the modifiable numbers of people
and thereby distort the resulting CBD work schedule.

All of the 83 modifiable industries are assigned
to one or another of the groups. For the most part,
the assignment is unexceptionable. There are however some borderline cases which could go into
more than one industry group. Usually, their assignment in this study is based upon considerations
of rescheduling.

In general, the grouping was produced by two
procedures. First, on a priori grounds, the industries were combined into aggregates. These grounds
were appropriate to the purposes of this study. They
include considerations of identifiability of the aggregate and the rescheduling capabilities of the industries.

The second procedure consisted of recomposing the
aggregates on the basis of the feasibility computations which are described in Chapter 7. The results
of the first several computations showed that some of
the groups should be modified, if possible, in order
to achieve a better rescheduling plan. In making
these modifications, the same criteria were employed
as in the original formulation of the groups.

Table 27 presents the present employment and the
modifiable portion of each of the seven industry
groups. As a whole, the seven groups contain 76.5
per cent of the total CBD employment. The remaining
23.5 per cent are in the industries not included
among the modifiable ones. 90.8 per cent of the

employees of the seven industry groups belong to industries considered capable, on functional grounds,
of modifying their schedules. This represents 68.4
per cent of the total CBD employment.

TABLE 27

Total and Modifiable Employment
in CBD Industries

Industry Groups	CBD Total	In Modifiable Industries
Production	469,399	416,557
Administrative offices	316,246	316,246
Business professions and services	151,005	151,005
Wholesale trades	226,731	223,877
Finance	143,265	122,260
Insurance carriers	126,979	119,095
Government agencies	130,994	71,122
Subtotal	1,564,619	1,420,132
Excluded industries	481,781	--
Total	2,046,400	1,420,132

The first group--which sets apart the production
industries from all the rest--consists of apparel and
other manufacturing, trucking and warehousing, and
factory type service industries. This is the largest
single group, with 416,557 employees. The remaining
industries--those which are not production--divide,
on various criteria, into six other groups. There
are the nongovernmental administrative offices,
drawn from a wide range of industry, which make up
the second largest group with 316,246 employees.
Next there are professional, subprofessional, and
service industries whose clients are primarily--though

not exclusively--other businesses, with 151,005 employees. The wholesale trades comprise the third
largest of the groups with 223,877 employees. The
financial group includes only a part of the industries usually classified in this category. They
are commercial banks, other business credit institutions, and part of the securities industry. Their
employment in modifiable industries amounts to
122,260 people. The insurance carriers form a
separate group with 119,095 employees. The last
group consists of governmental agencies of all
levels. Their modifiable portion has 71,122 employees.

       Many of the industry groups are divided into
subgroups. This was done to provide greater flexibility in rescheduling. In most instances, the subgroups have a distinguishable identity in addition
to common scheduling characteristics. These subgroups are explained in Appendix M.

Alternative Schedules

       Once the industries are grouped, it becomes
necessary to formulate their alternative possible
schedules--this time for the aggregate rather than
for the individual component industries. The basis
for formulating the group alternatives is furnished
by the capability of the component industries. In
keeping with the reasons for the grouping, the most
appropriate schedule is a uniform one for all members
of the group. Wherever possible, uniform schedules
are used. There are: earliest uniform schedules,
latest uniform schedules, and any other uniform ones.
However, not all members of the group have the same
number of possible alternatives; in some cases the
member industries do not all share a single similar
alternative. To meet these situations, other approaches are employed to formulate the group schedule. These include: an earliest possible schedule
in which all members are shifted to their earliest
possible times, which are not the same for all.
Similarly a latest possible schedule is sometimes
used. The details of these scheduling plans are
furnished in Appendix M.

It is self-evident that not all the possible
alternative schedules--whether of individual industries or of industry groups--are equally suitable or
preferable, even though they may be functionally possible. Wherever the groups have more than one possible schedule, the alternatives are ranked if there
are grounds for making the necessary choices. This
turns out to be an essential part of the procedure
for testing feasibility. Many possible combinations
of industries satisfy the cordon count criteria but
their scheduling patterns are less than desirable.

Various criteria are employed in ranking the
alternative possible schedules. In most instances
no change at all is regarded as the preferred alternative schedule. There are some cases, however,
where an alternative is considered better than the
one the industry now has. A second criterion is the
amount of time required by the change. A shift of
one hour--from 9:00 to 8:00 a.m.--is considered less
desirable than a half-hour shift. This is partly
based on simple considerations of convenience, and
partly on the diminished effect of longer schedule
changes introduced by the tolerance response modification table (see Chapter 5). The greater the time
of the shift, the smaller the proportion of people
who will tolerate the schedule change.

Third, with certain exceptions, a change to an
earlier time is considered preferable to a later one.
This is based on the findings of the sociological
study, in which there is a greater preference, willingness, and tolerability of earlier than later change.
This preference for an earlier shift, however, can
frequently not be satisfied on account of other considerations. But in ranking the alternatives, it is
unquestionably the preferred one in most cases. Thus
a change from 9:00 to 8:30 is preferable to one to
9:30, except in certain industries which require a
later starting time.

Finally, there are certain linkage criteria
which dictate the preference as to alternatives.
Where one significant industry has a restricted
choice or a preference for a particular time, other

industries whose schedules may be dependent upon it
are also given a schedule preference based on the
dominant industry.

Summary

Table 28 summarizes the industry groups and
their alternative schedules as set forth in Appendix
M. The schedules are classified into two categories.
The first category is the preferred schedules of the
groups, wherever preference could be decided from
available evidence. The no change alternative is
not included on the table. The second consists of
other possible schedules which, while not preferred,
might still be acceptable for work staggering. There
are other schedules of some of the groups which are
not included on the table. These are alternatives
which were ruled out in the evaluation of the available alternatives.

The data presented in Table 28 will be used in
the subsequent computations of feasibility. Schedules will be designated by the titles used in this
table. They will contain two terms: group and
starting time.

CONCLUSIONS

This chapter makes three contributions to the
unfolding analysis of the feasibility of work staggering.

First, it sets forth the theory of schedule
modifiability which was employed in the study. The
theory tells how the findings were obtained and it
helps explain what they mean. It is also an essential part of the support for the final results of
the inquiry.

Second, the chapter presents the findings as to
the modifiability of work schedules on functional
grounds. These findings are the basis for later
computations of the feasibility of work staggering.
However, to be usable, they must be further adjusted

TABLE 28

Alternative Schedules of Industry Groups
By Preference

Group	Preferred	Possible
Production industries		
Earlier subgroups	8:00	7:30
Later subgroups	8:30	8:00
Central administrative offices	8:30	9:30
Transportation company offices	8:30 or 9:30	8:00
Radio, television, and motion picture companies and organizations	9:30	8:30
Other administrative offices	8:30 or 9:30	8:00
Business professions and services	9:30	--
Wholesale trades		
Earlier subgroups	8:30	--
Later subgroups	8:30	9:30
Financial industries		
Commercial banks, public departments and business credit institutions	8:30	--
Commercial banks, earlier departments	8:30	8:00
Commercial banks, later departments, and security and commodity brokers, dealers, exchanges and services	9:30	--
Insurance carriers	8:30	8:00 or 9:30
Government	8:30	--

by the personnel determinants of schedule change.
The next chapter will describe the personnel determinants. It will show how they are applied to the
estimates of functional modifiability to produce a
forecast of probable response to schedule change.

Finally, this chapter defines the seven industry
groups which were developed in order to simplify the
rescheduling pattern, and explains how schedule
alternatives for these groups were formulated. The
findings of Appendix M, which gives detailed accounts of each group and its schedule alternatives,
were summarized; and they will prove useful in later
computations of feasibility.

CHAPTER **5** ACCEPTABILITY
OF SCHEDULE
CHANGE

Work staggering will require people to accept
changes in the times they start and stop work. Their
changes in work schedule may compel them to change
the times they journey to and from work, the times
they are at home, and the times they engage in social,
organizational, recreational, and other activities.
These changes in turn can affect the schedules of
their families, friends, and associates as well as
the schedules of the businesses, services, and institutions with which they deal. Thus, the rings of
consequence emanating from a change in CBD work
schedules can ultimately encircle the whole population.

These social effects of schedule change raise
two general problems for this inquiry. The first is
a problem of policy, and it confronts the community
as a whole, the places of employment in the CBD and,
on their account, this inquiry. Is a change of work
schedule sufficiently acceptable to the people to
warrant further inquiry into the feasibility of work
staggering--not to speak of actually instituting a
program? Or will schedule change engender enough
opposition and resistance--by those whose schedules
may be changed as well as by those indirectly af-
fected--to make work staggering unfeasible?

This policy problem has been resolved insofar
as the present inquiry is concerned. The people who
work in the CBD are favorably disposed to schedule
change as a way of relieving rush hour transit congestion. Not unexpectedly, there are some who object to schedule change, but they are too few and
too scattered to be considered a source of effective

resistance. The population's favorable disposition
toward schedule change is expected to influence the
people responsible for deciding about schedules and
about work staggering. They include employers, union
officials, and industry leaders, as well as city,
political, and community officials. Their decisions
will be governed, at least in part, by the attitudes
of their employees and constituents. Accordingly,
a policy of carrying through the inquiry into the
feasibility of work staggering is amply justified.

A second problem arising from the potential
social effects of schedule change confronts this inquiry. It is a problem of design, and it arises for
solution precisely because of the favorable attitude
of the people to schedule change. This design problem is: What characteristics of schedules do people
like and dislike? Their likes and dislikes will
serve as the constraints upon any redesign of scheduling in the CBD. The problem of design also has a
more specific meaning to this inquiry. It will answer the question: How shall the findings of functional capability be modified to satisfy the CBD population?

The evidence and reasoning by which the policy
and design problems were resolved will be presented
in this chapter. First, the source of information on
which these solutions are based will be described.
Thereafter, two sections will deal, respectively,
with the acceptability of schedule change by the rest
of the population, and with the personnel constraints
on schedule modifiability. The results achieved in
this chapter will produce a final determination as
to the modifiability of work schedules in the CBD.

THE SOCIOLOGICAL STUDY

The Staggered Working Hours Project made a study
of the people who work in the CBD. Its purpose was
to estimate their probable response to work staggering
It was a sociological study, employing the methodology
of survey research. The report of this study, a technical paper of the Project, is entitled "Receptivity

to Work Staggering, A Sociological Study." It was
written by Terence K. Hopkins in collaboration with
Amitai Etzioni and Immanual Wallerstein.

The sociological study obtained information
from a sample of 1,572 people working in over 230
places of employment. These places of employment
were selected randomly from the CBD establishments,
stratified by industry and size. The individual
respondents were also randomly chosen from within the
places of employment so selected. The sample as a
whole is considered representative of the people who
work in the CBD. Each return represents approximately 1,300 people.

The data were collected at the respondents' places
of employment, for the most part during the regular
work time. Each respondent first filled out a questionnaire and was then interviewed by a professional
researcher. The main topics covered were the journey
to work; the job, home life, and daily schedule; other
social relations and activities; participation in
public affairs; and receptivity to changes in work
time. On the average, better than one half-hour's
time was required of each respondent to complete the
questionnaire and interview.

The Staggered Working Hours Project chose the
method of survey research rather than other possible
ways of ascertaining attitudes and positions. In
this method, the respondents were individuals who
worked in the CBD and who provided the requested information about themselves. In particular, the
Project did not solicit information about attitudes
from any organizations, institutions, officials, or
leaders in respect to the probable response of the
population.

There were several reasons for choosing the
survey research method as against consultation with
personalities and agencies of the CBD. First and
foremost, this method was regarded as a more reliable
way of obtaining the required information than any
other. It is unlikely that leading personalities in
business and in the community would know, in the

desired depth, the feelings and the attitudes of their
employees and constituents. In fact, for them to obtain such information, they would have to conduct an
investigation very much like this one. Indeed, this
survey was designed to furnish the people responsible
for decisions about schedules with reliable information on prevailing attitudes and probable response
to schedule change.

Secondly, it was considered inappropriate to
institute discussions with responsible officials
about work staggering. Such discussions are considered a vital part of the procedure but they ought
properly to occur after the preliminary studies have
been completed.

Thirdly, the inquiry needs the kind of quantitative findings for its feasibility computations
which can be obtained by the survey research method.
This will become fully evident in the analysis of
personnel constraints on modifiability. These considerations dictated the form of investigation which
had to be undertaken for the purposes of the Staggered Working Hours Project.

Acceptability

If work staggering proves feasible, some of the
people who work in the CBD will be asked to accept
different work schedules. How will they respond?
This question, critically important to all those
responsible for work staggering, is exceedingly difficult and complex. It is a question raised now
about a response in the future--hence, a forecast.
It concerns future conditions which cannot be specified, but which will nevertheless influence the
response. The response too is complex, because
people can react in many ways to a schedule change.

The sociological study sought to answer the
question as sensitively as it was able. The study
is not an opinion poll nor are its answers simply
collections of individual opinions, feelings and
attitudes.

The information sought from respondents pene-
trated into many areas of motivation, interests, obligations, experience and goals in respect to work
schedules. From the collected replies, systematically analyzed, the study sought to reconstruct the
determinants of response to schedule change. Its
conclusions are drawn from this composition of the
CBD's relationship to work schedules.

There is no need to duplicate the report of the
sociological study in this chapter. The purpose here
is twofold: to justify an optimistic prognosis about
the acceptability of change in work schedules to relieve transit congestion, and to fashion personnel
constraints for the estimates of modifiability. Some
of the results of the sociological study will be
needed, not all; and they will be utilized as found
in the study, not justified here. The report expresses great sensitivity for the probabilistic
character of its findings and it extrapolates them
to the future with proper tentativeness and condition-
ality. In making use of these findings--the statistical tables, inferences and statements of conclusion--
the same restraints will be observed, but without
spelling out their limits. The limits must be taken
for granted, together with the report's statements
about the validity of its findings.

The notion of acceptability which will be explored in this section has two sides, both important
to any decision about work staggering. On the one
hand, acceptability denotes a favorable disposition
of the CBD people toward schedule change. The existence, extent, and depth of such a disposition will
determine whether the people are prepared for the
social changes induced by a change of work schedule.
The other side of acceptability is shown by the occurrence, if any, and extent of opposition and potential resistance to a program of work staggering.
Even if the people prove, in the main, hospitable to
schedule change, the magnitude, source, and location
of opposition and the nature of its potential expression must be assessed before reaching a decision
about the feasibility--on sociological grounds--of
work staggering. Both aspects of acceptability will

now be examined.   Thereafter, the appropriate conclusions will be drawn.

Preference, Willingness, Tolerance

The sociological study analyzed the sample's
response at several so-called response levels. It
was thus able to generate out of the data a startlingly systematic picture of the respondents' feelings,
desires, attitudes, and even probable behavior toward
schedule change, regularly varying according to the
level of response and the extent of change. To the
sociological study, these findings were of substantive and methodological value. Here, three of these
response levels are pertinent. They reflect possible
real circumstances under which a program of work
staggering may arise and come to fruition. They are
called the preference, willingness, and tolerance
levels of response. The study's definition and
findings of these responses will be presented next;
their relevance to a work staggering program will be
evaluated in the section dealing with personnel constraints.

Preference

The respondents were asked when they would prefer
to start and stop work, if they had a free choice
(and supposing the same number of hours as at present).
Their answer, given in actual times, expressed their
preference in as unrestrained and specific a way as
possible. The results are shown in Table 29.

TABLE 29

Per Cents of Sample Preferring Changed
Starting Times, by Minutes of Change

Minutes of Change	Per Cent Earlier	Per Cent Later
15 - 29	10	6
30 - 59	21	9
60 or more	12	6
Total	43	21

The numbers on Table 29 cannot fail to provoke considerable surprise. Only 37 per cent stated that they prefer their present starting times. (Changes of less than 15 minutes may be interpreted, for present purposes, as no change at all.) Sixty-four per cent prefer times other than those they now have. (Rounding causes the slight discrepancy in the numbers.) Of the totals preferring other times, 43 per cent would like to start earlier while 21 per cent want to start later.

There is thus double the desire for earlier than for later starting times. Equally as interesting, 48 per cent would prefer starting times of a half hour or more earlier or later than at present. Only 16 per cent of the total expressed the desire for a 15- to 29-minute change over the present. At all amounts, the pull toward earlier times was decidedly greater than toward later ones.

This preference for starting times other than present ones holds true no matter when the respondents now start work. This is shown by Table 30, which divides up the sample according to present starting times. Each row of the table is a different present starting time, and its 100 per cent total (added across) is distributed over the times the respondents would prefer to start. The table shows that there are people now starting at every present time who would prefer something different. Table 30 corroborates and amplifies the observations made about Table 29.

Combining the data of Table 29 with the respondents' attitudes toward present schedules, the study states

> . . . while most respondents reported being satisfied with their work times, yet most also preferred different work times. The reason is now clear: work times compared with other aspects of a job or with other times in a person's schedule are just not very important to

> the respondents. They are not psycho-
> logically salient elements nor are they
> something that most people care very
> deeply about. Hence they are 'satisfied'
> with them--why not?--but at the same
> time they prefer other ones. Of those
> who are 'very satisfied' with their
> present work times, almost one out of
> two (47 per cent) would prefer different
> times; about three out of four (73 per
> cent) of those who are 'fairly satisfied'
> or consider their present times 'all
> right' would prefer different times;
> and about five out of six (84 per cent)
> of those who are at all 'dissatisfied'
> (N=87) would prefer different times.
> Or, putting it the other way around,
> they would prefer other work times, but
> work times as such are so relatively
> unimportant to them that the existence
> of the preference does not give rise to
> dissatisfaction with the present hour.

From the viewpoint of work staggering, Table 29,
as interpreted, produces two useful conclusions. The
first may be expressed in language taken from the
sociological study.

> Work times are matter of fact
> features of most people's lives and
> are apparently treated as such by them.
> They are justified, if they are thought
> about at all, not on sacred or even
> traditional grounds, but simply on the
> grounds of habit by most and, at least
> in principle, on the grounds of ex-
> pediency by others. And so, if the
> reason justifying a change is a good
> one, they can be (indeed, perhaps ought
> to be) changed.

Schedule change, in short, may prove acceptable to the
population if it can relieve transit congestion.

TABLE 30

Per Cents of Sample, by Present Start Times,
Who Prefer Other Start Times

Present Start Time	Before		Preferred Start Times							After	
	7:15	7:30	8:00	8:15	8:30	8:45	9:00	9:15	9:30	9:30	Other
Before 7:15	60	4	16	2	2	0	9	0	2	4	2
7:30 (a)	26	47	16	0	5	0	5	0	0	0	0
8:00 (b)	15	11	56	2	5	0	9	0	0	1	2
8:15	6	10	26	24	12	4	10	0	0	2	6
8:30	6	5	28	5	28	4	19	1	1	0	1
8:45	1	1	15	7	27	22	17	1	3	5	1
9:00	2	1	12	1	24	10	31	3	8	6	1
9:15	1	1	9	1	11	4	24	17	18	12	2
9:30	0	0	5	0	4	3	22	4	43	18	3
After 9:30	2	0	5	0	5	2	16	1	7	56	5
Work Different Hours	6	0	21	0	6	3	26	0	9	18	12

(a) Includes 7:15
(b) Includes 7:45

193

The second conclusion which follows from Table
29, even with the interpretation, is that schedule
change can increase satisfaction with work schedules
by more closely approximating the people's preference.
Despite the nonsaliency of schedules as such, Table
29 discloses an unmistakable preference for times
different from present ones, and particularly in the
direction of earlier starting. These findings open
the door to work staggering not only as a means of
relieving transit congestion, but also as possibly
increasing the satisfaction of the working population with its work schedules.

Willingness

It is next of interest to know how much schedule
change people will be willing to accept. Willingness,
as defined by the sociological study, is "the limits
of subjectively acceptable change." It was measured
on the basis of questions which asked the respondents
how they would feel about having their schedules
changed by specific amounts of time ranging, in 15
minute intervals from zero to 90 minutes, both earlier
and later. The replies as such do not constitute the
findings of the study. The replies were used, in a
way described in the report, to construct an index of
willingness which reflects the individual respondent's
turning point from positive to negative feelings
about change in schedule. The results are not therefore opinions but considerably deeper probings into
the population's subjective feelings and attitudes
toward schedule change.

The willingness to change is expressed in the
form of a table which shows the per cent of people who
consider each amount of change acceptable. Table 31
gives the per cent in two forms: by each amount of
change and cumulatively. For present purposes the
cumulative table is the more revealing. It is constructed by assuming that people willing to change
their starting times by any stated number of minutes
would also be willing to change by a lesser amount.
This was tested in the sociological study and shown
to be warranted from the analytic results. Accordingly, the cumulative table gives the total extent of

willingness for each of the amounts of possible
change, both earlier and later.

TABLE 31

Willingness to Start Earlier or Later:
Per Cents of Sample by
Minutes of Change

Minutes of Change	By Each Amount		Cumulative	
	Earlier	Later	Earlier	Later
0	21	38	100	100
15	17	16	79	62
30	25	19	62	46
45	9	7	37	27
60	12	7	28	20
90	16	13	16	13

Several things stand out from Table 31. People
are more willing to start earlier than later (just as
they preferred to start earlier rather than later).
The cumulative array shows that almost two thirds are
willing to accept a half-hour earlier, and better than
one fourth, an hour earlier. The median per cents occur at thirty minutes earlier and 15 minutes later.
If there were a vote for changes in starting time,
these two changes would clearly be the winners--not
present times. These findings apply to the CBD work
force taken as a whole. It is important to know
whether the degree of willingness revealed by Table 31
differs for any particular segment of the population.
Tables 32 through 35 present willingness tables (on
a cumulative basis) for significant subdivisions of
the sample.

The tables disclose that the same characteristics--with but few exceptions--apply to the subgroups.

Differences in the degree of willingness might reasonably be expected from respondents having different present starting times. This expectation is investigated by Table 32 which shows the per cents who are willing to have their starting times changed by each amount.

The table shows that there are differences at the various present starting times, but they do not follow any discernible pattern, at least not one exposed by the factor of starting time alone. For example, the per cents unwilling to change at all, either earlier or later, differ for the various starting times. (This can be seen in the 15 minutes earlier and later columns. The difference between the amounts in these columns and 100 per cent represent the per cent unwilling to change at all.) But there are no evident patterns to these differences. A reasonable conclusion drawn from Table 32 would take note of the considerable similarity among the starting times in the general contours of willingness at the various amounts of change. The later percentage amounts tend to be low for all the starting times and the earlier percentage amounts tend to be high across the board--with a few minor and scattered exceptions. Table 32 thus produces the statement that the degree of willingness is not associated, in any apparent way, with present starting times.

Women employees, especially married ones, are often talked of as especially inhospitable to schedule change. They are considered locked into their work schedules by family and household obligations. This is reflected in the sample's response, but only to a small degree. Women are somewhat less willing than men to start earlier or later, but a substantial proportion of the women are still willing to change their work schedule. Married women show no clear differences in attitude from the total of all women. These observations may be gleaned from Table 33 which gives the per cent of willingness for the entire sample, all men, all women, and married women. In sum,

a somewhat greater reluctance to change schedules must
be expected from women than from men, but not enough
by far to consider them a distinct subgroup of the
population for the purposes of this inquiry.

On the other hand, there are some distinguishable patterns in the degree of willingness by occupations. The white-collar people seem somewhat less
willing to start earlier--by more than 30 minutes--
and later--by 30 minutes or less--than blue-collar
people, but not by very much. Table 34 gives the
willingness per cents by occupational group. The
first three rows are white-collar and the second
three are blue-collar occupations. Apart from the
modest amount of distinctiveness just stated, the
important fact disclosed by Table 34 is really the
similarity in the pattern of willingness of the occupations. Especially significant is the showing
of the employer group. Its degree of willingness
corresponds exceedingly closely, both earlier and
later, to the CBD total. There is one exceptional
occupation on Table 34. It is the unskilled group.
It shows a decidedly greater willingness to start
earlier and a noticeably lower willingness to start
later.

There is one final analysis which is important
to this inquiry--the extent of willingness by type
of establishment and by industry subdivision. The
places of employment in which the respondents worked
were classified according to four main kinds of
establishment--offices, commercial firms, plants, and
service firms. Each of these was further subdivided
according to industry, as far as the size of the
sample allowed. These results of this analysis are
shown on Table 35.

In general, Table 35 reiterates findings of
Table 34. The white-collar establishments--offices
and trade--differ from the blue-collar establishments--
plants and service--in the way described on the following pages. Within the plant group the two subdivisions are similar to each other. Within offices
and trade, however, there are some differences worth
noting.

TABLE 32

Per Cents of Sample, by Present Start Times, Willing to Start
Various Amounts Earlier and Later

Present Start Time	Minutes Earlier						0	Minutes Later				
	90	60	45	30	15	0		15	30	45	60	90
Before 7:15	38	47	51	57	75	100	100	63	54	48	44	40
7:30 (a)	11	27	27	59	75	100	100	37	5	5	5	5
8:00 (b)	27	40	47	71	79	100	100	51	42	31	29	22
8:15	22	36	46	66	80	100	100	60	48	32	26	16
8:30	15	23	32	65	78	100	100	60	46	25	15	11
8:45	7	14	29	57	83	100	100	59	36	19	11	7
9:00	14	29	39	66	84	100	100	64	47	26	20	12
9:15	9	21	26	51	77	100	100	70	54	28	21	11
9:30	11	26	32	54	69	100	100	75	61	38	24	11
After 9:30	32	37	45	59	70	100	100	63	49	32	28	21

(a) Includes 7:15

(b) Includes 7:45

198

TABLE 33

Per Cents of Men and Women Willing to Start Earlier and Later

Aggregate	Minutes Earlier						Minutes Later					
	90	60	45	30	15	0	0	15	30	45	60	90
Total	17	29	38	63	80	100	100	63	47	28	21	14
Men	21	35	43	68	82	100	100	64	50	32	25	17
Women, all	12	22	32	57	78	100	100	62	44	24	17	11
Women, married	12	24	33	56	75	100	100	64	40	19	14	10

TABLE 34

Per Cents of Occupational Groups Willing to Start Earlier and Later

Occupation	Minutes Earlier						Minutes Later					
	90	60	45	30	15	0	0	15	30	45	60	90
Proprietors, managers, officials, etc.	16	31	38	65	78	100	100	68	52	31	28	18
Professional, semiprofessional, etc.	14	28	40	66	80	100	100	68	56	36	24	14
Clerical and sales	13	24	33	60	81	100	100	63	44	23	16	10
Skilled labor; foremen	25	37	44	68	76	100	100	58	45	34	30	19
Semiskilled, all service	26	36	44	62	78	100	100	57	47	34	28	22
Unskilled	48	61	65	82	91	100	100	47	34	30	26	17

TABLE 35

Per Cents of Sample, by Type of Establishment and Industrial Subdivision, Willing to Start Earlier and Later

Establishment and Industry	Minutes Earlier						Minutes Later					
	90	60	45	30	15	0	0	15	30	45	60	90
						Cumulative Per Cents						
Office	12	25	36	63	81	100	100	65	48	28	19	11
Central administrative offices	10	25	34	65	85	100	100	62	42	20	14	10
Finance: insurance, etc.	14	23	35	62	83	100	100	63	45	27	17	12
Business-professional	11	28	41	65	81	100	100	74	60	36	22	12
Publishers	22	28	34	59	69	100	100	71	65	43	35	25
Government	11	27	36	58	77	100	100	63	44	27	19	6
Other office	11	24	35	61	78	100	100	54	39	23	19	6
Trade	17	26	31	57	79	100	100	66	48	29	24	19
Wholesale	13	22	28	56	79	100	100	66	47	26	21	15
Retail trade	30	38	41	62	80	100	100	63	48	35	30	28
Plant	22	33	41	64	78	100	100	58	44	28	23	17
Manufacturing	22	34	41	64	78	100	100	55	43	27	22	17
Other plant	24	34	43	67	80	100	100	62	46	29	24	16
Service	26	39	49	66	79	100	100	65	54	35	30	22

The publishing industry, an industrial subdivision of the offices, shows a unique pattern. It
is the first subgroup having greater willingness to
start later than earlier (although having also a
surprising 22 per cent willing to start 90 minutes
earlier). The business-professional people also show
a higher percentage of willingness to start later by
15, 30, and even 45 minutes. These two groups thus
identify a special body of attitudes toward schedule change. For the rest, the office groups conform
to the general office pattern.

The retail trade people also show a distinctive
response to schedule change. They appear more willing
to start earlier--especially 60 minutes or more--and
to start later--45 minutes and more--than most of the
other groups.

These special cases will be particularly significant in reconstructing schedules for the CBD as a
whole.

The general pattern of willingness for the CBD
as set forth originally on Table 31, reflects--with
but moderate variations--the response of most of the
subgroups. There are slight differences in the response of women as compared with men, and among white-
collar as compared with blue-collar groups. Worth
noting are the special features of the business, professional, publishing, and retail industries. For the
rest the general pattern characterizes the pattern of
the component groups.

Tolerance

Beyond what people prefer, or are willing to accept, the sociological study tells how much schedule
change they are willing to tolerate. The tolerance
level marks the dividing line between acceptance and
resistance to change. Resistance ranges from protest
to overt counter-activities such as quitting the job.
As defined in the sociological study, the tolerance
level indicates the extent of change that the respondents are prepared to "go along with behaviorally." It

is not itself a measure of resistance but only the boundary of nonresistance.   It is accordingly a response index of great importance to this study.

There are tables showing the per cent of the respondents who will tolerate varying amounts of schedule change, similar in form to the willingness tables.   Table 36 shows the per cents of the total sample who will tolerate varying amounts of change earlier and later.   Table 37 gives the cumulative per cents by present starting time.   The tolerance per cents of men, women, and married women are shown on Table 38.   The occupational tolerance percentages are given on Table 39.   Table 40 shows the percentages for type of establishment and industry subdivisions.

TABLE 36

Tolerance to Earlier and Later Starts:
Per Cents of Sample by Minutes
of Change

Minutes of Change	By Each Amount		Cumulative	
	Earlier	Later	Earlier	Later
0	7	14	100	100
15	9	10	93	86
30	20	21	84	76
45	13	10	64	55
60	12	8	51	45
90	39	37	39	37

TABLE 37

Tolerance to Earlier and Later Starts:
Per Cents of Each Present Start Time

Present Start Time	Minutes Earlier							Minutes Later				
	90	60	45	30	15	0	0	15	30	45	60	90
Before 7:15	55	68	70	81	90	100	100	95	89	74	70	66
7:30 (a)	53	69	74	85	100	100	100	79	74	58	58	58
8:00 (b)	50	64	72	86	94	100	100	83	73	59	54	47
8:15	44	52	68	86	90	100	100	80	76	54	40	34
8:30	38	47	59	82	92	100	100	84	72	48	40	34
8:45	30	39	60	84	95	100	100	86	74	52	39	32
9:00	36	52	67	87	96	100	100	88	77	55	43	33
9:15	27	39	54	77	92	100	100	86	74	54	42	28
9:30	42	53	63	88	93	100	100	92	82	53	49	41
After 9:30	46	53	66	88	93	100	100	85	77	51	44	42

(a) Includes 7:15
(b) Includes 7:45

TABLE 38

Tolerance to Earlier and Later Starts:
Per Cents of Men and Women

Aggregate	Minutes Earlier						Minutes Later					
	90	60	45	30	15	0	0	15	30	45	60	90
Total	38	50	63	83	92	100	100	86	76	55	45	37
Men	44	57	67	86	94	100	100	85	75	56	48	41
Women, all	32	44	61	83	93	100	100	86	74	51	40	31
Women, married	31	43	63	82	92	100	100	89	77	53	42	31

TABLE 39

Tolerance to Earlier and Later Starts:
Per Cents of Occupations

Occupation	Minutes Earlier							Minutes Later				
	90	60	45	30	15	0	0	15	30	45	60	90
Proprietors, managers, officials, etc.	40	50	65	86	94	100	100	87	78	55	46	35
Professional, semi-professional, etc.	30	48	66	88	96	100	100	91	80	59	45	33
Clerical and sales	34	47	61	83	94	100	100	87	76	54	43	34
Skilled labor; foremen	49	61	64	81	93	100	100	85	74	58	55	44
Semiskilled, all service	50	61	72	87	94	100	100	87	79	58	51	49
Unskilled	74	74	83	96	96	100	100	91	74	61	52	48

TABLE 40

Tolerance to Earlier and Later Starts: Per Cents by Type of Establishment and Industrial Subdivision

Cumulative Per Cents

Establishment and Industry	Minutes Earlier						Minutes Later					
	90	60	45	30	15	0	0	15	30	45	60	90
Office	35	48	63	86	94	100	100	88	78	55	44	34
Central administrative offices	39	50	62	88	97	100	100	89	76	51	42	33
Finance: insurance, etc.	38	48	63	88	94	100	100	87	77	55	43	36
Business-professional	34	49	66	87	94	100	100	90	83	62	48	34
Publishers	31	51	65	83	93	100	100	91	85	69	61	47
Government	34	43	56	76	90	100	100	80	69	47	36	27
Other office	29	45	60	84	91	100	100	82	71	46	38	29
Trade	41	52	62	81	95	100	100	88	79	58	49	42
Wholesale	36	47	60	78	95	100	100	88	77	58	48	41
Retail trade	54	64	66	85	91	100	100	88	85	60	54	46
Plant	41	53	67	84	93	100	100	84	72	52	43	37
Manufacturing	38	50	65	82	91	100	100	82	69	50	41	35
Other plant	48	59	70	87	94	100	100	88	77	57	47	41
Service	43	58	68	82	93	100	100	89	80	63	55	47

207

People will tolerate schedule change very similarly to the way they are willing to accept such
changes, but with an important systematic difference.
This difference is brought out on Table 41 which compares the three levels of response--preference, willingness, and tolerance. People will willingly accept more change than they actually would prefer to
have. They will tolerate more change than they are
willing to accept. Forty-three per cent of the
people prefer to start earlier, 79 per cent are willing to start earlier, while 93 per cent will tolerate an earlier starting time. A later starting
time is preferred by 21 per cent of the people, will
be accepted by 62 per cent, and tolerated by 86 per
cent.

The lower part of the table compares cumulatively the willingness and tolerance responses (the
preference response cannot be compared with the other
two because its 100 per cent includes both earlier
and later amounts.) Willingness and tolerance follow identical patterns. People are more likely to
tolerate earlier than later changes just as they are
more willing to accept earlier changes than later
ones. In each case the table shows they are prepared
to go along with more change than they declare themselves ready to accept willingly.

The tolerance tables disclose the same relationship to the willingness tables as disclosed by Table
41, some minor differences notwithstanding. There is
little discernible pattern to tolerance by present
starting time. As on the willingness index, so on
the tolerance index--women show up as less likely
than men to tolerate changes. Similarly the people
in blue-collar occupations will tolerate more and
larger changes than people in white-collar occupations
as was the case with their respective willingness
responses. Among the industrial subdivisions, the
business and professional establishments and publishers show greater tolerance toward later starting times. Further details of response may be seen
directly on the tables.

TABLE 41

Summary: Per Cents of Preference, Willingness, and Tolerance, by Earlier and Later Starts

Response Level	Minutes Earlier						Minutes Later					
	90	60	45	30	15	0	0	15	30	45	60	90
Preference		12		21	10	37	37	6	9	9	6	
Willingness	16	12	9	25	17	21	38	16	19	7	7	13
Tolerance	39	12	13	20	9	7	14	10	4	10	8	37
						Cumulative						
Willingness	16	28	37	62	79	100	100	62	46	27	20	13
Tolerance	39	51	64	84	93	100	100	86	76	55	45	37

Summary

The three response levels provide a valuable picture of the receptivity toward schedule change on the part of the people who work in the CBD. Beyond the specific details, the findings of the sociological study establish some significant ideas about the people and their schedules. First, they show that the majority of people who work in the CBD would really prefer different schedules from their present one. This offers a tremendous leverage to any plan for changing work schedules. Next, the contrast of the willingness and tolerance tables discloses that the people are prepared to go along with a very large amount of schedule change--indeed more than they want and certainly more than they prefer. Finally, the tables provide a remarkable quantification of these responses. The percentages depict very systematically the relationship one would expect among these three levels of response. The actual numbers will prove particularly useful in the formulation of constraints on modifiability.

Opposition To Schedule Change

Policy with respect to work staggering must take into account the nature and extent of potential opposition. Prudence demands raising the question: What resistance will work staggering encounter? Obviously there will be some resistance. The change in work schedules cannot avoid affecting some people adversely. From the viewpoint of policy it is essential to know in advance, if possible, if resistance will be widespread and if it will take a form which rules out any further thought of work staggering.

The sociological study addressed itself to the subject of opposition and resistance. Its findings provide indications of the causes of possible opposition, who the opponents might be, and the means they might employ. These, however, are only indications, not prophecies of the future. Yet they are the best information now available on the subject and must be fully exploited in reaching the required policy decisions.

The study finds, in the main, that opposition to work staggering is small and diffuse. It is not concentrated in any identifiable sector of the population. Opposition and resistance will probably take the form of individual acts rather than organized collective action. Accordingly, employees acting in concert or groups of constituents are not expected to exert strong organized pressures upon the people responsible for deciding about schedules or staggering.

The study itself develops these findings and conclusions with great sensitivity. They are presented fully in the report of the study. Here only the main results will be offered.

The Extent of Opposition

There is surprisingly little opposition to reasonable amounts of schedule change. This discovery is already foreshadowed in the preference, willingness and tolerance tables. On the basis of the study's findings the extent of opposition can be put in quantitative form. The study also shows where this opposition comes from primarily, and what its effects might be on work staggering.

The tolerance tables give the per cents of people who will not oppose each amount of change. An "opposition" table can be constructed by shifting these per cents by one interval in the direction of a larger amount of change. This shift is shown on Table 42. It is cumulative in the opposite direction of Table 36, from which it was taken. In order to show the increasing extent of opposition it assumes that anyone who objects to a 15-minute change will also object to a 30-minute change--an assumption shown in the analysis to be empirically valid.

As expected, the extent of opposition increases with the amount of change. Opposition at the 15-minute level is quite small, 7 per cent for earlier and 14 per cent for later changes. It may still be considered small at 30 minutes earlier and slightly

more serious at 30 minutes later. In both directions
there seems to be a noticeable stiffening after the
30-minute change. However, even at 60 minutes, only
about half the people express opposition to change.
It must be remembered that this opposition includes
a range of response from the mildest possible protest to quitting. It is known that the bulk of this
opposition is protest rather than other types of action.

TABLE 42

Opposition to Schedule Change (Nontolerance)

Minutes of Change	Cumulative Per Cent	
	Earlier	Later
0	0	0
15	7	14
30	16	24
45	36	45
60	49	55
90	61	63

Opposition is to be expected, and the data of
Table 42 offer estimates of its extent. In evaluating these estimates the information of Table 29,
the preference per cents, needs to be recalled. The
per cent opposing these changes must be balanced in
its attitude. Policies in staggering have to be
guided by both tendencies within the population.

Sources of Opposition

The sociological study offers some information about the sources of opposition to schedule change.

> The interviewers examined the respondents' answers on the ten willingness questions and asked those who had opposed one or more changes: "I see that you are unwilling to make (some) (any) change in the times you start and stop work. Why are you against such changes?"

> The answers clearly illustrate the main point. Of the 1,572 respondents, 111 gave only vague replies or none at all, and another 125, who had not opposed any of the changes, were not asked the question. The remaining 85 per cent gave almost 1,900 reasons why they were against making the change. If interpreted literally, about 10 per cent of the replies can be taken to reflect a psychological investment in things as they are. For example, some respondents said their schedule was just fine as it was, some said a change would 'throw me off schedule,' and so forth. All the other reasons for not wanting to change pointed directly to one or another existing commitment. About 5 per cent of the replies referred to transportation problems--car pools, bus and train schedules, etc. About 20 per cent referred to a variety of scheduled activities geared to work time-- stopping patterns, school patterns, school, another job, and so forth. And a few (less than 5 per cent) reflected a concern with interfirm or intrafirm schedules.

> The remaining 56 per cent of the replies concerned commitments at home:

> 16 per cent specifically gave con-
> flicts with the schedules of other
> family members as the reason, another
> 12 per cent said they did not want to
> get home too late, and 28 per cent of
> the replies (over two fifths of the
> respondents) said they did not want to
> have to leave home too early. In short,
> then, the answers reveal little vested
> emotion in present work time, but a
> fair amount of vested interest.

The study then offers its interpretation of
these findings.

> But why, then, resistance. . . ?
> The answer is of course straightforward:
> Having built around his present work
> times a scheduled set of <u>other</u> commit-
> ments, which <u>are</u> 'sacred' (relatively
> speaking), he is reluctant to change
> the former because of the implications
> of the change for the latter. He is
> committed to his present times deriva-
> tively. They are, as it were, locked
> in by the way he spends the rest of
> the day.

The study then reports upon an analysis of the
respondents' other scheduled commitments, for which
detailed data were collected in the survey. These
commitments were analyzed in respect to the respondents' willingness to modify their work schedules.
On the basis of these analyses, the study then concludes:

> It must be admitted that in design-
> ing the study we had viewed family syn-
> chronization as a key variable, in the
> sense that willingness would probably
> vary with it systematically, and that
> for families with two or more job hold-
> ers, staggering would very possibly en-
> tail serious disruption. We now think
> quite the opposite. As expected,

married women are less willing to change
than others, but the differences are not
great. Moreover, when we examine the
effects of specific household duties on
willingness, the small size of these effects is even more striking. And so far
from disturbing present intrahousehold
work schedules, staggering may even increase their integration. Certainly,
their present degree of integration is
not such that staggering can make matters very much worse. In short, the
net result of this and the preceding
analysis is that the respondents' present schedules both internally and in
relation to the schedules of others at
home, contain on the average more than
enough room to permit changes in work
times of the magnitude being contemplated.

Opposition to work schedule change originates
predominantly in other schedules, primarily at home.
Upon evaluating the information collected during
the investigation, the sociologists conclude that
these other schedules, particularly family synchroni-
zation, do not provide a very solid or unyielding
basis of opposition to work staggering.

Employees' Opposition

Any examination of employees' opposition to
schedule change needs to be set within a framework
of their general disposition to the issue. The
sociological study offers three general statements
about the over-all response of employees to schedule
change.

First, it finds that work times do not represent a crucial issue to the employee.

. . . work times do not seem to be
particularly salient or valued features
of jobs. . . . A reduction in salary,
a wholesale alteration of co-worker

relations (through say massive reallo-
cation of people among jobs)--these
would indeed touch on salient, valued
aspects of jobs and cause considerable
negative response. Work times are not
in this category: they fall within
what to employees is one of the least
important dimensions of jobs, working
conditions. So long as the more valued
aspects of their jobs remain the same,
as they would under staggering, changes
can be made in their work times without
materially affecting their attachment
to their present job.

Next, the study points out that there is a
widespread predisposition among employees to accept
a change in work schedules. It traces this predisposition to the prevailing authority structure
of the enterprise. ". . . <u>because work time changes</u>
<u>will be authoritatively introduced within employing</u>
<u>units, the reactions to the changes will be condi-</u>
<u>tioned by this general disposition to comply</u>. . . .
That this general disposition does underlie, and
give rise to, the observed response is indicated by
the fact that the disposition is more common among
those whose general position in the work force regularly puts them in situations where they must respond to other's authoritative directives."

. . . it follows that the staggering of work hours, if it receives the
support of executive personnel and is
implemented through organizational authority structures--as it probably must
be--can count on receiving a not unfavorable response from the great majority of workers, simply because they are
accustomed to accepting, and to adjusting to, organizational changes.

Third, the study shows that the majority of
employees regard work staggering as a justifiable
reason for changing schedules.

With this general disposition as background, it is now appropriate to look more closely at the opposition.

Individual Response

An indication has already been given in Table 42 of the opposition to schedule change. In Table 43 this material is supplemented by the per cent of respondents who replied they would quit their jobs if schedules were changed. It will be recalled that these same quits are included in the larger per cent. The difference between the two rows includes all responses short of quitting jobs--predominantly varying forms of protest.

TABLE 43

Anticipated Nontolerance of Schedule Change and Quits

| | Cumulative Per Cents | | | | | | | | | | | |
| | Earlier | | | | | | Later | | | | | |
Response	90	60	45	30	15	0	0	15	30	45	60	90
Non-tolerate, total	61	49	36	16	7	0	0	14	24	45	55	63
Quit	24	12	5	1	–			1	3	6	13	24

The per cents of quits include those who say they would quit as an individual protest against the change as well as those who would be compelled to quit in order to accomodate their work to the rest of their schedules. The table indicates that very few people even say they would actually quit their jobs. Even at an hour's change earlier or later only 12 and 13 per cent, respectively, say that quitting

would be their response to such a change. In general, therefore, there is little cause for concern
on this score by employers. If these figures materi-
alize, they would probably be readily absorbed within
the normal turnover rate, particularly since those
giving this response are those who are also least
attached to their present jobs. Nor would replace-
ments be lacking, if the preference figures are
taken into consideration. The crucial issue which
these quit data pose for places of employment concerns only key employees, whether in managerial or
subordinate positions. These are important enough
to raise very serious problems for individual firms.
All that can be said here is that one, supervisory
personnel are no more likely than others to oppose
schedule changes and, two, for the rest, ways of
adaptation will have to found or some firms will
probably be unable to modify their schedules. The
extent of noncompliance by firms for this reason,
however, should prove to be very small.

    With respect to these individuals who would
protest or quit, the study provides some additional
material which ought to interest employers. This
material must be understood as general findings
from a large-scale sample survey, to which individual
exceptions may always occur. On the basis of responses which were subjected to careful analysis,
the sociological study makes these general statements. "The people who would least tolerate changes
in their work times are those who are anyway marginally attached to their present jobs and would, presumably, be relatively intolerant of any organizational change. They are however a small proportion of
the sample. . . ."

        In short those marginally attached to
        their job are most likely to behave
        negatively in response to changes in
        their work time. It would thus seem
        that staggering can be implemented
        with little risk of alienating any
        employee other than those already
        alienated and looking for work else-
        where anyway. Moreover, since such

employees are a tiny minority compared
to the great majority who indicate a
strong attachment to their present job
the over-all effect would be small.

Organized Opposition

Within places of employment resistance to schedule change, as to any other organizational change,
can take a form of collective action. There are
many ways in which this might express itself, depending on the practice, experience, and capabilities of the work force. An attempt was made in the
sociological study to explore the opposition to
schedule change for any ingredients which might nur-
ture organized resistance. Specifically, the study
identified three possible sources of such resistance
and investigated each one. These are: opposition
by the authority structure itself, by informal organization of workers, and by the union. The findings on these three possibilities will be cited.

First, the study explored the responses of the
supervisory and executive respondents in the study,
and reports as follows:

> Our findings can be stated simply and
> briefly: comparisons between the one
> fourth of the sample who say they have
> a supervisory job and the other three
> fourths show no differences whatsoever
> between the two groups. There is con-
> sequently no reason to expect that the
> operative authority structures in the
> larger organization will magnify the
> reaction to staggering or provide a
> generally available means of mobilizing
> protest against changes in work hours.

Secondly, informal leadership was identified by
appropriate questions, and these respondents were
treated to special analysis. The study then concludes:

> There is no tendency at all for the
> more influential people to be against

changes in work times more than
others are. There is little likelihood, therefore, that the informal
influence structure will mobilize or
magnify the individual responses to
changes. Actually, the opposite seems
more likely. . . . It thus seems
reasonable to suppose that informal influence will be exercised in support of
changes in work times more often than
not.

Finally, the possibility of union intervention
was also explored. The study again finds:

. . . on the average union members
are no less receptive, and with respect
to changes to earlier times are more
receptive than others in the work
force. . . . There would seem to be
no reason to expect a collective
response through this channel, then,
that is in excess of the response
we would anticipate on the basis of
the aggregated replies of the individual members in the sample.

Conclusions: Employees

The possible effects of schedule change in
places of employment are carefully formulated in
the sociological study. It is appropriate to cite
them directly rather than summarize or paraphrase
them.

First, the study identifies the most probable
source of resistance to schedule change within the
place of employment.

As to the probable incidence of negative behavior in response to the more
likely amounts of change (15 and 30
minutes), there is nothing in the data
to indicate that it will be anything
other than random, relative to the major segments of the work force. No

category of the labor force shows any
marked tendency towards greater or lesser tolerance of changes in work times
than any other. This is to be expected
from our analysis of the place of work
times among the job features valued
most and least. Being matters of low
salience and value to employees generally, they do not provide a point
around which any particular group or
category can cohere; and not being emphasized or expressed by any particular
group or category, they can be changed
without any segment of the labor force
showing distinctive patterns of response. Again, then, this is one more
piece of information suggesting that
for any given amount and direction of
change, variation in reactions will be
largely on an individual basis. Not only are the actions unlikely to be organized on any substantial basis, but they
are unlikely even to be more pronounced
among one rather than another kind of
employee.

The study suggests, further, something about
how this individual reaction may be expected to
arise.

To a large extent, the range of changes
in work times that will be tolerated by
individual workers (that is, that they
will accept without verbally protesting
or actually quitting) depends upon a
general disposition to put up with organizational changes introduced 'from
above' by authoritative directives or
rulings. . . . Individuals will not
react to work hour changes in any new,
unusual, or random way. Whether the
changes are welcomed, tolerated, or
resisted, their behavioral reactions
reflect, in a general way, the insti-
tutionalized capacity of organizational

authority systems in our society to
introduce changes in work routines.
In particular settings, the behavioral reactions will reflect the
capacity of the particular organization's authority system to introduce such changes.

Next, there are some pertinent things relative
to collective action resisting work staggering.

As far as we can tell within the
limits of this study, there is no
sign that the more common mechanisms
of organizing and articulating individuals' interests--organizational
authority structures, informal influence patterns, and union grievance
procedures--would operate to produce
at the collective level a degree of
negative response in excess of that
foreseen by examining the probable
individual responses. None of the
strategically placed groups--
supervisory and executive personnel, informal opinion leaders in
work places, or union members--are
less receptive than the average person to proposed changes in work
times, and in some cases they are
more receptive. The usual modes of
collective action are thus unlikely
to facilitate the expression of individual discontent and may in fact
hinder it or even reduce its incidence. This means that negatively
reacting individuals are unlikely
to secure a return to the status quo
ante through such channels and will
probably have to do so by making adjustments at the individual level,
that is, by seeking alternative employment. In the light of the preceding discussion of that possibility,

it seems unlikely that more than
a very few will even try to do so.

These findings and conclusions support a policy
favorable to work staggering by employers. There
seems to be no reason to anticipate any significant
degree of opposition or resistance by employees,
certainly not enough to outweigh the favorable responses of the majority. Consequently, there should
be no general opposition from employers on the
grounds that their employees will object or will act
against a policy of schedule change.

Other Opposition

There is always a possibility that opposition
and resistance to work staggering will arise and find
expression through organs of community and political
opinion. Employees and their families, objecting to
a communitywide program of schedule change, may
utilize governmental and political instrumentalities
to give voice to their opposition and to stop a work
staggering program. Here again, the action in question lies in the future, under conditions which cannot really be foreseen or predicted. Nevertheless,
whatever light is available on this subject will
prove relevant to policy decisions.

As background to this topic, it is interesting
to examine the willingness and tolerance tables
based on the residence borough of the respondents.
These are shown in Tables 44 and 45.

The residents of Queens and Brooklyn show somewhat less willingness to accept schedule change both
earlier and later than the residents of Manhattan and
the Bronx, but about the same as the whole CBD sample.
The Staten Island residents show far less willingness
to accept change in either direction than the residents of the other boroughs.

TABLE 44

Per Cents by Residence Borough Willing to Start
Earlier and Later

Borough	Minutes Earlier						Minutes Later					
	90	60	45	30	15	0	0	15	30	45	60	90
Manhattan	22	34	40	62	77	100	100	66	54	35	28	20
Bronx	22	34	45	73	84	100	100	61	50	30	23	14
Queens	14	28	36	64	81	100	100	67	48	28	21	15
Brooklyn	16	28	38	63	83	100	100	64	46	28	20	12
Staten Island	7	18	25	58	73	100	100	52	45	15	8	4
Total	17	29	38	63	80	100	100	63	47	28	21	14

TABLE 45

Per Cents by Residence Borough Tolerant of
Earlier and Later Starts

Borough	Minutes Earlier						Minutes Later					
	90	60	45	30	15	0	0	15	30	45	60	90
Manhattan	39	53	69	86	95	100	100	88	78	58	48	40
Bronx	42	53	64	85	93	100	100	85	74	55	44	38
Queens	39	52	66	87	96	100	100	88	79	57	46	39
Brooklyn	38	52	61	81	91	100	100	85	74	50	41	32
Staten Island	48	52	63	82	100	100	100	80	73	58	51	44
Total	38	50	63	83	92	100	100	87	77	56	46	38

In contrast, the residents of Manhattan, Bronx, Queens, and Brooklyn show very similar degrees of tolerance toward schedule change, both earlier and later. Quite unexpectedly the Staten Island residents, while far less willing to accept change, show themselves far more tolerant of change than the residents of the other boroughs.

The finding from Tables 44 and 45 is that the response of the CBD as a whole is approximately the same as the response by the residents of the various boroughs, especially at the tolerance level. There would thus seem to be no need to worry about special community pressures in any of the city's major subdivisions.

On the general subject of opposition and resistance at the community and political level the sociological study reports briefly as follows:

> We asked several questions about public affairs, principally in order to assess whether and to what extent staggering may have political repercussions. Needless to say, any findings from such a study as ours bear on only one aspect of this possibility, particularly since if staggering becomes a political issue, it would probably be for reasons quite unrelated to our respondents' feelings and anticipated behaviors. The analysis is thus limited to the kind of question raised . . . regarding formal authority, informal influence, and union grievance machinery: to what extent is the existing political structure likely to provide a means for discontented people to organize and express their discontent collectively?

After analyzing the available data the study offers some brief conclusions.

Those whose present positions,
activities, or self-appraisals indicate that they would find it
easier than others to express discontent through political channels
are in no cases less willing than
others to start work earlier or
later on the average, and in several comparisons are more willing.
Once again, then, we conclude that
those who may oppose the changes
will have no special access to a
mechanism for organizing individuals' action, and hence that the
scale of whatever organized opposition may develop will probably be
no larger than that which would be
estimated by simply summing the
individual responses.

A Policy Toward Schedule Change

The findings of the sociological study, as reported in the preceding section, lead this inquiry to
a clear decision: to proceed further with the study
of the feasibility of work staggering. This conclusion is based upon an assessment of the probable
response of the people, and of the effects of their
response upon public and private officials. This
conclusion does not mean that public or private officials might not, for various reasons, oppose such
change. Their reasons may originate in the response
of their people or from other sources. At this
juncture, on the basis of available evidence, there
is simply no reason to discontinue the inquiry on
account of anticipated opposition to work staggering
by any significant segments of the population. This
policy conclusion applies only to the present study.
It is not necessarily appropriate for the decision
makers of the CBD, private or public. This study
evaluates the evidence of acceptability by its own
decision rule. In effect, so long as there is substantial evidence that the population will accept
and not resist a change, it is worthwhile to proceed with the inquiry. The decision makers of the

CBD will undoubtedly require a more stringent rule.

The Community

The evidence concerning the response of the
community is drawn, in this study, from a special
segment: the people who work in the CBD. These include many different kinds of people: married,
single, women both with and without household responsibilities, people of many different races,
creeds, and colors, all ranges of income and other
social criteria. It excludes members of the community who do not work in the CBD or who are not
employed at all, in particular the housewives. The
response of the community, while restricted to the
people who work in the CBD, is expanded, by the nature of the information collected, to reflect some
of the sentiment and circumstance of the other members of their households.

With respect to the community, the sociological
study produces two fundamental findings. First, it
discloses a wide acceptance of schedule change on
the part of employees. Their acceptance is further
analyzed with respect to domestic schedules and
interrelationships and has been found substantial.
The second finding is that no danger signals are evident in respect to schedule change. No special segment of the population nor any particular organized
body shows opposition or a hardening of negative
attitude toward schedule change. The community is
thus considered sufficiently hospitable to proceed
with the inquiry.

This conclusion does not presume to be a decision made for or on behalf of community officials.
They will ultimately decide their own positions according to their lights. It is rather a decision
for this inquiry and confined to the evidence of the
population response to the study.

Places of Employment

Individual firms decide their schedules in a
variety of ways and on the basis of many different

criteria. In some the employer decides unilaterally:
by fiat of the principal official, by consultation
with some or all of management, by consulting employees, or by other means. In others, schedules may be
fixed by collective bargaining or by accepting the
union's unilateral decision. Similarly, there are
many different criteria by which to fix schedules,
among which the preferences and desires of the employed work force often figure prominently. The
sociological study furnishes important and relevant
information about just this criterion. To the extent that places of employment take into account
the responses of their personnel, the findings of the
sociological study shed light upon one important element in their decisions about changing schedules.

In brief, the study shows that employees would
prefer, to a considerable degree, different schedules from the ones they now have; that they would
be willing to accept changes in schedules even
greater than the ones they prefer; and that they
would tolerate larger changes than those they express
a willingness to accept. The study also shows that
there are no danger signals arising from opposition
and resistance to a proposed schedule change. All
of these evidences of acceptability apply to stated
limits of schedule change.

The policy decision is reached that places of
employment, responsive to the sentiments of their
personnel, will in general lean favorably toward
schedule change in principle. This does not rule
out the possibility of some opposition based on
personnel considerations. Nor does it exclude negative decisions toward schedule change based on
other grounds. From the defined perspective of acceptability, this inquiry can safely conclude that
places of employment will take an affirmative attitude toward schedule change.

PERSONNEL CONSTRAINTS ON MODIFIABILITY

The ability of places of employment in the CBD
to modify their work schedules, on functional grounds

alone, is shown in Appendix Table 64. The notion of
functional modifiability, which was the basis for
constructing Appendix Table 64, intentionally omitted
three important determinants of work schedule. These
were: the attitudes of the people who work in the
CBD to schedule change, access to the local labor
market, and the special or unique situation of individual firms. These excluded determinants of
schedules must be added to Appendix Table 64 in
order to reach final estimates of schedule modifiability in the CBD.

The missing determinants will be supplied by
the findings of the sociological study. These non-
functional or personnel determinants of scheduling
will be derived in the sections to follow. The first
section will consider the problem of access to the
local labor market as a determinant of work schedule.
The second section will take up the response of the
employees, representing one part of the people who
work in the CBD whose attitudes toward schedule
change have not yet been incorporated in the estimates. The final section will deal with the response
of the employer and will also take account of the
residual problem of the special firm. After these
three factors have been analyzed, a procedure will
be developed for quantifying and applying the personnel constraints on schedule modifiability.

Access To Labor Market

One of the factors which will influence a firm's
capability of modifying its work schedule is its continuing access to the local labor market. It stands
to reason that a firm will be reluctant to adopt a
schedule which will cut it off from, or reduce its
access to, its supply of employees. The question
therefore arises: Will changes in schedule of the
magnitudes contemplated in this study affect adversely the access of employers to the local labor market?

This question will be answered by comparing
present and preferred schedules as reported by the
sociological study. This comparison will show that

people prefer quite a wide range of schedules different from their present ones. From this, the conclusion will be drawn that a labor supply exists
over a wide range of schedules. Hence, a firm which
modifies its schedule may restrict its access to
some employees but enlarge its access to others from
which it may at present be restricted.

The evidence of employees' preference in starting
times was presented in Tables 29 and 30. Table 29
shows most employees prefer other than their present
starting times. Table 30, subdividing the total
sample by their present starting times, shows that
the same preference structure occurs among people
now starting work at quite different times.

Additional evidence is presented in Tables 46,
47, and 48. These tables give the per cents of employees by present starting times and by their preferred starting times for three subdivisions of the
sample: occupations (46), types of establishments
(47), and industrial subdivisions of the office establishments (48).

From the evidence of schedule preference, two
pertinent conclusions may be drawn. First, since the
majority of employees prefer to start work at other
than their present starting times, a change in work
schedule need not reduce a firm's access to the local
labor market at all. In fact, there are undoubtedly
many kinds of change which would increase its accessibility. This conclusion applies not only to
the CBD as a whole, but to particular occupations in
which a firm may be interested; to the principal
types of establishment as well as to the various industrial subdivisions of the office establishments.
By and large, schedule changes of the kind contemplated by this study need not produce shortages of
labor supply to the firms and industries.

Second, access--as governed by work schedules--
to the local labor market is apparently not a very
vigorous determinant of work schedules. The tables
disclose that a majority of employees have accepted
employment at other than their preferred times. As

interpreted earlier in this chapter, this may mean
that people have considerable latitude in the schedules they can accept. But it also means that firms
do not necessarily fix their schedules to suit the
preferences of their employees.

On this evidence and reasoning, there is no
need for any additional constraint on functional
modifiability to preserve access to the local labor
market. Within reasonable shifts in schedule, introduced systematically and over the whole CBD, there
ought to be no difficulty in procuring a supply of
employees.

The Employees' Response

The sociological study furnishes at least three
sets of data showing the expected responses of people
to varying amounts of schedule change. Which of the
three levels of response is appropriate for determining schedule modifiability?

The answer to this question will be reached by
a process of analysis. It involves matching the
levels of response with the conditions under which
work staggering will most likely occur. Each level
of response was evoked by means of distinctive stimuli originating in the questions and their contexts.
To a sufficient degree, the way a proposal of work
staggering will reach and act upon employees can
also be envisioned. Comparing these two situations,
it will be possible to connect the levels of response to the potential events.

A work staggering program will reach the employees as a proposal to change their work schedules.
It will occur at work (regardless of any programs of
public education) and will consist of a definite
alternative schedule, proposing specific starting
and stopping times. As a community program for the
place of employment, a pressure to respond will inevitably be present. There will be differences among
firms in the actual procedures by which the proposal
will be handled--these will be considered below--but

no matter how it is processed, the constraints (or
stimuli) of a specific condition of employment will
be perceptible.

These circumstances do not correspond at all to
the sources of the preference level of response.
The preference level presupposed a free choice of
times and the absence of any restraints. As an issue in employment--and in the community--employees
will not be asked when they would most prefer to
start and stop work. Accordingly, the preference
level, however illuminating for other purposes, will
not be the employees' response in the actual employment situation.

Within any place of employment, if the issue
arises, the employees may be asked their views about
the proposed alternative schedule. This can take
place in two ways. If the subject arises within a
local union the issue may come to a vote of the membership. The employees will then express their views
by their vote. The second way in which employees
register their views, whether or not there is a local
union, is through a poll of employee opinion. In
either case, the employees are asked to state their
attitudes toward a specific alternative--whether or
not they would be willing to accept it.

The circumstances under which the employees'
opinions would be solicited, whether by vote or by
poll, correspond most closely to those which evoked
the willingness response. There would be a specific
proposal and the employees' feelings and attitudes
about it would be solicited. The best available
information about the probable outcome of such a
vote or poll is now offered by the willingness tables.
This should not be taken as meaning that a union vote
or an opinion poll, even among the same employees,
would necessarily produce the same results. The
willingness concept corresponds most closely to the
circumstance of both kinds of solicitation of opinion and the tables represent the only available data
about their probable response.

TABLE 46

Present and Preferred Start Times,
by Per Cents of Occupation

Start Time	Proprietors		Professional		Clerical		Sales		Skilled		Semiskilled Service		Unskilled	
	Pres.	Pfd.	Pres.	Pfd.	Pres.	Pfd.	Pres.	Pfd.	Pres.	Pfd.	Pres.	Pfd.	Pres.	Pfd.
Before 7:15	4	4	1	3	1	2	-	-	3	12	14	18	9	26
7:30 (a)	2	3	4	2	-	1	-	-	5	12	3	8	-	4
8:00 (b)	7	16	2	14	4	17	3	16	29	21	17	23	39	35
8:15	3	3	10	2	2	3	2	2	9	3	7	4	9	-
8:30	10	15	9	17	12	21	11	23	17	15	20	14	22	17
8:45	13	9	40	6	13	10	23	6	8	3	6	4	-	-
9:00	34	22	15	25	45	23	37	31	20	23	18	16	9	17
9:15	15	4	7	7	12	3	6	5	-	1	2	1	9	-
9:30	5	10	9	9	6	10	3	8	4	5	2	2	4	-
After 9:30	4	12	5	14	4	7	8	6	3	1	9	10	-	-
Other	4	3	-	3	1	2	6	3	1	5	3	1	-	-

(a) Includes 7:15
(b) Includes 7:45

234

TABLE 47

Present and Preferred Start Times,
by Type of Establishment

Start Time	Office Pres.	Office Pfd.	Trade Pres.	Trade Pfd.	Factory Pres.	Factory Pfd.	Service Pres.	Service Pfd.
Before 7:15	1	2	9	8	4	10	10	11
7:30 (a)	-	1	2	4	2	6	3	2
8:00 (b)	4	16	7	15	17	21	12	27
8:15	1	3	3	2	7	3	4	6
8:30	10	20	9	13	21	19	17	8
8:45	15	10	8	5	9	6	-	12
9:00	43	22	36	28	28	22	22	16
9:15	12	4	17	4	5	1	4	5
9:30	6	10	5	13	3	3	4	3
After 9:30	6	10	5	7	3	6	15	17
Other	3	2	-	2	2	3	9	3

(a) Includes 7:15

(b) Includes 7:45

235

TABLE 48

Present and Preferred Start Times,
by Office Type Industries

Start Time	Central Administrative Offices		Financial		Business-Professional		Publishing		Government		Other	
	Pres.	Pfd.	Pres.	Pfd.	Pres.	Pfd.	Pres.	Pfd.	Pres.	Pfd.	Pres.	Pfd.
Before 7:15	1	1	2	2	-	2	-	4	-	3	1	4
7:30 (a)	-	3	-	1	-	1	-	-	-	-	1	1
8:00 (b)	9	20	2	15	1	13	4	10	-	22	6	16
8:15	-	2	2	5	1	1	2	2	-	3	1	3
8:30	9	22	16	27	8	16	2	14	17	22	4	16
8:45	19	14	28	11	7	9	6	6	11	8	8	6
9:00	48	23	37	21	48	23	41	16	42	23	41	22
9:15	3	4	7	4	17	8	25	10	23	2	12	1
9:30	6	3	3	7	12	17	6	14	2	11	6	11
After 9:30	3	8	2	5	5	9	12	25	2	3	15	17
Other	2	1	2	2	2	2	2	-	3	3	4	3

(a) Includes 7:15
(b) Includes 7:45

236

Finally, assume that a decision has been made to introduce a new work schedule. This can be made unilaterally, with or without consultation of employees through a poll, or as a result of collective bargaining in which the members may or may not have voted on the issue. Regardless of the decision process, the place of employment is now assumed to have instituted an alternative work schedule. What then may be the expected response of employees? This circumstance-- the actual introduction of a new schedule--corresponds to the one envisaged by the tolerance level of response and by the opposition response of Table 43. The tolerance level seeks to capture the probable behavioral response of the employees: how they will act under actual conditions of a specific schedule change. The tolerance level indicates the proportion of people who will accept a given amount of change without protest and without quitting. The opposition table gives the per cent who will find a specified change intolerable and will respond to it by protesting or quitting.

On the basis of this analysis, a decision was reached to use the tolerance level as the personnel constraint on schedule modifiability. This level of response corresponds most closely to the real circumstances of the employment relationship, to the conditions under which an alternative schedule will occur, and to a behavioral response of the employees in the face of an actual event as distinguished from a proposal. The way it will be used and the meaning of the results it will produce will be described below in the section on application of the constraints.

The Employers' Response

The employer is a special occupational category insofar as work scheduling is concerned. He is the individual who makes the decision to modify--or not to modify--the work schedule in his place of employment, or who participates, as a management official, in making the decision. He may thus be owner, president, executive, manager, or even supervisor. He belongs to the employer occupation, regardless of

his rank and title, if he shares in the managerial
decision making process.

The employer is separated from the employees
because his response to schedule change reflects two
sources of attitude. Like the rest of the employees,
he is an individual with preferences, feelings, and
attitudes and with limits to his tolerance of schedule change. But different from the other employees,
he is also a decision maker about schedules--sole
or participating--for his place of employment. He
thus has two ties to the subject of schedule: a
personal one and an occupational one, and this differentiates him from the rest of the people who work
in the CBD in a way which is significant to this
study.

From this viewpoint, the employers' response to
schedule change is a contaminated one. It reflects
two sources of motivation, personal and occupational.
Individual employer respondents may have emphasized,
in their replies, one or the other of these sources.
It is most unlikely that any individual could suc-
ceed in separating his personal from his occupational
motivation, even if he tried. For the employer respondents as a whole, the tables unquestionably
reflect both. The response therefore of the employer
occupation is interpreted as giving a mixture of individual attitude and evaluation of the firm's capability of changing schedule.

To a considerable degree, the preceding analysis
of the employees' response applies to many of the
people classified as employers. A substantial number
in the employer category actually have employee status, even though they exercise parts of the employer
function. These will include supervisory, managerial,
and even some of the lower rank executive personnel.
As individuals their responses will conform, under
appropriate circumstances, to the willingness and
tolerance levels.

To the other members of this category who have
substantial decision making authority over schedules,
individual responses may still conform to the two

levels as interpreted earlier. But these responses
are evoked out of somewhat different circumstances.
If a proposal is ever made for schedule change in
the CBD, it may be expected to be offered with some
degree of firmness. There will be no coercion by
any authority, and no place of employment will be
obligated to accept any particular schedule. But
the proposal will emanate from responsible sources
with the support of local government, important institutions, trade associations, unions,and industry
organizations of the CBD and the rest of the city.
It will thus represent a communitywide program and
will be pressed upon the employers as a serious
proposal to which they must give a responsible
answer.

Under such circumstances, many of the conditions
which evoked the willingness and the tolerance responses will prevail. Specific proposals put forward in a responsible way and asking for a personal
reply correspond to the conditions which evoked the
willingness response. Similarly, the decision by an
industry to adopt a particular starting time will
confront each individual with the circumstances underlying the tolerance response--the need to act
with respect to the accepted starting times.

This analysis leads to the conclusion that the
tolerance level is the most appropriate of the three
levels of response by which to anticipate the employer's response to a proposed schedule change. For
him, too, the tolerance level measures what he will do
under actual conditions of a new schedule as against
the way he might vote at an industry or trade association meeting. The employer's response in the
tolerance tables are understood to embody both his
individual and occupational considerations, including
any special functional characteristics of his own
firm's scheduling. The use and meaning of the tolerance tables will be developed in the section which
follows.

The Special Firm

The studies of functional capability sought out
the general, common,and characteristic schedule

determinants of the CBD industries. By design, they
disregarded any of the special or unique circumstances of individual firms. These circumstances
are functional: They reflect special business and
competitive situations, or significant relationships
with suppliers or customers. Unquestionably, all
firms have some relationships of this kind, but
they do not necessarily govern schedules. Hence,
while they are prevalent, the number of firms which
must be regarded as exceptional from the viewpoint
of industry capability is considered small. Nevertheless, many or few, they remain to be taken into
account in the estimates of schedule modifiability.

As noted above, the employers' responses reflect two sources of motivation, personal and occupational. The occupational source must have given,
in a profound and systematic way, a special sensitivity to the unique functional characteristics of
the respondents' firms. These are precisely the
kinds of occupational factors which must be upper-
most in an employer's mind when he contemplates a
schedule change for himself and his firm. If they
were operative at all, they must have colored the
replies of all employers, not only those from the
exceptional firms.

A special accent will now be placed upon the
employers' responses to the survey. They will be
interpreted as containing an element of functional
capability, expressed through the medium of the
employers' acceptance of schedule change. They
will thus be treated as a corrective for the missing
special firm, as well as a general adjustment covering the employers' assessment of his firm's functional capability.

Personnel Constraints: Application

A procedure will now be presented by which to
apply the personnel constraints to the estimates of
functional modifiability. The purpose of this procedure is to adjust these estimates to account for
the personnel factors which affect an industry's
ability to modify its schedule. The procedure

contains a specification of the required adjustment
tables and the method by which the adjustments are
incorporated into the estimates of functional modifiability.

The tolerance response provides the required
personnel constraint on the modifiability of work
schedules. It embodies the personnel factors which
enter into a firm's whole capability. The tables
and their application will now be set forth.

A single tolerance table will be employed for
the purpose of applying the personnel constraints.
It is presented here as Table 49. This table shows,
for each present starting time, the estimated per
cent of the CBD work force who would tolerate each
alternative starting time. The main diagonal of
this table shows 100 per cent. This means that all
employees will tolerate their present starting times.
On each row of the table there are descending percentages moving to the right and to the left of the
main diagonal. These represent the declining percentages of people who will tolerate starting times
involving increasing amounts of change from their
present one.

This same table incorporates both the employers'
and the employees' response at the tolerance level.
This was made possible by the statistics. Table 39
shows the tolerance percentages by occupation and for
the total CBD. A comparison of the two reveals that
they are almost identical. It thus became possible
to use the one set of percentages to reflect the aggregate. If a separate table had been used to adjust
the data for the employer, the results would have
been insignificantly different from the results obtained by using a single table.

The method by which this adjustment table is
used will now be explained and illustrated. In
Chapter 4 the method of modifying industry schedules
to conform to new starting times was shown. This
method is now modified to incorporate the personnel
constraint by simply reducing the numbers of persons

shifted to conform to the percentages shown on Table
49.   Thus, if an 8:30 starting time is projected,
instead of transferring all the persons now starting,
say, at 9:00 to 8:30, the table indicates that only
87 per cent will find such a change tolerable and
this is the percentage which is shifted. The remainder are left at their original 9:00 time.   In
this same manner all shifts are made from present
to proposed starting times, reducing the numbers by
the percentages indicated on the table. Those who
are not shifted remain at their present time. No
allowance is made in the computation for a partial
shifting of schedule. The resulting table will then
reflect the industry's functional capability of
adopting the alternative starting time, as further
modified by the personnel constraints upon the
particular change.

TABLE 49

Personnel Constraints on Schedule Modifiability--
Per Cent of Each Present Start Time Who Will
Tolerate Each Alternative Start Time

Present Start Times	Alternative Start Times								
	7:30	7:45	8:00	8:15	8:30	8:45	9:00	9:15	9:30
7:30	100	79	74	58	58	58	58	--	--
7:45	94	100	83	73	59	54	51	47	--
8:00	86	94	100	83	73	59	54	51	47
8:15	68	86	90	100	80	76	54	40	37
8:30	47	59	82	92	100	84	72	48	40
8:45	35	39	60	84	95	100	86	74	52
9:00	36	44	52	67	87	96	100	88	77
9:15	--	27	33	39	54	77	92	100	86
9:30	--	--	42	48	53	63	88	93	100

    The effects of this procedure are shown on
Table 50. It may be compared with the exclusively
functional modification for the same industry presented on Table 22.

TABLE 50

Effects of an 8:30 Start Time on Schedules of the Wholesale Trades--
Functional Capability Adjusted by Personnel Constraints

Numbers of Employees

Start Time	Stop Time											Other	Total
	3:30	3:45	4:00	4:15	4:30	4:45	5:00	5:15	5:30	5:45	6:00		
7:30	0	0	3	0	9	0	0	0	0	0	0	20	32
7:45	0	0	0	0	0	0	0	0	0	0	0	20	20
8:00	0	0	519	0	2,792	0	6,025	0	0	0	0	416	9,752
8:15	0	0	0	0	0	243	420	0	0	0	0	4	667
8:30	0	0	550	1,035	65,642	44,662	52,419	1,131	5,548	0	0	2,209	173,196
8:45	0	0	0	0	2	525	1,500	13	39	0	0	2	2,080
9:00	0	0	0	0	64	137	7,549	425	6,270	24	474	228	15,171
9:15	0	0	0	0	0	0	0	1,425	56	0	0	11	1,492
9:30	0	0	0	0	0	0	108	59	159	9	226	107	667
Other	493	0	2,494	0	126	131	303	265	298	0	521	19,022	23,653
Total	493	0	3,566	1,035	68,634	45,698	68,323	3,319	12,370	33	1,220	22,039	226,731

243

CONCLUSIONS

At the outset of this chapter two main problems were identified as arising from the social consequences of schedule change. They were a policy problem--whether or not work staggering was sufficiently acceptable to proceed with the inquiry--and a design problem--how to incorporate the needs of the people into estimates of schedule modifiability. The evidence and reasoning leading to the policy decision have been set forth in sufficient detail to establish its justification. Similarly the reasoning and procedure for the solution of the design problem were developed in the presentation of the personnel constraints on modifiability. The problems of the chapter are thus brought to a suitable conclusion.

It may be of interest, from a methodological point of view, to point out that the solution of the design problem gives a continuous and varying solution to the policy problem. By adjusting the estimates of functional modifiability on the basis of the tolerance tables, the policy issue is resolved by a computational procedure. For each schedule alternative, the percentage of people who will tolerate the required amount of change represents the number about whom an affirmative policy decision has been made. The number who will not tolerate the amount of change, and who as a consequence will not be shifted to the new starting time, reflect the numbers of people for whom a negative policy change has been made. The greater the extent of the shift, the fewer the numbers of people who are transferred to the new starting time. By this procedure a separate policy decision is made on each computation. The procedure is thus sensitive continuously to the policy implications of schedule change.

6

FORECASTING
CORDON COUNTS

A method is required by which to forecast the subway cordon counts resulting from an alternative work schedule in the CBD. Since the desired counts are measures of future behavior--under specific conditions of schedule change--a forecasting method is needed, not merely a computational procedure.

This chapter will produce a forecasting equation capable of testing the effect of alternative CBD work schedules upon subway traffic measured at cordon stations. The equation will apply to mornings and to the journey to work. It is assumed that any transit relief which alternative work schedules produce in the morning will also accrue, with reasonable variations, during the return trips in the late afternoon.

Two analyses will be required to derive and present the forecasting equation. Each will occupy a section in the remaining portion of this chapter. The first section will identify and quantify the components of the relationship between present work schedules and present cordon counts. This will provide the materials for constructing the forecasting equation.

The second section will derive the forecasting equation. It will not be the same as the equation of relationship, but it will utilize that equation as its foundation. The analysis will derive the forecasting equation and will show the restrictions and conditions governing its application.

At appropriate places in this chapter, the results will be given in general symbolic terms, since
the equations are mathematical statements. Appendix
S presents the definitions of the terms and the two
equations.

WORK SCHEDULE AND CORDON COUNT--
THE PRESENT RELATIONSHIP

To develop a forecasting equation, there must
be a systematic relationship between work schedule
and cordon count. Such a relationship is assumed to
exist in the real world: It produces the rush hours.
It should then be possible to represent the reality--
the flow of passengers to their places of employment,
within specified time intervals--by mathematical
statement: an equation. On the basis of such a relationship, expressed mathematically, the forecasting equation can be constructed.

The desired relationship has to possess two
characteristics, to prove useful in developing the
forecasting equation. First, the elements of the re-
lationship--the terms of the equation--must be derived from known phenomena and from satisfactory empirical data. It is possible to construct the equation of present relationship by numerical methods
alone. Let one variable be the present cordon count
(a 1 X 11 vector) and the other the work schedule
(also a 1 X 11 vector). Then formulate the function
which produces the one from the other. This was
done and the results, while computationally correct,
proved unsatisfactory. They provided no information
about the meaning of the terms of the equation.
Therefore, when constructing the forecasting equation, the results were not useful. It was impossible
to take into consideration the consequences of schedule change upon the relationship of the two phenomena.
The elements of the relationship are the behaviors of
people, and they must be known in order to utilize
the equation for forecasting purposes.

The second characteristic of the relationship

equation concerns the time intervals of each variable. Work schedules are fixed predominantly on
quarter-hourly intervals which must be preserved if
the equation is to be useful. Similarly, the cordon
counts and transit scheduling are based on 20-minute
intervals, which must also be maintained in the equation. It is obvious that cordon counts and work
schedules are closely related on, say, a three-hour
basis. This large time interval is useless for
present purposes. Nothing will be satisfactory but
the customary intervals of employment and subway operation.

The work of conducting the forecasting equation
will be begun, in this section, by establishing the
equation of relationship between work schedule and
cordon count. First, the nature of the problem will
be exposed. Thereafter, a series of adjustment factors which progressively convert the work schedule
statistics into cordon counts will be presented.
When this is completed, the results will be evaluated.

The Problem

Work schedules and subway traffic are undoubtedly related--and closely--as experience and reason indicate. But the actual statistics do not corroborate
experience, at least not to the extent required by
this study. And it is the statistics of the relationship, not the reality itself, which provide the materials by which to construct the desired equation.
This lack of close relationship creates an exceedingly difficult problem, both for the immediate subject
and for the rest of this study. It will only be
partly solved, hopefully enough for the needs of the
later computations.

The lack of close relationship between work
schedule and cordon count statistics shows itself in
two ways: aggregately, and by the dissimilarity in
the distributions of the two sets of data.

The October, 1962, cordon count reports that
1,206,540 people passed through the twenty cordon

stations into the CBD between 6:20 and 10:00 a.m.
These included all riders, both those going to work
in the CBD and all others. Since the period contains
the rush hours, presumably most of the riders were
traveling to work in the CBD.

Between 6:30 and 10:30 a.m. (a period equivalent to the cordon intervals) about 1-3/4 millions
of people are scheduled to start work in the CBD.
Two thirds cross the subway cordons to work. This
yields a total of 1,160,000 of employee-riders as
compared with the total of 1,206,540 passengers,
leaving only 46,500 of all other riders.

For many purposes, this aggregate comparison
might be regarded as remarkably successful. There
is no reason to expect that two sets of statistics,
drawn from wholly different sources and even different times, should converge so closely. But for this
study, the result is inadequate. To produce the computations of feasibility, the aggregate difference--
without the manipulations to be developed in this
chapter--will prove excessive.

The dissimilarity in the distributions of the
two sets of statistics is shown by Figure 11. It
gives the number of subway riders entering the CBD
during 20-minute intervals, and the number scheduled
to start work at 15-minute intervals. For some purposes these two series are not comparable because
their interval lengths differ. However, this will
not affect the interpretation to be made here.

The figure reveals many likenesses in the two
phenomena. It shows that their general contours are
similar--both rise to a peak and fall; that the cordon count peak precedes the work schedule peak--
which it should since people cross the cordons before reporting to work. Moreover, if the work schedule line were reduced by the one third who do not
cross the cordons, the two lines would show even more
general similarity than they actually do. These considerations notwithstanding, the serious differences
may now be noted.

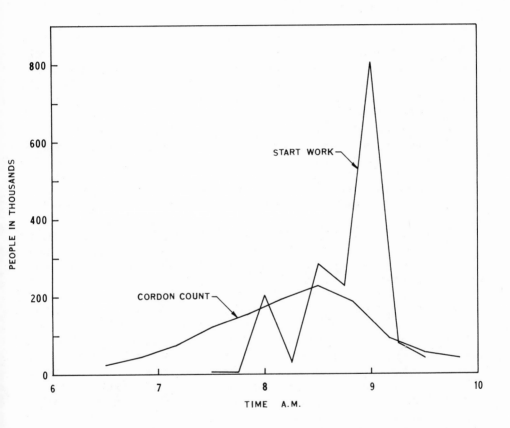

FIGURE 11
CORDON COUNT ENTERING THE CBD
AND NUMBER OF PEOPLE STARTING WORK

249

The cordon count shows a smooth, continuous rise to a peak, and then a similar drop afterward. The work schedule rises jaggedly, with three peaks at 8:00, 8:30, and 9:00 a.m. The cordon count build-up begins as early as the 6:20-6:40 interval, while the work schedule does not show any sizable magnitude until 8:00 a.m. The time lag exceeds the half-hour difference in the peaks, and can scarcely be charged to increased travel time from cordon station to destination during the earlier hours.

These differences in contour are substantial and significant. There is no simple and direct relationship between the two phenomena. The fact that about 200,000 people are scheduled to start work at 8:00 does not provide any useful information about the size of the cordon counts during intervals up to--or later than--that time. Even more to the point, if the number starting work at 8:00 were increased to 300,000, it would not be possible to tell--from the relationship shown on Figure 6.1--which cordon intervals would be increased by the additional 100,000 and which would be decreased, and by how much.

It is possible, as noted earlier, to construct a mathematical bridge between the two sets of data. The work schedule numbers multiplied by a suitable matrix can be made to yield the cordon count. This would make it possible to assign the present 200,000 at 8:00 to cordon intervals. But would they be the correct ones? And when the additional 100,000 are scheduled to start at 8:00, would they obey the same mathematical rules of distribution among the cordon intervals? None of this can be known because the activities which the mathematical bridge represents are unknown. To use such a device for forecasting ought to be avoided, if at all possible. The distribution rule which it embodies is drawn from the present relationship of work schedule and cordon count. When work schedules are changed, the relationship must also be expected to change. If the behavioral reality behind the mathematical expression is unidentified, it becomes impossible to adapt the equation of relationship to the circumstance of modified work schedules.

Figure 11 corroborates the prevailing under-
standing that work schedules and subway traffic are
related. But the relationship is too distant for
the purposes of this study. As it stands, it cannot
connect the two series in a useful way. Even more,
it cannot serve as a basis for computing the effects
of alternative work schedules in the CBD.

For this study, Figure 11 poses two issues.
Practically it reveals that a more serviceable equation of relationship is required than the one which
might be derived from the data on which the figure
is based. More profoundly, however, it points to
the need for explaining the discrepancies between
these two series. Any equation of relationship upon
which forecasts are to be based presupposes an under-
standing of the behavior of people which gives rise
to the discrepancies depicted on the figure. It is
not sufficient to evolve a computationally satisfactory method of going from work schedule to cordon
count. It is necessary also to know the behavioral
elements which intervene into this relationship, so
that the terms of the equation can be used properly
in forecasting the cordon counts after work schedules
are changed.

The System

Despite the statistics, work schedule and cordon
count are systematically related. Their relationship is produced by three principal elements: by
the people who participate in it, by the sequence of
activities in which they engage, and by the timing
of people and activities. The two phenomena, linked
together by these elements, constitute a system.

The Participants

The way the two phenomena are related by their
participants is shown in Figure 12. Each has its
set of participants, and their sets intersect for
one aggregate: the people who cross subway cordons
and who are journeying to work in the CBD.

FIGURE 12

PARTICIPANTS IN THE RELATIONSHIP

PEOPLE WHO WORK IN THE CBD AND ARE PRESENT AT WORK, BY MEANS OF TRANSPORT	PASSENGERS TRAVELING THROUGH CORDON STATIONS, BY DESTINATION		
	CBD		BEYOND CBD
	TO WORK	OTHER	
BY SUBWAY : THROUGH CORDONS			
OTHER			
BY OTHER MEANS			

The people who cross the subway cordons are given at the column headings of the figure. They are divided into two main groups: those whose destinations are in the CBD and those who travel beyond (but by subway, passing through exit cordon stations). Of the two, only the first is of interest, and it also contains two subgroups: those going to work in the CBD and those headed to other kinds of destination. Only the passengers going to work--the first subgroup--are participants in the relationship, as the diagram shows.

The people who work in the CBD are given in the rows of Figure 12. The total employment of the CBD is reduced to the number who are present at work on any normal working weekday. The remainder is divided into two groups on the basis of their means of transportation to work. One group uses the subway, the other all other means. The subway riders subdivide further into two groups: those who pass through the cordons and those who do not (but enter the subway within the CBD--from home, railroad, bus, car, or other). Of these, only the first are participants in the relationship.

These two main groups intersect at only one

aggregate: the people who cross subway cordons on
their journey to work. There are no other intersec-
tions of the two populations. A measurement problem
thus arises to quantify this common aggregate. It
will be treated later in this section.

The Activities

The activities which interconnect the two phenomena are shown diagramatically on Figure 13. The
figure shows the sequence of activities by which subway passengers proceed from the cordon stations to
their places of employment in the CBD. After crossing the cordon, they continue to ride to their destination station (which may involve one or more transfers). They exit at destination stations and walk:
directly to their places of employment, or to some
intermediate stop such as an eating place or something else, after which they proceed to work. Deviations from this sequence of actions are negligible
in quantity, and probably irregular in occurrence.

FIGURE 13

CORDON STATION-TO-WORK ACTIVITIES

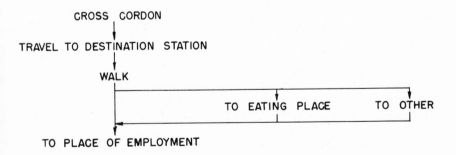

Timing

The two phenomena--linked by participants and
activities--are also joined together by time. Their
time relationship has two parts. One is activity

time--the amount which each activity in the sequence, as shown on Figure 13, requires for its performance. The total of this first part is the sum of all activity time, including such waiting, delays, and other random events which make up the normal journey to work.

The other part is the time between the last activity in the sequence--arrival at place of employment--and work schedule. When the participant has completed all the activities of the system, he reaches his place of employment. He may be early, late, or on time. In the relationship between work schedule and cordon count, this arrival-schedule variation must be incorporated.

The Composite

The system of work schedule and cordon count consists of the elements combined in some appropriate way. The elements were described in observable, phenomenological terms--as people, activities, and time. They may easily be abstracted into the variables of an equation of relationship, each one representing one of the terms which make cordon counts functionally related to work schedules. The description also indicates the operations which link the variables: the reductions of groups, and the distribution of people over time. A mathematical statement of the system can be produced from the description.

The next two steps in constructing the equation will be undertaken together. The elements and operations of the equation will be identified. At the same time, their numerical coefficients will be produced. These coefficients consist of specific numbers--in the form of scalars, vectors, and matrices--which provide the quantities by which work schedules become progressively modified into their corresponding cordon counts.

The Measures

The elements of the process have to be measured in order to provide the coefficients of the

relationship equation. Thus, if travel time is required between cordon station and destination, some
amount is needed. The amounts, for this and all the
other elements, will be presented here.

The process contains six measurable elements.
They will be presented in reverse process order,
starting from work schedule and proceeding backward
to the cordon count. This order is preferred because
all computations will follow the direction from work
schedule to cordon count. These elements are: present at work, lateness, cordon crossing, arrival,
travel-cordon interval assignment, and cordon station
distribution.

In considering the quantities assigned to these
elements, two things will stand out as significant.
The first is the analysis which produced each of
them. This will provide the elements and their
quantification with the definitions and meanings
which are needed in adapting them for forecasting
purposes. The second is the data and method by which
each was quantified. No claim is made that all elements in the process are represented, nor that the
quantities are final and definitive, nor that they
are applicable to other problems than the one at hand.
They are a first attempt to identify and measure the
relationship of work schedule and cordon count. They
are the most that could be achieved with the available data. As presented, they suit the needs of
this study.

Present At Work

The numbers of people shown on the work schedule tables include all those who work in the CBD,
both those present at work on any given workday and
those who are absent. It will be immediately obvious that subway passengers include only those who
are present at work. Accordingly, the employment
totals need to be reduced by an appropriate amount
so as to make them correspond to the numbers of
people present on any typical work day.

The reduction factor for this purpose was obtained from a survey of office absenteeism conducted regularly by the Commerce and Industry Association of New York. Table 51 gives the average annual absenteeism rate for offices in New York City for the years 1958-62. Over this five-year period a typical rate of absenteeism was 3 per cent. This amount serves as the basis of the adjustment. Accordingly, all work schedule numbers will be modified by a factor of 97 per cent so as to reduce total employment to the number estimated actually at work on a typical working day.

TABLE 51

Office Absentee Rates, Annual Daily Averages,
1958-62

Year	Daily Rate
1958	3.02
1959	2.80
1960	3.02
1961	3.04
1962	2.92

Source: Office Absenteeism and Turnover, Commerce and Industry Association, Fourth Quarterly Report, 1961 and Four Year Average, 1958-61; and Fourth Quarterly Report, 1962.

The small magnitude of this adjustment calls for a justification. The employment statistics themselves may be incorrect to a factor greater than this adjustment. Moreover, on statistical grounds the variation of the work schedule data from true values may exceed this amount. The use of this

adjustment may, therefore, worsen an existing underestimate of a prevailing overestimate. Hence, the
use of the factor may be questioned.

Its use is justified, however, on two grounds.
The first is that it is substantively correct to
include such a factor regardless of its magnitude.
The actual adjustment may, in fact, be lower than
it should be, but this does not gainsay the inherent
validity of the correction. Any equation of relationship of the two magnitudes must reflect this
offset to total employment. Secondly, there is a
need for reducing the total of employment to bring
it into better conformity to the cordon count statistics. Even this small percentage of reduction
is helpful in the desired direction.

Lateness

The work schedule times do not necessarily reflect the actual behaviors of the employees. In the
first place, the meaning of official starting time,
insofar as employees' conduct is concerned, depends
on the practices of the individual places of employment. Individual enterprises interpret the starting
time in various ways. Some make it the latest time
employees may punch time clocks without being considered late. Others treat it as the time employees
are required to cross the threshhold of the employer's premises. Some employers interpret the times
very strictly and obligate their employees to adhere
to the authorized times. Others allow substantial
leeway in either direction, early or late. The work
schedule study has brought to light many practices
by individual industries in regard to observance of
work schedule times.

In the course of the field studies it became
evident that a considerable amount of modification
of work schedules, both authorized and unauthorized,
actually takes place. People start earlier and stop
earlier than their official times. They also start
later and stop later than their official times. For
example, employees in the public departments of commercial banks must begin their work before the

official opening and starting time of 9:00 a.m.
People in retail and personal service industries
frequently begin before their official starting time.
Many executives, owners, managers, and employers,
especially of small enterprises, start earlier or
later than their stated starting times. Similarly,
at the close of the day there are varied practices.
Early stopping is by no means uncommon, especially
to avoid traffic congestion. Also late stopping,
whether as paid overtime or not, is quite common.
The regular work schedules denote the policy, the
legal commitment, the collective bargaining arrangement, and other official time specifications. Where
people's behaviors are concerned, however, allowance
must be made for some degree of deviation from the
schedules.

     For the topic at hand, the actual conduct of
employees is critically important. In any plan of
work staggering the official schedules are the devices which are subject to modification. However,
in the relationship of schedules to transit traffic,
it is the actual behaviors of people which create
the flow of traffic. Hence a method must be discovered by which to translate work schedules into
people's actual behavior.

     The first step in this process is to modify
the schedule data by the amount of lateness prevalent
in the CBD. Unfortunately, no specific studies of
lateness were found. Several were contemplated by
this Project, but for various reasons were not undertaken. Fortunately, from the resources of its own
research material, the Project was able to fashion
an acceptable substitute--a lateness adjustment
table. A full description of the data and methods
employed in constructing the table are contained
in Appendix N.

     Actually, two lateness adjustment tables were
constructed. One introduces lateness as a modifier
of work schedules starting at 8:00 a.m., the other
at 8:30 a.m. There is no basis of choice between
these two tables insofar as data or methods are
concerned. Lacking independent evidence, no

convincing assessment may be made as to their respective correspondence to actual behavior. The
only test is the way they adjust the work schedule
statistics.

The lateness adjustment tables, on the basis
of the sample data from which they were constructed,
apply to the total CBD working population. They
must therefore be used directly with the work schedule tables (as modified by the present-at-work adjustment). When so used they convert the original
work schedule data into the numbers of employees
actually starting work in the CBD by 15-minute time
intervals during the morning peak period.

The effects of the first two adjustment factors--
per cent present and lateness--are shown on Figure 14.
It gives the original CBD work schedule, and its
reduction by the per cent present (97.0) and the lateness adjustment starting at 8:30. (This one is used
because it provides the better result.) The present-
at-work adjustment makes an almost unnoticeable
change in the graph. The lateness adjustment shows
its first effects at 8:30, and then continues through
the rest of the distribution. It reduces the numbers
at 8:30, 8:45, and 9:00, and increases them at 9:15 and
9:30. Its effect is to shift people from their scheduled times to later actual starting times.

Cordon Crossing

The relationship under examination deals with a
special segment of the CBD working population--the
people who pass through subway cordons on their
journey to work in the CBD. Some of the people in
this segment of the population use other means of
transport before entering or after leaving the subway: Their special characteristic for present purposes is that they cross subway cordons to work. It
should also be noted that even this segment does not
include all persons who use the subway to work. A
substantial per cent of the people who work in the
CBD enter the subway within the CBD. These are
principally the people who arrive by other means of
transportation: by train, bus, ferry, or private

car. This group, however, does not belong to the
segment now under consideration.

One of the most obvious sources of discrepancy
between the work schedule and cordon count statistics
is the fact that the work schedules include all employees, both those who cross the cordons and those
who do not. In order to reduce the difference between the two series it becomes necessary to exclude
from the work schedule statistics all employees except those who cross subway cordons. The journey-to-
work portion of the sociological study provides very
detailed information on modes of travel. Estimates
of the proportion of cordon crossers of the total
population were therefore computed from the survey
data. Appendix O describes the data and the method
by which these estimates were made.

Two different adjustment factors were computed
for reducing the total population to those crossing
subway cordons. One is a fixed percentage of 67.1
per cent. This is the per cent of the total sample
which crosses subway cordons to work. (Another 9.6
enter the subway within the CBD. This gives an
estimated total 76.7 per cent of the people who work
in the CBD as subway riders to work.) The second
adjustment factor provides percentages of cordon
crossers by the times they actually start work. The
table discloses noticeable differences in the percentages at the various actual starting times. Some
variation might be expected because of the different
industry and occupational composition of the various
hours of the CBD work schedule. Accordingly, this
more elaborate presentation of the adjustment factor
was computed.

Both--the single and multiple (by start time)
percentages--are available for purposes of computation. In the test applied to present work schedules,
the multiple percentages are considered to provide
a slightly better result.

FIGURE 14

NUMBER OF PEOPLE WHO WORK IN THE CBD,
BY SCHEDULED START TIME
AND BY PRESENT-AT-WORK AND ACTUAL START TIME

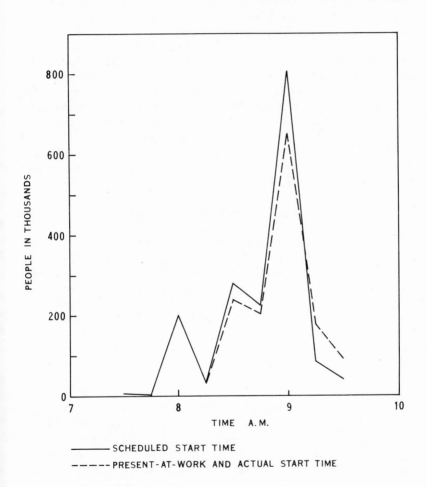

SCHEDULED START TIME

PRESENT-AT-WORK AND ACTUAL START TIME

261

The cordon crossing tables are computed on the
basis of actual start times. This means that they
have to be applied to work schedule data after the
adjustment for lateness. However, if applied to the
original work schedule data, it implies that lateness
is disregarded in the calculation; or alternatively,
that employees are assumed to start work at their
official starting times.

Figure 15 shows the further modification of
the work schedule table produced by adding the lateness adjustment. The figure also gives the work
schedule and its modification by the per cent present and lateness adjustments. The most pronounced
effect of this adjustment is to reduce the numbers
by an over-all one third. The figure actually uses
the multiple percentage table, so that the result--
not apparent on the figure--is a somewhat different
reduction at each time.

The Arrival Adjustment

From the viewpoint of subway traffic, the time
a person arrives at work is a more sensitive determinant of travel time than his official work schedule. The discrepancy between work schedule and
cordon count may arise, at least in part, precisely
because arrival times differ from official schedule
times. The sociological study provided information
on this subject. Appendix P presents a full account
of the original data and the construction of arrival
adjustment tables.

From the evidence of the sociological study, as
summarized in the arrival tables, the people who
work in the CBD have a practice to which very little
attention has heretofore been given. If these results are to be believed, considerable portions of
the CBD working population arrive at work well in
advance of the time they actually start work. (The
time they actually start means, of course, that lateness is already taken into account.) Now it is logically necessary that a person arrive at work before
he actually starts work. A difference, however small
must be expected in the two times. The evidence of

the tables indicates that the proportions of people
who arrive early are fairly large--on the average
59 per cent--and that they arrive anywhere from 15
minutes to an hour or an hour and a half before their
actual start times. The credibility of these findings is discussed in Appendix P.

The arrival table whose construction is described
in Appendix P incorporates both arrival at work and
arrival at a place of breakfast in the CBD, whichever
occurs earlier. Thus, for all but perhaps an in-
finitesimal fraction of the CBD working population
the arrival tables can be designated as arrival at
the first CBD destination. It is noted that the
tables are constructed for that portion of the total
population which crosses the subway cordons to work,
not for the entire CBD working population. They
therefore must enter the computation after the CBD
working population. They therefore must enter the
computation after the CBD population has been divided
between cordon crossers and all the rest.

There are two arrival tables presented in the
Appendix. One is a uniform set of percentages to be
applied to each actual start time. The other is a
table with particular sets of percentages for each
individual actual start time. Accordingly, the first
distributes the employees at each start time by the
same set of percentages, while the latter allows for
differing arrivals by people who actually start at
varying times.

The effect of the arrival adjustment upon the
modification of the work schedule is shown on Figure
16. This includes the progression of adjustments
given in preceding figures, as well as the modification produced by the arrival adjustment. It shows a
dramatic change in the distribution. The jaggedness
of the other three is eliminated, the peak is sharply
reduced, and the numbers are redistributed to the
earlier times. Figure 16 uses the variable percentage
table for the arrival adjustment because it produces
a more satisfactory result.

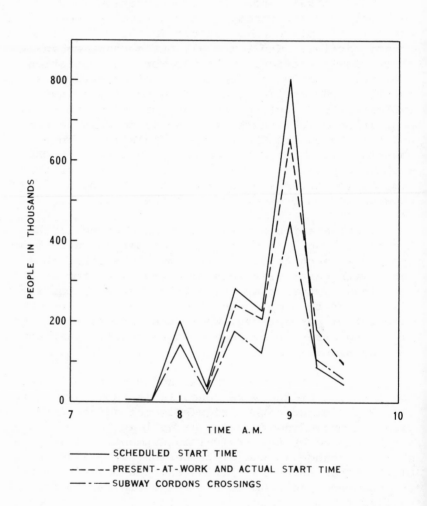

FIGURE 15

NUMBER OF PEOPLE WHO WORK IN THE CBD,
BY SCHEDULED START TIME,
BY PRESENT-AT-WORK AND ACTUAL START TIME,
AND BY SUBWAY CORDONS CROSSINGS

——————— SCHEDULED START TIME

— — — — — PRESENT-AT-WORK AND ACTUAL START TIME

—·——·—— SUBWAY CORDONS CROSSINGS

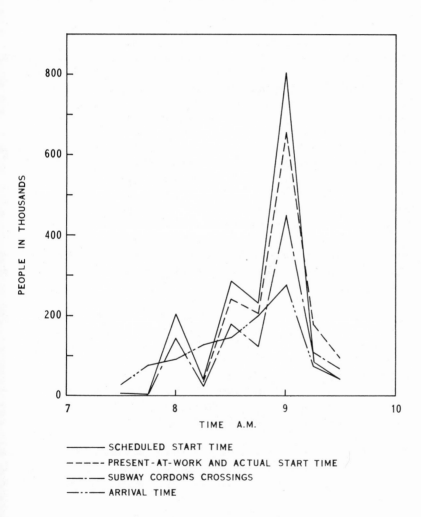

FIGURE 16

NUMBER OF PEOPLE WHO WORK IN THE CBD,
BY SCHEDULED START TIME,
BY PRESENT-AT-WORK AND ACTUAL START TIME,
BY SUBWAY CORDONS CROSSINGS,
AND BY ARRIVAL TIME

PEOPLE IN THOUSANDS

TIME   A.M.

———— SCHEDULED START TIME
————— PRESENT-AT-WORK AND ACTUAL START TIME
——.—— SUBWAY CORDONS CROSSINGS
——..—— ARRIVAL TIME

265

The Travel-Cordon Interval Assignment

The next two adjustments to the work schedule data will be considered together. These adjustments provide for travel time from cordon station to destination and the transfer from a 15- to a 20-minute time interval. They are dealt with together because they are incorporated into a single set of adjustment tables.

An obvious reason for the difference between the cordon count and work schedule is the travel time between cordon station and destination. This travel time consists, for all but an exceedingly minute proportion of the population, of two distinct parts. One part is train time (including transfer time) between cordon station and destination station. This time can be determined with a high degree of accuracy It consists of the train running time plus an allowance for transfer time. The second part is walking time from the train to the persons' destination, whether work or eating place. Some people may have other prior destinations or may use another means of transport after leaving the subway in the CBD. These, however, are considered to be so few that neglecting them will not affect the resulting statistics.

Travel time also has another dimension which was quantified by the sociological study. The actual train time from cordon station to destination needs to be weighted by the proportion of people traveling from each cordon station to each destination station with the CBD. The nature of these data and their use in constructing the travel-cordon interval adjustment are described fully in Appendix Q.

The second component of this adjustment consists of a device by which to relate the 15-minute interval of the work schedule data (as by now modified) to the 20-minute cordon count interval. The table incorporates this factor, again as weighted by travel time.

This element produces twenty-one separate tables one for each cordon station and one composite table f

the CBD as a whole. These tables enter the computation after the arrival has been computed, and they
carry total employment from arrival at work to passage through each cordon station.

The effect of this factor will be shown below,
in the evaluation of the equation of relationship.

The Station Distributions

Taken together, the adjustments deliver the
total cordon crossing employment to each cordon station and to the composite of all the stations. It
is next necessary to subdivide the total into the
number traveling through each station. For this
purpose another adjustment is needed--the per cent
per cordon station.

Two possibilities are available for distributing the total to the individual station. One is
to use a single per cent of passengers for each cordon station representing its average proportion of
the total a.m. rush hour count. This single percentage would be applied to each number resulting
from the preceding computation. It would assign
the fixed per cent of the total to each cordon interval of the station. The other method is to use a
percentage for each interval of each station. These
percentages are obtained by computing, for each cordon interval, each station's per cent of the interval
total. They are given in Appendix Table 23.

For purposes of computing the relationship, the
second method--multiple per cents per station--was
used. This was determined on logical grounds. The
single percentages per station will reduce the totals
to station distributions closely resembling the CBD
total. Since the station patterns differ (see
Appendix Table 7), such a result would be undesirable.
Hence, to give effect to the particular contours of
each station, the multiple per cent method was used.

The effect of this final factor will be taken
up in the evaluation of the equation of relationship.

The Equation

All the elements of the relationship for which
suitable data are available have now been derived
and quantified. The results will be briefly examined
and thereafter the equation of relationship will be
formulated. An evaluation of the equation will conclude this section.

A system linking work schedule and cordon count
was described at the outset. It was abstracted into
three elements, the participants, the activities, and
timing. Figures 12 and 13 diagrammed the composition
of the first two elements. It is now appropriate to
compare the results of the derivations with the described structure of the system.

The first element of the relationship is the
participants. They were shown in Figure 12 to be the
intersection of the people who cross the subway cordons and work in the CBD. Three of the adjustment
factors deal with the participants. The present-at-
work factor and the cordon crossing adjustment reduce
the working population to the subgroup which crosses
the cordons to work. The cordon station assignment
table distributes the employee-passenger group to
the individual cordon stations through which they
travel. Thus, the horizontal population shown on
Figure 12 has been suitably refined to the participants in the relationship.

It has not been possible, however, to find the
subset of all subway passengers crossing the cordons
who are traveling to work in the CBD. Thus the verti
cal population given on Figure 12 remains whole.
There are no data available by which to subdivide the
passengers crossing cordons into the subgroup of
participants in the relationship. The problem was
briefly discussed in Chapter 2 and will again be
treated late in this chapter. For the present, the
problem remains open and unsolved.

The second element of the relationship consists
of activities, as shown on Figure 12. The activities

were measured, in the adjustment tables, by the
times they require. All the activities shown on the
figure are incorporated in the tables by suitable
allowed times. The possible individual and minor
exceptions to the activity pattern were not taken into account.

The third element, time, is represented in the
remaining three adjustment tables. The lateness and
arrival adjustments redistribute the participants by
the times at which they actually start work and arrive at work. These are the two factors which connect the sequence of activities with the work schedule. They make up the final difference--plus, minus,
or zero--between the time people arrive at work and
the time they are scheduled. The travel time-cordon
interval assignment also distributes the participants
by time. The first part accounts for all the activity shown on Figure 13--from crossing the cordon to
arriving at the destination. The second part is
supposed to be entirely statistical--it regroups the
numbers taken from the 15-minute work schedule intervals into the 20-minute cordon count intervals. It
should have no effect on the results other than this
systematic expansion of the intervals. These three
tables cover all the time components of the relationship.

Out of these elements, now represented by the
various adjustment factors, the equation of relationship can be constructed. No equation can consist
only of these elements because they are the only
ones for which suitable tables (coefficients) could
be computed. Undoubtedly, other elements ought to
appear in the relationship equation. A factor reducing the cordon count to the people who work in
the CBD is clearly essential--but not available.
Later it will be seen that a more refined way of con-
necting work schedule to cordon station is desirable--
but also not yet available. The equation, necessarily limited by the elements which can be successfully
quantified, is not for that reason unacceptable. It
remains to determine by actual computation--just how
effective it really is.

The elements were also quantified in the preceding section, but the quantities can only be evaluated in combination, as they operate in the whole
equation of relationship. Each table is individually
evaluated insofar as possible in the appendix in
which it is derived.

The equation of relationship will now be formulated mathematically, but in simplified form. The
terms will be defined and then the equation will be
presented. A full definition of terms and the complete equation is given in Appendix R.

Let:

A = the present CBD work schedule
p = the per cent present at work
D = the lateness adjustment
K = the cordon crossing adjustment
E = the arrival adjustment
T = the travel time-cordon interval as-
    signment
S = the per cent per cordon station in-
    terval
G = the computed cordon count

Then, the equation of relationship is:

$$G = p\,A\,D\,K\,E\,T\,S$$

In words, the equation works as follow:

The computed cordon count (G) is produced by
multiplying the CBD work schedule (A--the number
scheduled to start work at each time) by each of the
factors in the order given--the per cent present at
work (p), the lateness adjustment (D), the cordon
crossing adjustment (K), the arrival adjustment (E),
the travel time-cordon interval assignment (T), and
the per cent per cordon station interval (S).

Evaluation

The ultimate question now arises: Is this
equation acceptable? Ordinarily this question is

answered by comparing the computed results with a
standard. If the difference between the standard
and the computation is, by some criterion, not excessive, the equation is judged acceptable. In the
present case, however, there is no truly reliable
standard. The conclusion will have to be reached,
at least in part, by qualitative rather than quantitative means.

The evaluation will have two parts. In the
first, the equation will be applied to the total
CBD, treating all the individual cordon stations as
a single aggregate. This is the way the preceding
analysis was conducted. In the second part, the
equation will be evaluated for the individual cordon
stations.

The Total CBD

The computation (G) for the total CBD is presented in Figure 17. The figure also contains the
October, 1962, cordon count (as modified by the cordon interval pattern and the truncation adjustment.
See Chapter 2.) For present purposes, Figure 17
should be compared with Figure 11, which presents
the original work schedule data along with the October, 1962, cordon count. The comparison of the two
figures reveals the effectiveness of the equation.

Using the present work schedule (Figure 11) and
the October, 1962, cordon count (Figures 11 and 17)
as standards of comparison, the equation of relationship proves highly successful. By means of the
equation, the work schedule is converted to a computed cordon count which closely resembles the actual
one. In particular, the equation reduces the peak,
eliminates the jaggedness, and redistributes the
numbers to earlier and later times. It produces a
distribution whose contours are similar to those of
the cordon count.

The effectiveness of the equation goes even
further. During the early and late periods--up
to 8:00 and after 9:00--the computed count falls

below the actual, with the gap narrowing toward 8:00
and widening after 9:00. If the gap is interpreted
as the subway passengers whose destinations are not
places of employment in the CBD--the other riders--it
corresponds very closely to what might reasonably be
expected. As the rush hour approaches the peak on
both sides, the number of riders who are not travelin
to work in the CBD diminishes. The computed amounts
in the periods 6:40 to 8:00 and 9:00 to 10:00 are thu
startlingly close to what actual conditions are
thought to be.

On the other hand, the computed amounts for the
period 8:00 to 9:00 exceed the actual ones--a result
which is wholly illogical, if correct. There cannot
be more passengers who work in the CBD than the total
number of passengers. Just as in the other intervals
the amounts between 8:00 and 9:00 should be less than
or equal to, but by no means greater than the actual
cordon counts.

At this juncture, the issue raised in Chapter 2
again appears. Are the cordon counts accurate, particularly during the 8:00 to 9:00 rush hours? It
was argued, on various grounds, that the counts
understate the number of passengers during the congested intervals. If this is so, then the computed
counts during these intervals are not incorrect
simply because they do not accord with the computed
ones. If the true counts were known, the computed
counts might prove correct--or at least not so far
from the true ones as from the reported ones.

To evaluate the equation, it is thus necessary
to treat the cordon count in an unusual way. Based
upon previous findings, the October, 1962, count--as
modified by the cordon interval pattern and the truncation adjustment--serves as an acceptable standard
for all intervals except during 8:00 to 9:00, when it
is too low. On this basis, the equation is judged an
effective and valid expression of the relationship
between the CBD work schedule and the total CBD
cordon count--if the count were entirely accurate.

FIGURE 17

ACTUAL AND COMPUTED CORDON COUNTS

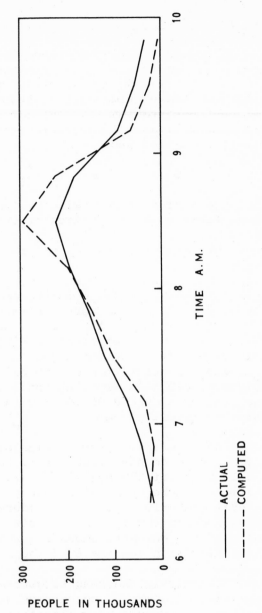

273

The Individual Stations

The same equation was used to compute cordon
counts for each of the twenty entering cordon stations. This was done by applying the individual
stations' travel time-cordon interval assignment and
per cent per station interval adjustment factors to
the computations. The equation was thus changed
slightly, as follows:

$$G^z = p\ A\ D\ K\ E\ T^z\ S^z$$

The superscripts z following G, T and S signify that
these terms apply to particular stations (z).

The results of these computations can be readily
summarized.

In all cases, the computed amounts are free of
the jaggedness of the work schedule, and the contours
are quite similar to the station counts. They also
fall below the cordon counts during the intervals
before and after the congested period, thus allowing
the same interpretation of the gap as was made for
the total CBD. As with the total CBD, the computed
amounts during the 8:00 to 9:00 intervals are higher
than the reported ones.

The principal discrepancies between the computed
and reported counts occur during the congested period,
the location of the peak interval. In fourteen of the
stations, there is no discrepancy, apart from the
general one arising from the underestimate of the
actual cordon counts. But in six of the stations, the
shape of the computed amounts was judged only in fair
conformity with the shape of the reported.

In general, the results corroborate the conclusion reached above in connection with the total CBD.
The equation proved very effective for fourteen of
the stations, and fairly so for the remaining six.

Summary

Within the limits required by this study the investigation produced a satisfactory and useful result. The adjustment factors, as identified and quantified, bring the work schedule statistics into sufficient conformity with the cordon count to serve as a basis for constructing the forecasting equation. The results are regarded as successful and effective first achievements, not as the final terms and parameters of the relationship in question.

The Reconstructed Cordon Count

The difference in the 8:00 to 9:00 amounts--as between the reported cordon count and the computations of the equation--will produce difficulties later in this study. It is accordingly desirable to make yet another modification in the count.

A reconstructed cordon count for the eleven intervals, 6:20-10:00 a.m. is given in Table 52. This table was developed by using the October, 1962, cordon count (modified by the cordon interval pattern and the truncation adjustment) for all except the three intervals in question, 8:00 to 9:00. For these intervals, the computations produced by the equation of relationship are used.

This method of reconstruction makes no allowance for passengers other than CBD employees during the three intervals. Such an allowance seemed inappropriate because of the crudeness of the method and because the results have to serve computational needs more than substantive ones. The reconstruction adds a total of 113,294 to the count, or 9 per cent. By interval, the additions are: 4,060 or 2 per cent to 8:00-8:20; 69,510 or 31 per cent to 8:20-8:40; and 39,724 or 21 per cent to 8:40-9:00. These are substantial increases, both over-all and during the later two intervals.

TABLE 52

The Reconstructed Cordon Count

Intervals	The October, 1962 Count, Adjusted[a]	The Computed Cordon Count	The Adjusted Minus the Computed	The Reconstructed Cordon Count
6:20-6:40	25,582	27,056	-1,474	25,582
6:40-7:00	43,995	16,539	27,456	43,995
7:00-7:20	74,844	36,850	37,994	74,844
7:20-7:40	121,283	101,960	19,323	121,283
7:40-8:00	156,689	149,776	6,913	156,689
8:00-8:20	198,934	202,994	-4,060	202,994
8:20-8:40	225,249	294,759	-69,510	294,759
8:40-9:00	186,824	226,548	-39,724	226,548
9:00-9:20	93,982	65,098	28,884	93,982
9:20-9:40	52,992	21,832	31,160	52,992
9:40-10:00	37,249	6,735	30,514	37,249

[a] Adjusted for cordon interval pattern and truncation.

THE FORECASTING EQUATION

The equation of relationship applies to present
work schedules and cordon counts. From this relationship, an equation for forecasting cordon counts,
given alternative work schedules, will be wrought.
For reasons which will appear shortly, it is not
possible, either theoretically or even computationally, to proceed directly from the equation of relationship to the forecasting equation.

The development of the forecasting equation
will occupy three sections in this portion of the
chapter. Immediately following, the problem in constructing the forecasting equation will be presented.
There it will be shown that the adjustment factors
contained in the equation of relationship must be
examined for the applicability to the forecasting
equation. The next section will analyze the adjustment factors. It will reach conclusions respecting
their suitability, both qualitative and quantitative, to the forecasting equation. The final section will present the equation, define its properties, and specify the procedure for applying it.

The Problem

It would be reasonable to suppose that alternative work schedules could be transformed into cordon
counts by using the equation of relationship. This
would simply require substituting, in the equation
of relationship, the alternative for the present
schedule and thus produce a forecast of employee-
passengers. This procedure rests on the premise that
the journey-to-work process, including all its
elapsed time requirements, will remain unchanged
under the alternative work schedules. Unfortunately,
this direct and simple method proves unacceptable,
for several reasons.

First, its results would understate the cordon
counts by some unknown amounts, representing the
other riders in the subway. This underestimate can
be avoided by using a net difference method in

computing cordon counts. In this method, the numbers of people starting work, according to present
schedules, are subtracted from the numbers in the
alternative schedules, giving a remainder or net
difference in the numbers scheduled to start work
at each time. These net differences, some positive
and some negative, are then added to the appropriate
interval counts, producing the changes in the cordon
counts corresponding to the effects of the changed
work schedules. The net difference method, under
existing circumstances, is a valid one and is
actually employed in the final forecasting equation.
But this method cannot be used without first determining where the subtraction must take place--at the
scheduled start, actual start, arrival, or crossing
the cordons. This requires a prior solution of the
second difficulty.

The second reason for not accepting, a priori,
the equation of relationship as a forecasting equation stems from strong theoretical considerations.
The adjustment factors employed in the equation of
relationship represent and quantify the travel practices of the people who work in the CBD under present schedules. A change in work schedules will affect the basis of these travel practices. Indeed,
it may even affect the behaviors of the people whose
work schedules are not changed. Hence, it cannot be
assumed that the adjustment factors operative under
present schedules will continue under changed ones.
A change in work schedules can produce changes in
travel by various means. The change in schedule
itself, disregarding all other consequences, may
compel some people to modify their travel arrangements. It can modify the time requirements for certain essential interoccupational relations, which
may, as a consequence, produce changes in travel
patterns. This change in schedule may--and it is so
intended--produce some relief in subway congestion,
and this can cause consequent changes in travel
practices. There are also many other kinds of
changes in personal and social life which might follow from modifications in work schedules and thereby
affect the travel practices of the people who work
in the CBD.

These considerations go to the bases of the adjustment factors as well as to their particular percentages. They raise the questions: Will these factors continue to operate under conditions created by alternative work schedules? And if so, in the same amounts as at present?

The applicability of the adjustment factors to the forecasting model will be analyzed in the three sections which follow. The first section will deal with the present-at-work, cordon crossing, and travel time-cordon interval assignment factors. It will show, after brief examination, that they are immediately adaptable to the forecasting equation. The second section will deal with the per cent per cordon station and will show that station forecasts cannot be made. The third section will analyze the lateness and arrival adjustments. It will disclose the use and limitation of these adjustment factors in forecasting the effects of work schedule change.

Present-at-Work, Cordon Crossing, and
Travel Time-Cordon Interval
Adjustments

The adjustment factor for the per cent of employees at work can be used in the forecast equation exactly as in the present relationship one. The 97 per cent is regarded as unrelated to work schedule and unaffected by interoccupational relations or subway congestion. Nor are there any grounds for the belief that this per cent will shift systematically in any direction within the proximate future. Hence, it will be retained in the forecast model.

Cordon Crossing

The cordon crossing adjustment employed in the relationship between present schedules and present cordon counts used a different percentage for each of the actual starting times. These percentages, as described in Appendix O, were taken from the sociological study. The information they convey is that the subway riders or cordon crossers

form different proportions of the employee group at
different parts of the normal work day. The varying
percentages in the table give effect to these different proportions of subway riders.

The forecasting problem which this table creates
is: Will these proportions change if work schedules
are changed? Alternatively, are the proportions by
time independent of work schedules? If they are independent of work schedules, then the same adjustment table can be used for forecasting. If, however,
the proportions using the subway at various times actually depend on work schedules, then the same table
cannot be used for alternative schedules as for the
present ones, since under the alternative schedules
people will be traveling and arriving presumably at
different times.

It seems obvious that the percentages crossing
subway cordons are not independent of work schedules.
The differing proportions reflect industry and occupational schedules, which in turn draw upon varying
proportions of subway riders and nonsubway riders.

It follows that a change in work schedules will
change the proportions of the cordon crossing table.
If an industry whose labor force is made up of subway riders is shifted to an earlier or later time,
this shift will unquestionably modify the proportions. Unfortunately, there is no way of determining the changes in proportions which might follow
work schedule changes. The loss of contact with individual numbers, as noted earlier, is partly responsible for this. But even more so, the degree of
detail which would be necessary in the basic statistical data to trace out the effects of schedule
change on subway rider proportions by 15-minute intervals would be enormous and far beyond the scope
of this study. Fortunately, this loss is not a significant one for the results being pursued.

In lieu of a cordon crossing percentage table--
or set of tables--reflecting alternative schedules
for various segments of the working population, the

average percentage will be employed for each time interval. The sample per cent of the total population
who cross cordons to work is 67.1 per cent. This is
the adjustment factor which will be used in the forecast.

Travel Time-Cordon Interval Assignment Factor

The travel time-cordon interval assignment
tables are composed of two bodies of data. They are:
(1) the travel time from cordon station to destination station; and (2) the 15- to 20-minute interval
assignment table.

It is considered unlikely that a change in
schedule will affect any of these underlying factors
in a systematic or significant way. Accordingly,
the travel time-cordon interval assignment tables
will be retained for the forecasting equation in the
same forms and quantities as in the present relationship equation.

Per Cent per Cordon Station

At its next-to-last operation, the relationship
equation calculates the number of passengers per interval of each station--as though all CBD employee-
passengers traveled through each station. This is
the result of the computation of pALKET. The last
operation reduces these totals to the number estimated for each station interval. Two reduction
tables were developed for this purpose, one a single
percentage for all intervals of each station; the
other a multiple set of percentages, one for each interval of each station. Both were tried, and only
the latter--the multiple percentages--produced satisfactory results in the relationship equation.

The question now arises: Which if any of these
tables can be used in forecasting?

It turns out, after analysis of the problem,
that neither can be used. The consequence is that

forecasts cannot be made for the individual stations.
However, this does not prevent aggregate forecasts
for the total CBD.

The single per cents per cordon station cannot
be used because they impose the cordon interval pattern of the total CBD upon the station forecasts.
This imposition occurs because the single per cent
assigns a fixed proportion of the CBD total--or net
difference--to each station interval. This is precisely what happened when the single percentages
were used in the relationship equation--each station's count was a miniature replica of the CBD.
But, it was shown in Chapter 2 that the individual
stations have very distinctive patterns, and that
many of them differ markedly from the CBD pattern.
Hence, if the total is forced upon the individual
stations, the resulting forecasts will be inaccurate.

The multiple percentages per cordon station cannot be used in forecasting because they distribute
the station passengers on the basis of present work
schedules, not the new ones. The percentages are derived from the prevailing cordon counts. They, in
turn, are governed by the times people now travel to
work--presumably to meet present work schedules. If
schedules are changed, the numbers per station interval will also change. And the percentages per station interval must also be expected to change in accordance with the new schedule. Moreover, the
diverse cordon interval patterns suggest that the
effects of any alternative work schedule will be experienced differently by the individual stations.
Therefore, the station interval percentages must be
expected to change in different ways. To distribute
the total CBD passengers--or the net differences--on
the basis of the old percentages will inevitably distort the results and make them useless.

Since neither set of tables can be used, it follows that forecasts cannot be made for the individual
stations. An aggregate forecast for the total CBD
can be made, but the totals per interval cannot be
distributed to the stations in any meaningful way.

To forecast the station counts, the entire procedure of establishing a forecasting method would
have to be revised. This would be desirable, but
the necessary data are not now available. In essence, it would be necessary to distribute both the
present and alternative work schedules by cordon
station before any of the subsequent computations
are begun. To make this distribution, it would be
necessary to establish the patterns of employment by
cordon station passengers. This in turn would require still other computations, both as to present
and alternative distributions by industry, schedule,
and cordon station. In effect, the relationship
would have to be established in twenty ways--one for
each station, and probably by industry. Apart from
the magnitude of such a task, the essential data are
not at hand.

The Arrival Adjustment

The lateness and early arrival adjustments pose
computational and theoretical problems. The computational problems arise from the multiple percentage
tables in which each row (start time) has its own
set of percentages. The theoretical problems are
those stated earlier: Will these adjustments remain
in effect under conditions of alternative work schedules? And if so, according to what percentages?

The computational problem resolves itself, at
least in part. The lateness adjustment must remain
the same in the forecasting equation as in the equation of relationship, if it is used at all. There
is no available basis for adapting it to the particular conditions created by the computations under alternative work schedules. This, however, creates
less difficulty than it might at first appear. The
lateness percentages were virtually the same for all
times except 8:30 a.m. Hence, the use of these percentages in most of the shifts will make little difference in the results. The 8:30 percentages are
slightly less than the others. There will therefore
be a bias toward reducing the amount of lateness on
the part of those people shifted from 8:45 and 9:00

a.m. to 8:30. This, however, accords with certain
conclusions reached later in this section.

The arrival adjustment can be adapted to the
forecasting computations. It will be recalled that
two tables were prepared for the arrival adjustments:
one with different sets of percentages for each
starting time and one with a uniform set of percentages were utilized in the equation of relationship. A reasonably satisfactory adaptation can be
made by using the uniform percentages for arrival
under the alternative work schedules.

The theoretical problem pertains to the travel
behavior of people after work schedules have been
changed. This behavior is now expressed by the lateness and arrival tables. For forecasting purposes,
it is necessary to decide whether the tables will
continue in effect at all; and if so, whether their
percentages will be modified in any way by an alternative work schedule. But before reaching any decision concerning quantities it is necessary to consider the behavior which the tables quantify. Will
people continue to arrive early and late after their
schedules have been changed? It may then be asked:
How might a change in work schedules affect the procedure and the timing of people's arrival at work?

Analysis of the Problem

Arrival at work is an individual act which each
person times, insofar as he can, to suit his requirements: personal, family, other, social, work, and
the like. It is an act, however, which is governed
or restricted to a significant extent by certain
identifiable external conditions. The play of individual behavior occurs within the limits allowed
by these externals. The only possibility of forecasting future arrival practices lies in discovering
how these external, nonindividual, nonpersonal factors control arrival now. Then, by projecting them
into the future--when schedules will have changed according to some systematic plan--it might be possible
to forecast future arrival patterns.

Of these external determinants, the principal
one is subway congestion. Some people arrive early--
others come late--because they cannot get subway
transportation when their work schedules need it, or
because they choose to avoid the worst of the crush.
In either case, the result is the same: early or
late arrival. A second determinant resides in occupational practices. Certain occupations are known
to come to work early in order to get a head start
on the day's work. These include executives, owners,
managers, supervisors, and others with independent
occupational responsibilities. Similarly, many occupations in the business-professional category are
persistent late arrivals.

There are also many other determinants of arrival
times, but which are less distinct or which affect
fewer numbers of people. Among these are transportation arrangements under which some people use cars
(pools), trains, or buses having fixed schedules,
and then take the subway through the cordon stations.
Another important determinant of arrival is the tolerance of the place of employment to arrival before
or after the scheduled time. Beyond these, there
are the purely personal and social reasons which
will undoubtedly operate no matter what happens to
the external conditions.

The forecast of early and late arrival which
will be developed here will be based upon two lines
of inquiry. The first and most important will be an
analysis of congestion as a determinant of arrival.
The second will be a more general appreciation of
how schedule change and its occupational effects
might be expected to influence arrival.

The general results of the inquiry will be
stated at once.

First, it will be shown that the early and late
arrivals depend largely on whether subway capacity
is sufficient to meet the demand for service. Hence,
any forecast of the arrival adjustments must be associated with an anticipated level of traffic in the
system in relation to capacity.

Second, it will be urged that the rearrangement of work schedules as projected in this study--regardless of their effects on congestion--will create a predisposition to reduce the present amounts of early and late arrival at work.

Finally, it will be concluded that some minimal amount of early and late arrival, growing out of personal and individual considerations, will inevitably remain.

After the analysis, it will be possible to apply these general results to constructing the forecasting model.

Arrival and Congestion

Early and late arrival will now be shown to be a by-product, at least in part, of subway congestion. This will tend to confirm the common assertion that people come to work early or late in order to avoid subway congestion. The finding, however, will produce other far-reaching consequences for the forecasting of cordon counts and for work schedule changes.

Train congestion is measured by the ratio of passengers to capacity. It is not necessary, for present purposes, to decide when the ratio is too high, or what the ratio might be at the boundary between a comfortable and an uncomfortable ride. It is valuable merely to establish that congestion is measured by these two quantities: capacity and the number of passengers. They furnish a basis for investigating the relationship between arrival and congestion.

The relationship of capacity to the number of passengers during the October, 1962, cordon count is shown graphically on Figure 18. The figure provides two cordon counts, one the actual and the other the reconstructed count. For present purposes, the reconstructed count is the more suitable, although the conclusion will not differ no matter which one is

FIGURE 18

CAPACITY AND CORDON COUNT

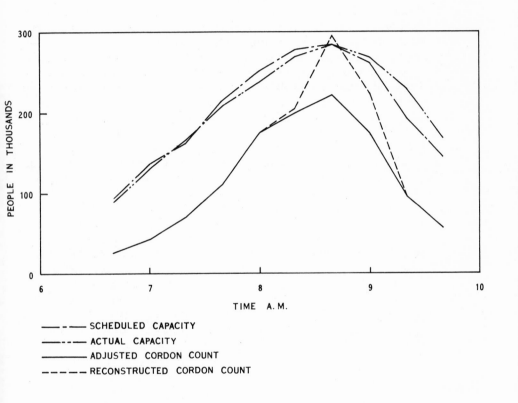

SCHEDULED CAPACITY
ACTUAL CAPACITY
ADJUSTED CORDON COUNT
RECONSTRUCTED CORDON COUNT

used. The fact that the reconstructed count exceeds
capacity at the peak causes no concern. The Transit
Authority's measure of capacity is explicitly less
than the maximum, and considerably below the observed numbers of people in cars. (See Chapter 2
and Appendix H.)

Similarly, there are two capacity lines--both
derived from the October, 1962, cordon count--one the
actual capacity and the other the scheduled capacity.
For the interpretations about to be made, the differences between the two are negligible. Accordingly,
reference hereafter will be made only to capacity
without distinguishing between them. It should also
be noted that there is no question about the accuracy of the capacity data as there has been about
the cordon count statistics. The capacities are
based upon the number of trains and cars which are
obtained from observations, full counts, and records.
Hence, they do not suffer from the deficiencies of
the cordon counts.

Figure 18 shows that during the peak period,
8:20-8:40, the trains had their greatest congestion
whether measured by the actual or reconstructed
counts. In the intervals next to the peak, 8:00-
8:20 and 8:40-9:00, congestion was less than the
peak, but still high. The trains were about 75 per
cent full during the earlier interval (by both
counts) and during the later interval about 67 per
cent full by the actual count. The per cent full
diminishes as the figure proceeds outward along the
slopes of the curves.

Figure 18 must now be interpreted with reference to the problem under investigation: the relationship, if any, between subway congestion and
arrival. This interpretation will require one additional datum which is shown on Figure 19. This may
be called the "absolute" demand for passenger service, by people who work in the CBD, at all cordon
stations during 20-minute intervals. Figure 19 presents both cordon count and the actual capacity

FIGURE 19
CAPACITY, CORDON COUNT, AND ABSOLUTE DEMAND

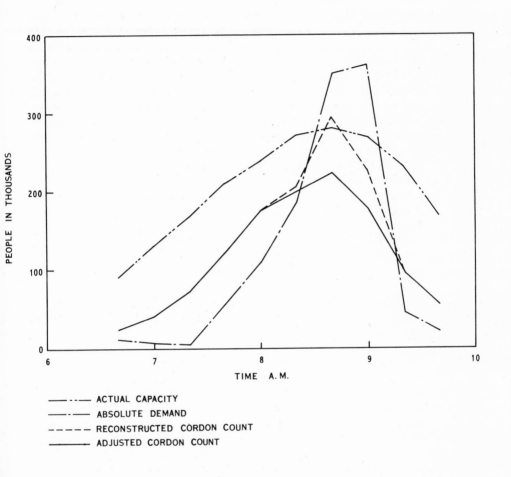

————·—— ACTUAL CAPACITY
————·—— ABSOLUTE DEMAND
— — — — RECONSTRUCTED CORDON COUNT
———————— ADJUSTED CORDON COUNT

statistics given on the previous figure along with
the additional one of absolute demand.

The absolute demand consists of the present
CBD work schedule adjusted for the number present
at work (97.0 per cent), the number who cross subway
cordons (67.1 per cent), and for travel time and cordon interval assignment. These are the same adjustment factors derived in the earlier section of this
chapter. Explicitly excluded are the lateness and
early arrival adjustments. The resulting statistics,
as shown on Figure 19, are the numbers of people
under present schedules who would cross subway cordons during each interval--if they arrived at work
on time ($\pm$ 7 1/2 minutes)--neither late nor early.
This is their "absolute demand for service." It
should be noted that demand of riders other than
those who work in the CBD is excluded from these
data.

At the present time the capacity of the system
at the cordon stations during a 20-minute interval
is somewhat below 300,000 passengers. This is a
little more than the actual capacity. Thus, the actual capacity shown on Figure 19 is at or only a
little below, the system's capacity during the peak
period.

Figure 19 makes it clear beyond any doubt that
the subway system cannot satisfy the absolute demand
for service by the people who work in the CBD during
the peak period of 8:20-8:40, nor during the next
highest period, 8:00-8:20. It cannot satisfy this
demand at its actual, scheduled, or full capacity.

Because the absolute demand for service is
greater during these two peak periods than the system's capacity, there is an excess unsatisfied demand during these periods. This excess consists of
the people whose work schedules would require travel
during these peak periods, but who cannot ride the
subway then because it is already overcrowded. The
excess demand for service must, therefore, be met at
other times (or by other modes of travel). A redistribution of passengers by travel times is forced

into being by the existence of a capacity limit.

This redistribution is revealed by Figure 19. The absolute demand is greater than the cordon count during the two peak intervals, but is less than the cordon count in the other intervals. The excess of people who cannot ride the subway during the peak intervals apparently shift their travel to earlier or later intervals, when the cordon counts show more people than the work schedules furnish. These people must be the ones who create the early and late arrival percentages. Forced to travel at times other than optimal, from the viewpoint of work schedule, some people arrive early and others late--the choice depending, among other things, on the amount of lateness which their places of employment will tolerate.

If people were able to travel to work on the subway at times most convenient to their work schedules, the cordon counts would assume the shape of the absolute demand line on Figure 19. Since the system's capacity cannot satisfy the absolute demand, the people who work in the CBD must modify their travel times. The result, achieved over many years of adaptation by passengers and by the Transit Authority, takes the form of the cordon count. These counts are not the real demand for passenger service by time interval. They are a distortion of the real demand--a distortion whose measure is provided by the early and late arrival adjustments.

From Figure 19, a second generalization is drawn. The limitations of subway capacity which compel people to travel earlier or later than their schedules require give rise, as a principal cause, to the lateness and early arrival practices. Moreover, the people who shift their travel times from the peak create congestion in the intervals to which they shift and thus cause people who travel in these intervals to modify their travel times. The effects of capacity limitations are not confined to the peak period, but are diffused over the intervals preceding and following it. This spreads the early and late arrival practices to other work schedule times.

Other Determinants of Arrival

There are many other determinants of early and late arrival, in addition to congestion. Most of these are personal and individual, and there is no way of telling how they will be affected by a change in work schedule and its concomitant effects. It is presumed here that some people will continue to arrive early and others late no matter what happens to work schedules, and that there will always be some small amount of adjustment required. It is possible, however, to consider briefly other identifiable determinants and to consider how they might be affected by the projected change in work schedules.

The two determinants which will be examined are interoccupational relations and work schedules. The first, interoccupational relations, governs arrival in a negative kind of way. One of the reasons lateness is tolerated in many CBD establishments is because it does not interfere with interoccupational relations during the very early part of the day. The question therefore arises: Will schedule change in the CBD affect this determinant? Work schedules also stimulate an inquiry because they will undergo change. All other things being equal, how will the change in work schedules as such affect arrival times? Because both of these determinants are closely related, they can be discussed together.

The schedule changes which are projected in this study ought to produce a tendency to arrive at work on time, or at least closer to on time than at present. This is based on two assumptions about people and places of employment. The first assumption is that for many people, early arrival entails a waste of time. Given a choice, they would prefer to arrive closer to their scheduled starting time. The consequence of this assumption is that in any readjustment of schedules, people will, if possible, reduce the amount of early arrival. The second assumption is that places of employment find lateness, for many reasons, an undesirable conduct. From this it follows that the toleration of lateness

on the part of places of employment will tend to diminish if there is any increase in its amount.
These assumptions may now be utilized in assessing
the consequences of the projected schedule changes.

The schedule changes projected in this study
will, by design, modify the times of interoccupational relations. In general, every effort has been
made to take up the slack in the time for interoccupational relations. Thus, for example, the business-
professional occupations which are predominantly
scheduled to start at 9:00, but which, in fact,
actually start at 9:30 or later, have been set
at a 9:30 starting time. All other things being
constant, the lateness prevalent among these occupations will be reduced significantly by the proposed
schedule changes. Similar adjustments have been
made for others.

The conclusion is therefore reached that the
tolerance of lateness as a consequence of interoccupational relationships ought to be substantially reduced by the schedule changes projected in this
study. Not only the tolerance, but the feasibility
of such lateness can be expected to diminish. It is
therefore concluded, on this ground alone, that a reduction in the lateness adjustment might be anticipated after a change in work schedules.

The schedule changes as such also ought to con-
duce a reduction in early and late arrivals. The
principal changes projected in this study are away
from 9:00 to 8:30 and earlier and to 9:30. The
shifts to earlier starting schedules will enable
large numbers of people, who now arrive early at
work, to maintain their present travel times and
still come to work on time. This will have the net
effect of reducing the early arrival percentages.
On the other hand, the shift to 9:30 starting time
applies to the principal occupations which now contribute to lateness. Their new starting times will
coincide much more closely with their actual arrival
times. Understandably, there will be some changes
which run opposite to these general patterns, but

the ones just described form the majority of changes.

Out of this reasoning, only a very modest conclusion can possibly be justified. It is that the
projected schedule changes will create a tendency
toward somewhat less early and late arrival. It is
not actually possible to quantify this tendency.
But the belief that it will occur will have useful
consequences in forecasting the arrival adjustments.
For one thing, it lends strength to a decision not
to expand the present tables or to provide for more
early and late arrivals than are now shown on them.
It urges that the tables will remain as they are or
contract in the direction of the scheduled starting
times. Additionally, the claim will support any argument from other sources that the present arrival
tables be contracted for purposes of forecasting.

Conclusions: The Arrival Adjustment

It is now possible to formulate the appropriate
use of the lateness and early arrival adjustments
for forecasting purposes. The terms employed in the
formulation will be defined first. Thereafter the
forecast of arrival behavior, as derived in the preceding section, will be stated.

The terms requiring definition are: capacity,
degrees of the lateness and early arrival adjustment,
and real demand for service.

Capacity denotes the number of riders, seated
and standing, who can be transported through the cordon stations by trains with the standard maximum number and type of cars regularly used on each line,
operating at minimum efficient headways, during a 20-
minute interval. A capacity can be defined for each
cordon station, and by addition, for the system.

The comfort level is defined as approximately
75 per cent of the car capacities.

Degrees of lateness and early arrival adjustments signify certain graded modifications of the

original tables. Their definitions and derivation
are given in Appendix T. The degrees correspond to
the amounts of early and late arrival expected under
the conditions to which they apply. The maximum degrees of lateness and early arrival are considered
to be the amounts shown on Appendix Tables 76 and 83.
This is based on the judgment that the projected alternative work schedules will probably not increase
the amount of early and late arrival. The minimum
degree of lateness and early arrival adjustment provides for the least amount of such practice which
can be expected, on practical grounds, to occur.

Demand for subway service by the people who
work in the CBD is measured by the number of people
who pass through subway cordon stations during 20-
minute intervals. Absolute demand is defined as the
demand which would occur if the riders were to arrive
at their CBD destinations on time, without any early
arrival or lateness. Real demand is defined as the
demand which would occur if early and late arrival
did not exceed the minimum degree of the adjustments.

The forecast of early and late arrival refers
to expected future behavior of the people who work
in the CBD and applies to the work schedules projected by this study. It is limited by the conditions embodied in the ensuing statement.

First, the analysis showed that a relationship
exists, at present, between arrival times and train
capacity. This relationship has causal interconnec-
tions, and therefore, may be presumed to continue
under forseeable future conditions. The analysis
could not establish how much of the arrival adjustment arises from the capacity limitations and how
much from other sources. But it is safe to conclude
that capacity is far and away the principal determinant of the amounts of the adjustment.

The analysis also disclosed that the arrival adjustment and capacity are functionally related. The
magnitude of the arrival adjustment is governed

(with certain possible minimal restrictions) by passenger capacity in relation to demand for service.
This functional relationship may be stated as follows: The closer the system's capacity corresponds
to real demand, the lower the arrival adjustments
will be. These adjustments may be expected to reach
some irreducible minimum when real demand is equal
to or less than the capacity in all time intervals.
This functional relationship provides the basis for
forecasting the arrival adjustments, and for their
use in the general forecasting model.

The relationship may be explained more concretely by applying it to transit traffic. It says that
the people who work in the CBD, except for some irreducible minimal number, can be expected to travel to
work so as to arrive on time and with as little
early or late arrival as reasonably possible. If
the subway capacity and schedules provide a sufficient amount of space, people will then travel at
these times and will thus bring the arrival adjustments to their irreducible minimal percentages. If,
however, the system's capacity and schedules are
less than the amount required to serve the whole
riding population, some will have to reschedule
their trips to earlier or later times. They will
then increase the amounts of the arrival adjustments.

The forecast of the arrival adjustment is thus
a conditional, not an absolute one. The amount of
the adjustment will depend on whether or not the
real demand exceeds capacity in any 20-minute interval or not. Hence, in order to determine whether
a minimal arrival adjustment is to be used or not,
it is necessary to know what the real demand will be
in each corresponding interval.

There are certain convenient guides for making
the necessary determinations. The capacity of the
system as a whole in any 20-minute interval is now
about 300,000 passengers. If a computation of real
demand produces more than this number during any interval, a greater than minimal arrival adjustment
will have to be utilized. Similarly, if the 300,000

limit is approached in more than some minimal number
of intervals, the Transit Authority may not be able
to supply the service. In making the necessary determinations, it will always be necessary to refer
to the total system capacity and the possible levels
of scheduling which the system can provide.

The Comfort Level

The use of this conditional forecast will encounter one further problem. The application just
described has assumed that train schedules will be
based on the present maximum capacity levels utilized by the Transit Authority. However, the Authority has indicated that it might be able to lower its
capacity levels for scheduling purposes to the so-
called comfort level, which is approximately three
quarters of the capacity level now used. The use
of this lower, comfort level standard would provide
a much improved ride.

The introduction of the comfort level capacity
adds still a further complexity to the use of the
arrival adjustment. While the Transit Authority
might schedule its trains according to the comfort
level--thereby providing more trains during the
period before and after the present peak--the riding
public will not necessarily elect to travel according to the comfort level. To the contrary, with
more train space available, the riders can be expected to travel even more in conformity to their
real demand than they now do. In order to bring
about a train loading equal to or less than the comfort level, it would be necessary to produce a real
demand for service equivalent to train capacity as
measured by the comfort level. Early and late
arrival can be expected to diminish to a minimum
only when the real demand for service will not exceed the comfort level capacity of service in each
of the 20-minute intervals.

THE FORECASTING EQUATION AND
ITS APPLICATION

The final forecasting equation embodying the results of the preceding analyses will be presented in this concluding section. The equation will be given in general form. Its structure will be explained and then the equation as a whole will be appraised. Finally, the method of applying this equation and of interpreting its results will be explained.

Before presenting the equation, it is essential to define it, and to specify what it is intended to forecast and what it is not.

The forecasting equation provides a method by which to compute the total subway cordon count entering the CBD, assuming an alternative work schedule is instituted in the CBD. The alternative work schedules whose effects are to be forecast are limited to those projected by this study. These alternatives embody certain systematic characteristics which were taken into consideration in constructing the equation. Other possible schedule changes having different properties will not necessarily be converted into cordon counts by the forecasting equation developed in this chapter.

This equation forecasts cordon counts as a consequence only of alternative work schedules and their immediate effects upon congestion and inter-occupational relations. Everything else is held constant, under a vast and pervasive ceteris paribus assumption. The equation assumes that all other factors affecting the amount and timing of subway travel (by people who work in the CBD, during rush hours) remain unchanged. These include among other things, the volume of employment in the CBD, the volume of subway traffic, fares, substitutability among modes of transport, and the like.

From this it follows that the equation does not claim to forecast future cordon counts, not even on the basis of a changed work schedule in the CBD.

The alternative work schedules are assumed as given
conditions of the problem. The forecasting equation
makes no attempt to determine what schedule will in
fact be instituted in the CBD. Nor does the equation allow for forecasting the development of other
factors affecting the volume and timing of subway
traffic. These are all held constant, under the
ceteris paribus assumption. A forecast of future
cordon counts would require forecasts of all these
other determinants. Such an effort falls far outside the range of this study, and is not essential
for the results being pursued here.

The Forecasting Equation

The forecasting equation will now be stated in
a general form. The terms and definitions of this
equation are the same as those in the equation of relationship with a few additions and changes to be
noted. For clarity's sake, the forecasting equation
is presented in three steps. The first computes the
net change in arrival time. The second computes the
net change in cordon counts by 20-minute intervals.
The third, by adding the net change in cordon counts
to the reconstructed October, 1962, cordon count, produces the forecast.

The Forecasting Equation

In addition to the terms of the relationship
equation, let:

    B = an alternative work schedule
    D' = lateness adjustment (by appropriate degree)
    K' = cordon crossing adjustment = 67.1 per cent
    E' = arrival adjustment (by appropriate degree)
    F = TS, the travel time-cordon interval assign-
         ment for the total CBD
    C = the reconstructed October, 1962, cordon
         count
    H = the forecasted cordon count, based on work
         schedule B.

Then:

(1) 97.0 per cent (BD'K'E'-ADKE) = net change in
    arrivals

(2) 97.0 per cent (BD'K'E'-ADKE)F = net change in
    cordon counts by 20-minute intervals

(3) 97.0 per cent (BD'K'E'-ADKE)F+C = H

The first line uses the net difference method
to compute the net change in the number of people
arriving in the CBD. The net difference is calculated after the application of the adjustment factors. This procedure can now be justified on the
ground that the adjustment factors have been adapted,
insofar as possible, to the amounts they will assume
under the forecasted conditions. Below, in describing the application, the use of these factors will
be made specific.

The second line distributes the arrivals to an
aggregate station by 20-minute intervals.

The third line actually states the full equation. Since the second element in the parenthesis,
ADKE, remains the same for all computations, it is
in effect a constant for purposes of computation.

In this equation the two adjustment factors are
the same as in the equation of relationship: present-
at-work and travel time-cordon interval. The cordon
crossing adjustment is modified from a multiple basis
to a single percentage for all times. The lateness
and early arrival adjustments are represented in the
alternative schedule portion of the equation by
three degrees of adjustment. These are given in
Appendix T.

Appraisal

This equation is accepted as a serviceable
method for accomplishing its purpose. It is expected to forecast cordon counts under the conditions defined just above. The results will be

approximations of the cordon counts for the purpose
of assessing the capability of alternative schedules
to relieve subway congestion.

The validity of this equation can be investigated only indirectly, not by the test of experience.
First of all, the equation has to be used long before
there would be any opportunity to test it. Indeed,
a test could not even be designed except by accepting
the results of the equation which experience would
thereafter be expected to test. But even if this
were done, experience is far more complex than the
equation, with its ceteris paribus assumptions. Experience would therefore produce results which reflect many other possible determinants, not only alternative work schedules, and hence it would not
necessarily provide a definitive test of the forecasting equation.

The validity of this equation can be analyzed
a priori only by reference to its method of construction and to the data employed in developing its parameters. In order to assess the method and the data,
the text of this chapter and its appendixes spell
out the procedures in considerable detail. In accepting the equation as serviceable for the purpose
at hand, it is recognized that improvements in it
might be made by better data and by the discovery of
other adjustment factors which belong in the journey
to work process.

Application

The procedure for utilizing this equation to
forecast cordon counts and to interpret the results
is specified as follows:

First, the cordon counts arising from any projected alternative work schedule are computed, using
the minimum degrees of the lateness and early arrival
adjustments. This establishes the real demand for
subway service arising from the particular alternative work schedule.

Next, the real demand during each 20-minute interval is compared with capacity.

The results of this comparison dictate the subsequent steps. If real demand is equal to or less than capacity, then the computations will have produced a forecast of the cordon counts. If the real demand is equal to or less than three quarters of the capacity, then the alternative work schedule will be judged capable of producing a comfort level of transit subway traffic.

CORDON COUNTS WITHOUT CONGESTION

A short but critical digression must now be made. It will establish the cordon count criteria for testing the feasibility of work staggering. Before presenting the combined schedules of industry groups, and their consequent cordon counts, the standards by which they are evaluated must be explained. The theoretical basis for the cordon count criteria has already been put forward. Subway traffic is to be reduced to the comfort level, at least. This level was defined in Chapter 2 and Appendix H. It turns out that the comfort level cannot be applied simply and directly to the forecasted cordon counts, nor is it a sufficient criterion for the test of feasibility. Appendix U explains why, and how the problem is solved. The results will be summarized here.

Once the criteria are available, the digression proceeds one brief step further. Using the cordon count standards, it presents the optimum work schedule for the CBD. This is the schedule which satisfies the cordon count criteria. The optimum schedule sets the stage--the possibilities as well as the limits--of the feasible combinations of industry groups' schedules, which are presented in Chapter 7.

The cordon count criteria divide into two parts. The first pertains to the congested intervals as identified in Chapter 2. They are: 7:40-8:00,

8:00-8:20, 8:20-8:40, and 8:40-9:00. The second part concerns the intervals before and after the congested ones, in particular those not now congested but which are immediately affected by the shift of people away from the congested intervals. Each of these will be established in the present section.

The Congested Intervals

The feasibility tests are to be applied to the total CBD cordon count for 20-minute intervals, not to the individual station counts. In so doing, delicate assumptions are made about important characteristics of subway traffic--about the distributions of origins, destinations,and work schedules of passengers. These are adequately explained elsewhere in the study. Unfortunately, the state of quantitative information about these matters simply does not allow a more detailed computation of traffic at the individual stations. Hence, all computations of subway passengers resulting from modified work schedules must be made for a global CBD cordon count.

The appropriate criterion of feasibility is thus the comfort level for the total CBD treated as a single station. To compute such a criterion would appear to be a simple matter, since all the required capacity data are at hand: trains per 20 minutes, cars per train, and comfort level per type of car. This simple procedure, however, is wrong and if used will produce erroneous results. It will set a comfort level for the system which is far higher than the present traffic, even at its worst.

Why? Because the twenty cordon stations are not all congested, and many of them have so little traffic that they are scheduled considerably below their capacity. In Chapter 2 a special analysis of cordon counts was made in order to determine the net excess of passengers--the irreducible number of excess passengers at each station after its number of trains per 20-minutes and number of cars per train were raised to their maximum capacity. The results are given in Table 13. Only seven of the twenty

stations have such irreducible excess. Two others
have a negligible amount (eight passengers during
one interval). Effectively, thirteen stations can
be completely relieved of congestion by raising
their schedules to no higher than comfort level capacity, and many of them do not require full capacity.

If the comfort level is fixed for the system as
a whole, the whole increase will occur in the underutilized stations, which will be brought up to their
full capacity. But this will not be a realistic comfort level capacity. Scheduling more trains in the
uncongested stations will not relieve conditions in
the congested stations where no more trains can be
run. This calculation will fix a high comfort level
for the system, higher than the present peak load.
But the congestion would persist in the seven congested stations because no relief can be given them
through increased train schedules. This way of setting a comfort level for the total system simply
misses the mark.

A quite different approach is needed in order
to fix the comfort level cordon counts for the system. The question must be asked: By how much must
the cordon counts be reduced during each of the four
congested intervals so that the net excess will be
removed from all of the stations shown on Table 11?
To this question too there is an apparent answer
which is wrong. The number is not the total excess
during each interval. If, for example, the total
cordon count during the 7:40-8:00 interval were reduced by 1,134--the total net excess during that in-
terval--the 125th and St. Nicholas station would
still have almost as much net excess as is shown on
the table. Theoretically, it would lose only its
share of the 1,134 passengers; the rest would be distributed among the other stations according to their
share of the total count during the interval. To relieve this station of its net excess, the total CBD
count must be reduced by an amount, of which this
station's share is 1,134. This number is easily
estimated: 1,134 divided by the station's percentage
of total system cordon count.

This procedure gives rise to Table 12, the equivalent net excess passengers for each station during each interval. The table is a preliminary one, calculated before the correction based upon the reconstructed cordon count. A corrected calculation may be found in Appendix U which provides a full explanation of the development of the CBD comfort level standards.

The criteria arising from this method (as developed in Appendix U) are shown in Table 53.

TABLE 53

The Comfort Level of the Total CBD During
Selected A.M. Intervals, Entering the CBD

Interval	Comfort Level Standard
7:40 - 8:00	146,700
8:00 - 8:20	166,600
8:20 - 8:40	206,600
8:40 - 9:00	195,700

A question may be raised about these standards. If the 8:20-8:40 interval can carry 206,600 people at comfort level, why can't all the others? Why, in fact, can this not serve as the general standard for the congested intervals and for those before and after? The reason is that each interval has to have its own standard, based on eliminating the irreducible amount of congestion from all the stations. If this standard were applied to the other intervals, the congestion would be increased, not reduced.

The Other Intervals

The intervals before 7:40 a.m. and after 9:00 a.m., while not now congested, must inevitably be affected by a shift of passengers away from the congested intervals. Accordingly, some guidelines have to be set so as to avoid transferring the congestion to them.

It turns out that only two problem situations arise. The first of these concerns one of the intervals before 7:40. Some work schedule combinations increase one of the early intervals. This produces an earlier interval greater than the 7:40-8:00 one. Two issues thus arise. First, is a bimodal distribution undesirable from the point of view of scheduling? It may be, but so long as the size of the hump—the height of the first peak against the drop following it—is not excessive, it ought not create any insurmountable scheduling difficulties. Second, at what point will the new peak become congested? It is not possible to determine this with any exactness because congestion, as already shown, occurs long before the system capacity is reached. The presence of congestion in any interval depends upon the flow of passengers through individual stations. Here again, a rule of reason has to be applied. So long as the first peak remains within the range of adjacent standards, it is regarded as acceptable.

The second problem arises at the 9:00-9:20 interval. It expands very rapidly as employees are shifted to 9:30 starting times. The rule was adopted here of not allowing the 9:00-9:20 interval to exceed the 8:40-9:00 interval. This rule assumes that the two intervals have reasonably similar traffic patterns and hence can be handled with some security by using the same comfort level standards.

Noncongesting Work Schedules

At this point, given the forecasting equation and the cordon count criteria, a hypothetical question is raised. What work schedule, if any, will produce cordon counts satisfying the comfort level criteria? The answer is a valuable introduction to the industry group combinations.

To answer the question, a series of trials was
conducted. In these trials, hypothetical work schedules were formulated and their resulting cordon
counts were computed by means of the forecasting
equation. Each hypothetical schedule was based on
the results of the preceding trial, with the goal of
reducing the deviations between the forecasted cordon counts and the cordon count criteria. This continued until a schedule was found whose resulting
cordon counts differ from the criteria by very small
amounts. This trial schedule--based only on numerical formulations, not upon industry group schedules--
is considered the optimum.

The trial and error method may seem roundabout.
A more direct one is to invert the forecasting equation and calculate a true optimum schedule, given
the desired cordon counts. This method was tried
and the results deserve mention. No schedule could
be produced which satisfied the four interval stand-
ards--that is to say, no schedule except one which
had millions of people starting at one time and negative millions at another. The values in the adjustment matrices cannot be combined with the cordon
count standards to produce meaningful numbers of
people starting work. There must be some deviations
from the standards in order to obtain real work
schedules. This has to be borne in mind when evaluating the results of the industry group combinations.

Table 54 gives the optimum schedule. It also
shows the present CBD schedule and the net changes
which are required in order to produce the optimum.
Table 55 contains the resulting cordon counts based
upon the optimum schedule. Table 56 gives the deviations from standard for each of the four congested
intervals. Both the last two tables contain the
data for each of the four degrees of travel time
practices.

Before drawing the appropriate conclusions
from these tables, a significant point must be made.
It turns out that the optimum schedule is not a practicable one. It requires a net increase of 271,500

people to start work at 7:30 a.m. No such increase
is possible, at least within the capabilities assigned to the industries in this study. The maximum
net increase, on the basis of the expected response,
is 61,800, which leaves a deficit of 209,700. As
will be seen, the deficit is made up primarily by increasing the number starting at 9:30, with some
small increases (and consequent deviations from cordon count standards) in the other start times. The
optimum numbers of the other times are as stated in
Table 54 and they may be used for drawing some pertinent conclusions.

TABLE 54

The Present and Optimum Work
Schedules of the CBD

Time	Present	Optimum	Required Net Change
7:30	8.9	280.4	271.5
7:45	2.3	2.3	-
8:00	205.8	276.0	70.2
8:15	30.9	30.9	-
8:30	286.7	266.0	- 20.7
8:45	224.9	153.5	- 71.4
9:00	808.6	460.4	-348.2
9:15	84.7	81.9	- 2.8
9:30	43.9	145.3	101.4

The table shows that the excess number of
people starting work at 9:00 a.m. is about 350,000,
representing 43 per cent of the number now scheduled
at that time and 17 per cent of the total CBD

employment. The fact of excess at 9:00 a.m. is uni-
versally known; it is useful to establish just how
much it amounts to.

The rest of the table produces quite unexpected
findings. There are excess people at 8:30, 8:45,
and 9:15. The net increase which can be absorbed at
8:00 is very small. This means that the excess now
starting at 9:00 cannot be shifted to 8:30, 8:45,
and 9:15 unless people now starting at those times
are first shifted to 7:30 and 9:30. Nor is 8:00 a.m.
a substantial receiving time, unless again there are
people first shifted out of it.

According to Table 54, a minimum of 443,100
people have to be shifted in order to produce acceptable cordon counts. To bring this about, even more
have to be rescheduled--to make additional room at
8:00 a.m., and to make gradual transfers from 9:00
to 8:30 and 8:30 to 8:00.

These findings establish some very important
qualitative characteristics of any possible work
staggering in the CBD. First, a large number of
people--upward of 443,000--will have to accept
schedule change. Second, the most desirable alternative start times--8:30, 8:45, and 9:15--are already overcrowded. A substantial number of people
will have to accept 9:30 and 8:00 as their new
starting times.

Table 55 is of interest in showing how the different degrees of change in travel time practices
affect the computation of the resultant cordon
counts. The degrees were originally formulated as
a way of taking into account the possible changes in
travel time practice which might result from changes
in work schedule and reduction in subway congestion.
It was argued that the substantial amounts of early
and late arrival, practiced under present conditions,
might tend to contract if schedules were changed and
congestion relieved. Hence, the arrival and lateness
matrices ought to be modified. However, since no one
knows whether such change will occur, and if it

TABLE 55

Computed Cordon Counts Produced by Optimum Work Schedules

(000)

Cordon Interval

Degree	6:20 6:40	6:40 7:00	7:00 7:20	7:20 7:40	7:40 8:00	8:00 8:20	8:20 8:40	8:40 9:00	9:00 9:20	9:20 9:40	9:40 10:00
- 0	72.0	74.4	133.7	146.0	143.2	169.1	202.9	150.1	105.4	60.3	39.7
- 5	58.2	68.5	144.2	140.4	145.8	167.8	204.1	164.5	111.3	60.6	39.2
-10	44.5	62.7	154.7	134.5	147.3	167.4	205.9	179.5	117.8	60.1	38.2
-15	29.8	56.4	165.0	128.4	147.6	167.4	208.5	195.6	125.3	59.0	36.8

should, by how much, an arbitrary device was worked
out, the degrees of reduction. The matrices were
shifted toward their main diagonals by amounts reflecting 5, 10, and 15 minutes of reduction in early
and late arrival, giving four degrees of change, 0,
-5, -10, and -15 minutes. All computations of cordon counts are made on all four bases.

No amount of reasoning produces any light on
the probable course of this behavioral practice, although much was attempted. Roughly one third of the
people starting work during the main morning period
will have to undergo schedule change. Of this group,
some who now come late will be shifted to a later
time. Presumably their lateness will diminish. Similarly, some who now arrive early will be shifted to
earlier starting times, and they too may reduce the
amount of early arrival. Moreover, the two thirds
who are not shifted ought to find better travel conditions, thereby reducing their need to arrive early
or late as a way of avoiding congestion. But some
who now arrive early will be shifted to a later
start, and some who are now late will be shifted to
earlier start times. How might they respond? Out
of all this comes a slight indication that a reduction in early and late arrivals might occur, but it
is entirely speculative and qualitative.

The resulting cordon counts, computed according
to the four degrees, will prove very useful in analyzing the industry group combinations. Their usefulness arises from a consequence of the computations. It will be observed on Table 55 that the
principal effect of the degrees is to shift the cordon count flow to later times. As the degrees increase, they show greater concentrations of people,
first at the 7:00-7:20 interval, and then toward the
later intervals. This is a systematic consequence
of the numerical properties of the gradually modified
matrices. The industry group combinations will be
computed to all four degrees. These computations
will show how much change in travel time practice
can occur before a given combination begins to produce subway congestion. The degrees thus provide a

valuable condition to the ultimate test of feasibility. It will be used in Chapter 7.

TABLE 56

Deviations from Standards of Four Congested
Intervals, by Congested Cordon Counts,
Produced by Optimum Work Schedules

	(000) Cordon Interval			
Degree	7:40 8:00	8:00 8:20	8:20 8:40	8:40 9:00
- 0	- 3.5	+ 2.5	- 3.7	-45.6
- 5	- 1.0	+ 1.2	- 2.5	-31.2
- 10	+ .6	+ .8	- .6	-16.2
- 15	+ .9	+ .9	+ 1.9	-

Table 56 sheds important light on the subject of conformity with standards. Although the schedule shown on Table 54 is considered optimal, it nevertheless produces cordon counts which deviate from the comfort level criteria. As mentioned earlier, it is not possible to reduce all deviations to zero on account of the values contained in the adjustment matrices. The optimum schedule got about as close to conformity with standards as possible. Larger deviations will have to be expected when the CBD schedules are composed out of industry group combinations.

SUMMARY

The cordon count criteria which will be employed in the feasibility tests were presented in the section now ending. They consist of the comfort

level criteria for the total counts entering the CBD
during each of four intervals from 7:40 to 9:00 a.m.
Supplementing them are the more general criteria governing the intervals before and after the four congested ones.

As a by-product of the comfort level criteria,
an optimum work schedule for the CBD was calculated.
It yields several findings which are important to
Chapter 7. In particular, it shows that 7:30 and
9:30 are the principal starting times to which
people can be shifted, and that 8:00 can receive a
few. It shows also that 8:30 and 8:45 are already
congested and, together with 9:00, must be relieved
of people. These are exceedingly narrow constraints
within which a feasible work staggering plan must be
constructed.

Finally, the cordon counts produced by the optimum schedule give notice that the comfort level
standards can only be approached, not perfectly satisfied, by CBD schedules resulting from the industry
group combinations.

7

The climactic problem of the study now arises: Can CBD work schedules be modified to relieve subway congestion during rush hours? The essentials for answering the question are in hand. The present work schedules of CBD industries were presented in Chapter 3. The industries' maximum capability of modifying their schedules was developed in Chapters 4 and 5. The forecasting equation worked out in Chapter 6 will convert alternative work schedules into their resulting cordon counts, incorporating in them a forecast of probable compliance. It remains to bring these elements together and show what they yield.

They yield quite a few possible ways of modifying CBD work schedules which will reduce subway congestion. Some ways are better than others: They offer a more suitable pattern of CBD work hours, or they produce better subway conditions, or both. Five possible schedules stand out as exceptionally suitable. They are variants of two main patterns by which the CBD can be rescheduled. The choice among them depends upon the emphasis placed upon various criteria. The question of the feasibility of work staggering as a way of relieving subway congestion during rush hours may be regarded as settled, on the basis of these results.

It is settled, however, within a limiting framework of assumptions and conditions. Those already made have been explicitly stated in appropriate places in preceding chapters. They apply especially to the statistics employed in the analyses, and to many aspects of behavior which were quantified by

sample studies. There were also crucial assumptions
about things for which statistics do not exist. All
of these, and their justifications, were amply exposed. The feasibility of work staggering, as will
be shown in this chapter, is not independent of the
conditions and assumptions laid down earlier in the
study.

There are also other assumptions and conditions
which will arise in the course of this chapter, as
the exposition of the final results goes forward.
It is appropriate to enumerate the general ones at
this point.

First, the tests of feasibility will be applied
to the CBD as a whole, and not to the individual
cordon stations. This is a shortcoming made necessary by the limitations of data. In so doing, it is
assumed that the unique characteristics of the individual stations are either adequately accounted for
by the procedures employed, or that they will not
suffice to invalidate the results. This problem was
discussed in Chapter 6, where the conclusion was
reached that the individual station calculations had
to be abandoned.

Second, all of the tests will be applied to
entering the CBD during the morning rush hours.
This assumes that by relieving the morning rush, the
evening conditions will also improve. The assumption will not be left unexamined. Some partial
checks into evening conditions which support the assumption will be reported later in the chapter. However, the conclusion of feasibility is based upon
detailed tests only of morning conditions.

Third, there are two major sets of behavioral
indeterminacies among the materials brought together
for the final tests. One set, as discussed and illustrated in tables in Appendix V, pertains to compliance with proposed modifications in schedule. It
is imbedded in the two concepts of modifiability:
functional and tolerable. The other set, dealt with
in the text of the chapter, concerns the possible

changes in travel practices which might arise as a consequence of reduced subway congestion. It is brought to the final computations in the form of the four degrees of reduction in the lateness and early arrival matrices. The fact that both behaviors are represented by alternative estimates means that one cannot be sure how people will act in these two circumstances. Judgments about them will be made during the course of the chapter.

A stylistic matter must also be noted. This chapter deals with numbers--people starting and stopping work, crossing cordons, and others. Almost always, they are forecasts of future behaviors. It stands to reason that any statement of how people will be expected to act is at best an estimate, not a measurement of an already observed event. Such statements, to avoid misunderstanding, ought to spell out the limits within which they are made and any other conditions which adhere to them. In general, the estimates and forecasts will be stated without the appropriate caveats. At times, they will be carried to a detail--to the last one of hundreds of thousands of people--which is totally unjustified, except to minimize rounding errors. This ought to be received as a stylistic trait, not as a characterization of the materials.

It must be understood that all forecasts are, at best, expected results. If all assumptions hold good, they will vary from the future actual ones by modest and tolerable amounts. But they might also vary by substantial amounts even if the assumptions are not destroyed by actual events. This general caution applies also to the final conclusions of feasibility.

To present the results properly, there must be a good deal of accompanying explanation. This does not mean that they are unclear, nor that they are too complex. Quite to the contrary, they have the simplicity and clarity which such a far-reaching change in community practices requires. But in presenting them for the first time--indeed, in showing

that they are justified and worthy of acceptance--it
is necessary to furnish the definitions, explanations, reasoning, and computations by which they
were produced, as well as their limitations.

The chapter builds to its conclusion in two
main sections. The first part will establish the
cordon count criteria employed to test feasibility
and will also present the optimum work schedule for
the CBD. The second part will set forth and evaluate the five feasible schedule combinations of the
CBD.

THE FEASIBLE SCHEDULES

Five combinations of industry group schedules
emerge from the testing as feasible ways of staggering work hours in Manhattan's CBD. They were discovered by combining the alternative schedules of
the industry groups, as given in Table 28, in all
possible ways, and by evaluating the resulting combinations against the criteria of feasibility. Of
the 1,492,992 possible combinations in Table 28, the
five satisfied the criteria better than any of the
rest.

The testing procedure consisted of combining
the schedules, eliminating the unlikely combinations,
converting the suitable ones into cordon counts, and
then evaluating them by the appropriate criteria.

The way schedules were combined may be illustrated by describing a single combination. One alternative schedule is selected from each industry
group, including no change as a possibility. Each
schedule is represented by the net changes in the
numbers of people starting work at each start time,
as given in the tables of Appendix V. The net
changes of each member of the particular combination
are added together to produce the total net change
at each start time. Some of the totals will be positive and others negative. These total net changes,
plus and minus, are then added to the present CBD

schedule--that is, to the total numbers now starting
work at each start time. The positive net changes
increase the CBD totals, the negative ones decrease
them. The result is a modified CBD schedule embodying the changes arising from the combination.

Every possible combination was actually computed by going systematically through all of the
alternative schedules of all the industry groups.

In principle, the combinations were next converted into cordon counts by means of the forecasting equation. However, to avoid a vast amount of
unnecessary computation, many of the combinations
were eliminated by applying certain interim criteria.
The experiments which produced the optimum work
schedule also showed the numbers of people at each
start time--both too high and too low--which would
not possibly satisfy cordon count standards. Thus,
a set of constraints or boundaries were constructed
for the principal start times. If any combination
produced numbers which fell outside these boundaries,
the combination was automatically rejected. The
ones which were not rejected were then screened for
scheduling pattern. Those which contained undesirable group alternative schedules were eliminated.
The number of combinations was thus reduced to include only those which gave promise of satisfying
the standards of feasibility. These were converted
into their resulting cordon counts.

The feasibility criteria were applied to these
results. The cordon counts were compared with the
standards established in the preceding section. The
ones which deviated excessively from the standards
were discarded. The remaining ones were then evaluated in respect to their over-all schedule patterns.
Those which met the criteria of satisfactory schedules were judged to be feasible.

The five feasible combinations satisfied both
sets of criteria better than any of the other

combinations. Nevertheless, quite a few of the others were almost as good as the five; indeed, some of
them met one or the other of the criteria better
than any of the feasible combinations. The existence of these many nearly feasible ones gives enormous support to the general finding that work staggering is feasible. They demonstrate that feasibility is not an accidental or fortuitous or even random outcome of a vast number of combinations. A
general trend in the direction of feasibility is
evident as the combinations of schedules are gener-
ated. Of all the combinations which conform, in
some degree, to the criteria, the five chosen ones
stand out as best.

One final matter has to be taken up. It concerns the procedure described above, but its significance is vast both for the computation and the
results. In combining the schedules, as just described, the net changes in numbers of people were
employed as the data. But, it will be recalled,
two different kinds of net change data were presented in Appendix V: the maximum response and the
expected response. The numbers, for any given alternative, are quite different from each other.
Very different results are produced by the combinations employing one or the other of the data. A
question of choice thus arises. Which of the net
changes should be employed in combining work schedules and thereby in determining the results of any
modifications in the CBD?

The expected response data were used to compute the feasible combinations for several reasons.
First, it is highly improbable that the total CBD
or any of its groups would respond to a proposed
schedule change by shifting all its employees. As
pointed out in Chapter 4, individuals, firms, and
possibly even subdivisions of industries might prove
incapable of adopting a schedule which is considered
functionally possible for the industry taken as a
whole. There may be exceptional cases. Some industries composed of a few large firms or otherwise
well organized might adopt a new schedule in its

entirety. Undoubtedly such possibilities would be
offset by others in which an industry or subdivision
would wholly not accept the new schedule. Accordingly, except for setting the upper limits, the maximum
response is regarded as a highly improbable one.

The expected response furnishes an estimate of
the probable compliance for the CBD taken as a whole.
For some industries it is an optimistic estimate,
perhaps better than will actually turn out. For
others it is a conservative estimate, a lower expectation than will actually occur. The refinements of
forecasting, industry by industry, are simply not
available. For the CBD taken as a whole, and for a
reasonable period of time after a work staggering
program is instituted, the expected response furnishes a credible measure of the extent to which the
modified schedules will be adopted.

Nothing can be said about the duration of this
response. Undoubtedly, a work staggering program,
once instituted, will experience defections as well
as laggard compliance. Moreover, there will undoubtedly be adaptations by other industries which
will further affect the over-all CBD schedule. It
lies quite outside the scope of available forecasts
to estimate these things, however significant they
may become.

The expected response is thus a forecast level
placed reasonably below the maximum capability of
industry and hopefully within an acceptable range of
the actual response. It is used with full awareness
of its limitations, both statistical and conceptual,
but with the conviction that it provides the best
available estimate of the probable over-all behavior
of the CBD industries and people.

Finally, the expected response injects into the
computational procedure a very significant criterion
of feasibility--the acceptability of schedule change
to the people who work in the CBD. The numbers who
can change schedules is deliberately reduced from
the industry totals by the proportion of people to

whom the change is unacceptable. The net changes
contain only the people who--on the basis of the sociological study--will find schedule change tolerable. This highly important criterion of feasibility
is introduced into the procedure before it starts,
as a correction to the numbers available for schedule change.

THE CONSTANT SCHEDULES

Eight of the industry groups have the same
schedules in each of the five feasible combinations.
They are: the earlier and later production groups,
the four administrative office groups, the business
professions and services group, and the insurance
carriers. Table 57 gives the start times of each of
these groups.

TABLE 57

The Constant Schedules, by Industry Group

Group	Schedule
Production industries	
Earlier subgroups	7:30
Later subgroups	8:00
Administrative offices	
Central administrative offices	9:30
Transportation company offices	9:30
Radio, television, and motion picture companies and organizations	9:30
Other administrative offices	9:30
Business professions and services	9:30
Insurance carriers	9:30

TABLE 58

The Net Changes in the Numbers of People
in the Constant Schedule Groups at
Each Start and Stop Time

Start Time	Net Change
7:30	61,803
7:45	− 81
8:00	61,437
8:15	− 11,734
8:30	− 76,714
8:45	− 54,661
9:00	−279,408
9:15	− 13,812
9:30	313,171
Stop Time	
3:30	13,160
3:45	7,782
4:00	62,340
4:15	− 817
4:30	− 42,349
4:45	− 61,386
5:00	−227,498
5:15	2,199
5:30	187,175
5:45	22,889
6:00	19,851

The production groups must start at 7:30 and
8:00, as noted earlier. The other six office groups
have to shift to 9:30. In only two cases--the business professions and services group and the radio,
television, and motion picture companies and organizations group--is 9:30 the preferred time. For the
others, as shown on Table 28, 8:30 is preferred to
9:30 as a starting time. Unfortunately, their first
preference cannot be met. Work staggering will have
to depend upon their adopting the 9:30 starting time.

The effect of these group schedules upon the
total CBD is given in Table 58. The table shows the
net changes at each start time and stop time, based
upon the expected response, for the fixed groups.
These numbers were obtained by adding together the
net expected response columns of the net change tables of Appendix V, for each of the fixed groups.
If these net changes are compared with the required
changes to achieve an optimal schedule, as given on
Table 54, the progress toward a feasible outcome
may be measured. Of the required 271,500 at 7:30,
61,800 are supplied by the fixed schedules, and no
more will become available. This leaves a deficit
of 209,700 which will have to be shifted to other
times. The available space at 8:00 is reduced to
8,800. Instead of requiring a reduction at 8:30,
the shifts by the fixed groups have now opened
places for an additional 56,000 people. 8:45 and
9:00 are still overcrowded, by 16,700 and 68,900 respectively. There is room for an additional 11,000
at 9:15, but it will not be used because of the half-
hour interval pattern for rescheduling. The fixed
groups make a substantial change in the total CBD
especially by opening 8:30 and relieving 8:45 and
9:00.

THE VARYING SCHEDULES

The differences in the five feasible combinations are produced by six of the industry groups.
They are: the earlier and later wholesale trades,
the three finance subgroups, and the government

agencies. These groups and their alternative schedules, by each of the feasible combinations, are giv-
en on Table 59.

TABLE 59

The Varying Schedules, by Industry Group

| Industry Groups | The Combinations | | | | |
	1	2	3	4	5
Wholesale trades					
Earlier subgroups	n.c.	n.c.	n.c.	8:30	n.c.
Later subgroups	n.c.	n.c.	n.c.	n.c.	8:30
Financial industries					
Commercial banks, public departments, and business credit institutions	8:30	n.c.	8:30	n.c.	n.c.
Commercial banks, earlier departments	8:30	8:30	8:30	n.c.	n.c.
Commercial banks, later departments, and security and commodity brokers, dealers, exchanges, and services	9:30	9:30	9:30	9:30	9:30
Government	8:30	8:30	n.c.	n.c.	n.c.

The five feasible combinations are variants of
two basic schedule patterns, which are defined by
the wholesale and finance groups. In the one pattern, the wholesale trades are not changed and the
finance groups are. In the other, the reverse holds
--the finance group is (largely) unchanged, while

one of the wholesale trades is shifted to 8:30. The
government schedules do not help define either pattern. The first three columns of Table 59 contain
one pattern, the last two columns, the other.

The wholesale trades have no schedule change in
three of the combinations. In two of them, one of
the subgroups shifts to 8:30. While no change is
the preferred alternative for these industries, the
preferred alternative time, if one is needed, is
8:30. For the wholesale trades, the alternatives
are satisfactory. However, from the viewpoint of
work staggering, the no change is preferable.

There are two distinct patterns for the finance
subgroups. In the first, the earlier and later subgroups shift to 8:30 and 9:30 respectively, each a
preferred time; and the public subgroup shifts to
8:30 for two combinations and remains unchanged for
one. The dominant characteristic of this pattern is
a schedule change for the finance group, with a
variant possibility for the public subgroup. The
second pattern is quite different, having essentially a no change characteristic. Only the later subgroup goes to 9:30 in both combinations. Both patterns are considered satisfactory for the finance
group as a whole. Probably the second--the one with
least change--is preferable to the group because it
involves the least amount of adjustment. But for a
work staggering program, the first pattern--the one
with the changes but with the options for the public
subgroup--is the better.

The government agencies shift between their
preferred alternatives, no change and 8:30. Here
again, for work staggering purposes, the 8:30 alternative is preferable.

Of the two patterns, the preferred one for work
staggering is the first--the one in which the wholesale trades are unchanged and the finance group is
shifted. Within this pattern, the preference is for
the combinations in which government shifts to 8:30.
From a scheduling viewpoint, there is no preference

as between no change or an 8:30 start for the public
subgroup of finance.

The second pattern is a very acceptable one.
It is less preferred than the first because it re-
lies upon the wholesale trades rather than upon finance and government for compliance with the new
schedules. As noted in Appendix M, the diffuse
character of the wholesale trades makes them a less
secure base for staggering than the other groups.
However, it requires only one of the groups to
shift. As between the two, the earlier or later,
there is no clear basis for making a choice. As a
practical consideration, in the event staggering is
instituted, the wholesale trades might be reexamined
and a choice made of individual trades from both
subgroups until a sufficient number of shifts are
obtained.

Table 60 shows the net changes of all the variable groups at each start and stop for each of the
five feasible combinations. It will be noted that
they differ primarily in their effects upon 8:30,
8:45, and 9:00. They treat 9:15 and 9:30 very much
the same.

THE FINAL SCHEDULES

The fixed and variable schedules can now be
brought together and appraised. Table 61 presents
the final schedule for each of the five feasible
combinations, showing the starting times of each of
the industry groups. The first three combinations
(in the first three columns) belong to the first
pattern: no change for the wholesale trades and
change for finance. The second two are the other
pattern: change in one of the wholesale trades and
minimal change in finance.

The consequences of these combinations upon
work schedules are shown in Tables 62 and 63. Table
62 gives the net changes for each of the combina-
tions--the net numbers of people who would be

TABLE 60

The Net Numbers of People of the Variable Schedule
Groups, by Each Combination, Changing
at Each Start and Stop Time

| Start Time | Combinations | | | | |
	1	2	3	4	5
7:30					
7:45					
8:00					
8:15					
8:30	85.7	65.9	55.4	82.1	58.7
8:45	−21.6	−11.6	−12.9	−12.3	−27.2
9:00	−88.4	−78.9	−67.2	−93.4	−56.6
9:15	− 1.5	− 1.4	− 1.2	− 2.7	− 1.1
9:30	25.8	25.9	25.9	26.3	26.3
Stop Time					
3:30					
3:45					
4:00	.3	.3		.1	.4
4:15	3.6	3.6	3.2	.7	.3
4:30	61.5	51.5	40.3	44.7	16.0
4:45	4.6	− 3.8	3.3	− 5.0	24.9
5:00	−89.0	−70.7	−68.9	−31.4	−51.4
5:15	− 2.5	− 2.5	− .2	− 2.3	− 1.7
5:30	21.4	21.6	22.5	− 5.8	13.9
5:45			.1	.1	− .1
6:00	− .1	− .1		− 1.0	− 2.3

TABLE 61

The Five Feasible Schedule Combinations

Industry Groups	The Combinations				
	1	2	3	4	5
Production industries					
Earlier subgroups	7:30	7:30	7:30	7:30	7:30
Later subgroups	8:00	8:00	8:00	8:00	8:00
Administrative offices					
Central administra-					
tive offices	9:30	9:30	9:30	9:30	9:30
Transportation com-					
pany offices	9:30	9:30	9:30	9:30	9:30
Radio, television,					
and motion pic-					
ture companies and					
organizations	9:30	9:30	9:30	9:30	9:30
Other administrative					
offices	9:30	9:30	9:30	9:30	9:30
Business professions					
and services	9:30	9:30	9:30	9:30	9:30
Wholesale trades					
Earlier subgroups	n.c.	n.c.	n.c.	8:30	n.c.
Later subgroups	n.c.	n.c.	n.c.	n.c.	8:30
Financial industries					
Commercial banks,					
public departments,					
and business credit					
institutions	8:30	n.c.	8:30	n.c.	n.c.
Commercial banks, ear-					
lier departments	8:30	8:30	8:30	n.c.	n.c.
Commercial banks,					
later departments,					
and security and					
commodity brokers,					
dealers, exchanges,					
and services	9:30	9:30	9:30	9:30	9:30
Insurance carriers	9:30	9:30	9:30	9:30	9:30
Government	8:30	8:30	n.c.	n.c.	n.c.

TABLE 62

The Net Changes in Numbers of People of All Groups,
by Each Combination, at Each Start and Stop Time

	(000)				
Start Time	1	2	3	4	5
7:30	61.8	61.8	61.8	61.8	61.8
7:45	- .1	- .1	- .1	- .1	- .1
8:00	61.4	61.4	61.4	61.4	61.4
8:15	- 11.7	- 11.7	- 11.7	- 11.7	- 11.7
8:30	9.0	- 10.8	- 21.3	5.4	- 18.1
8:45	- 76.2	- 66.2	- 67.6	67.0	- 81.9
9:00	-367.8	-358.3	-346.6	-372.8	-336.0
9:15	- 15.3	- 15.2	- 15.0	- 16.5	- 15.0
9:30	338.9	339.1	339.1	339.5	339.5
Stop Time					
3:30	13.2	13.2	13.2	13.2	13.2
3:45	7.8	7.8	7.8	7.8	7.8
4:00	62.7	62.7	62.3	62.5	62.8
4:15	2.8	2.8	2.4	- .1	- .5
4:30	19.2	9.1	- 2.1	2.4	- 26.4
4:45	- 56.8	- 65.2	- 58.1	- 66.4	- 36.5
5:00	-316.5	-298.2	-296.4	-258.9	-278.9
5:15	- .3	- .3	2.0	- .1	.5
5:30	208.5	208.7	209.4	181.4	201.0
5:45	22.9	22.9	22.9	22.9	22.8
6:00	19.8	19.8	19.9	18.8	17.5

TABLE 63

The CBD Work Schedules Produced by
the Five Feasible Combinations

Start Time	Present	(000)				
		1	2	3	4	5
7:30		70.7	70.7	70.7	70.7	70.7
7:45		2.2	2.2	2.2	2.2	2.2
8:00		267.2	267.2	267.2	267.2	267.2
8:15		19.2	19.2	19.2	19.2	19.2
8:30		295.7	275.9	265.4	292.0	268.6
8:45		148.6	158.7	157.3	157.9	143.0
9:00		440.8	450.3	462.0	435.8	472.6
9:15		69.5	69.5	69.7	68.3	69.8
9:30		382.9	383.0	383.0	383.4	383.4
Stop Time						
3:30		46.0	46.0	46.0	46.0	46.0
3:45		16.9	16.9	16.9	16.9	16.9
4:00		135.3	135.3	135.0	135.1	135.4
4:15		26.2	26.2	25.8	23.2	22.9
4:30		227.0	216.9	205.7	210.2	181.4
4:45		160.6	152.2	159.3	151.0	180.9
5:00		444.7	463.0	464.7	502.3	482.3
5:15		85.9	86.0	88.2	86.1	86.7
5:30		416.4	416.6	417.3	389.2	408.9
5:45		48.0	48.0	48.0	48.0	47.8
6:00		83.1	83.1	83.1	82.1	80.8

330

shifted to or from each of the starting and stopping
times. Table 63 gives the final CBD schedules which
result from the addition of the net change to the
present CBD schedule. (It will be noted that the
net changes are identical for the starting times of
7:30, 7:45, 8:00, and 8:15; and very similar for
9:15 and 9:30. The principal differences among the
combinations occur in the three starting times of
8:30, 8:45, and 9:00. The same characteristics may
be seen in Table 63.)

It is of interest to compare the final CBD
schedules with Table 54, which contains the optimum
CBD schedule. The comparison shows that the feasible schedules contribute only 70,700 to 9:30 instead
of the required 280,400, leaving a deficit of
209,700. Most of this deficit is made up by shifting 383,000 to 9:30, instead of the optimal 145,300,
or about 238,000 more than required. 7:45, 8:00,
8:15, and 9:15 are undersupplied by the feasible
combinations by small amounts. How serious these
differences from the optimal schedule are can only
be determined by the resulting cordon counts.

These five possible CBD schedules--produced by
the feasible combinations--can now be appraised on
the basis of the two sets of governing criteria:
the cordon count standards and the schedule criteria.
The amount of change they require will also be investigated.

The Resulting Cordon Counts

The total CBD cordon counts which each of the
schedules produce--according to the forecasting
equation of Chapter 6--are given in Table 64. The
counts are given four ways: one for each of the
four degrees of arrival time practice. These counts
must now be tested for their conformity with standards during the four congested intervals, and for
their contours during the other intervals.

The four congested intervals are evaluated by
calculating their differences from the comfort level
standards. These calculations are given on Table 65.

TABLE 64

The Forecasted Cordon Counts Resulting from the Five Combinations, by Each Degree of Travel Practice

Cordon Count (000)

Combination	Degree	6:20 6:40	6:40 7:00	7:00 7:20	7:20 7:40	7:40 8:00	8:00 8:20	8:20 8:40	8:40 9:00	9:00 9:20	9:20 9:40	9:40 10:00
1	0	31.2	48.3	89.7	133.6	144.1	177.5	206.6	186.1	166.6	80.2	44.8
	5	26.8	46.0	86.2	125.6	144.9	176.9	207.1	194.1	182.8	80.7	43.1
	10	22.4	43.6	82.7	117.2	144.5	177.3	208.1	201.4	202.3	80.0	40.3
	15	17.7	41.1	78.9	108.6	142.9	178.4	209.3	208.1	225.6	78.7	36.8
2	0	31.1	48.2	89.5	133.0	140.8	174.9	210.4	188.4	167.0	80.4	44.8
	5	26.8	45.9	85.9	125.0	142.2	173.2	211.2	196.8	183.2	80.8	43.1
	10	22.4	43.6	82.5	116.8	142.4	172.3	212.5	204.4	202.7	80.1	40.4
	15	17.7	41.1	78.8	108.2	141.4	171.8	214.3	211.3	226.0	78.7	36.8
3	0	31.1	48.2	89.3	132.6	138.9	172.5	212.5	190.6	167.4	80.5	44.9
	5	26.8	45.9	85.8	124.7	140.6	170.2	213.0	199.5	183.6	80.9	43.1
	10	22.4	43.6	82.3	116.5	141.1	168.7	214.1	207.5	203.1	80.2	40.4
	15	17.7	41.1	78.7	108.0	140.5	167.5	215.7	215.1	226.3	78.7	36.8
4	0	31.2	48.3	89.7	133.6	143.8	178.1	207.3	185.3	166.4	80.2	44.8
	5	26.8	46.0	86.2	125.5	144.7	177.3	208.3	193.1	182.6	80.7	43.1
	10	22.4	43.6	82.6	117.2	144.3	177.4	209.8	200.0	202.2	80.0	40.3
	15	17.7	41.1	78.9	108.6	142.7	178.2	211.7	206.2	225.5	78.7	36.8
5	0	31.1	48.2	89.2	132.6	138.9	171.0	211.9	192.1	167.9	80.6	44.9
	5	26.8	45.9	85.8	124.6	140.6	169.0	211.7	201.4	184.1	81.0	43.2
	10	22.4	43.6	82.3	116.4	141.2	167.8	212.0	210.0	202.6	80.3	40.4
	15	17.7	41.1	78.7	107.9	140.5	166.8	212.5	218.3	226.8	78.8	36.8

TABLE 65

The Deviations of the Five Feasible Combinations
from Cordon Count Standards, by Degree

Degree	Cordon Interval	Combination (000)				
		1	2	3	4	5
- 0	7:40-8:00	- 2.7	- 5.9	- 7.9	- 3.0	- 7.9
	8:00-8:20	10.8	8.3	8.0	11.5	4.5
	8:20-8:40		3.9	6.0	.7	5.3
	8:40-9:00	- 9.6	- 7.2	- 5.0	-10.4	- 3.6
- 5	7:40-8:00	- 1.9	- 4.6	- 6.2	- 2.1	- 6.2
	8:00-8:20	10.3	6.6	3.7	10.7	2.4
	8:20-8:40	.6	4.6	6.5	1.7	5.1
	8:40-9:00	- 1.5	1.2	3.9	- 2.5	5.7
- 10	7:40-8:00	- 2.2	- 4.3	- 5.6	- 2.4	- 5.6
	8:00-8:20	10.7	5.7	2.1	10.8	1.2
	8:20-8:40	1.6	5.9	7.5	3.2	5.4
	8:40-9:00	5.7	8.7	11.9	4.4	14.4
- 15	7:40-8:00	- 3.9	- 5.4	- 6.3	- 4.1	- 6.2
	8:00-8:20	11.8	5.2	.9	11.6	.3
	8:20-8:40	2.8	7.7	9.1	5.1	6.0
	8:40-9:00	12.4	15.7	19.4	10.6	22.7
Total positive deviations		66.8	73.5	76.9	70.3	73.0

The numbers on Table 65 state the number of
passengers, in thousands, above (plus) or below
(minus) the standards--during the 20-minute interval
for all of the twenty stations. To interpret these
deviations from the standards, the positive numbers
are the more important, and the negative ones may be
disregarded. The positive numbers are the numbers
of passengers exceeding the comfort level and thus
measure the residual amount of discomfort for the
riders. The negative numbers signify cordon counts

which are lower than the comfort level, and while
unfavorable from the cost viewpoint, are advantageous to the riders. It so happens that the negative numbers are always small, and hence pose a
negligible cost problem.

It is recalled, in appraising the forecasted
cordon counts, that zero deviations for the four intervals are impossible to obtain, simply on account
of the arithmetic of the adjustment matrices. Hence
some deviations must be expected. Further, even if
zero deviations were possible, they would not necessarily inspire greater confidence in the findings
than do reasonably small ones. The universe to
which the data apply is a fluctuating one, hence in
reality there must be deviations. Some of the data
employed in the calculations are estimates obtained
from samples, and they too must differ from true
values by some amounts. This also makes for deviations from the standards. The issue, in interpreting the results, is not whether the cordon counts
conform perfectly to the standards or not, but
whether the deviations are within tolerable limits.
In the present instance, these limits cannot be
quantified as they might be in less complex assem-
blages of statistics. Instead, a rule of reason can
help in evaluating the deviations, as will now be
shown.

Of the four congested intervals, the most critical is the third, 8:20-8:40. It has seven congested stations and its cordon count must be reduced
from 294,800 to 206,600, or by 88,200, the largest
amount of the four intervals. According to Table 65,
the third interval in all four degrees for all the
five combinations shows deviations ranging from 0 to
9,100. At the worst, instead of a reduction of
88,200, there would be 79,100. This must be ad-
judged, on any reasonable grounds, as an entirely
satisfactory improvement in travel conditions during
the third interval.

The second most congested interval is 8:00-8:20.
It has three congested stations and its passenger

load must be reduced by 36,400, or from 203,000 to
166,600. The deviations from the 166,600 standard
of this interval, as shown by Table 65, range from
300 to 11,800. Of the twenty deviations, eight are
above 10,000 and twelve are below 9,000. The worst
cases--10,300 to 11,800--provide from three quarters
to two thirds of the desired relief. One of the
congested stations will be completely relieved and
the other two will benefit to the extent of three
quarters to two thirds of their requirements. The
highest deviations are the fewest; most are well below 9,000. Despite the deviations, the second interval will also derive ample benefits from any of
the five schedules.

The fourth interval, 8:40-9:00, is the third
most congested. It has three stations, and its cordon count must be reduced by 30,900, from 226,500 to
195,600. The deviations for this interval range
from 0 to a high of 22,700. The -0 degree has no
deviations and -5 has very little. In the -10 degree, there are three combinations with low degrees,
but two exceed 10,000. The -15 degree has serious
deviations, with only two or three of the combinations reasonably within bounds of tolerability. The
weak situation of this interval with regard to deviations occasions no surprise. It is particularly
sensitive to the shift of people to the 9:30 start
time.

For the fourth interval, a dividing line is
arbitrarily set at 15,700. A deviation of this size
is about one half of the desired relief, but it will
provide about three fourths of the relief required
by the second most congested station and about all
for the third. At this level of deviation, three of
the combinations are satisfactory in -15 degree.
The other two are unsatisfactory. However, it
should also be noted that even these two will still
relieve the fourth interval, although not by as much
as they should if the relief is to be considered
sufficient.

The first interval, 7:40-8:00, has only one
congested station and to relieve it the cordon count

must be reduced by 10,000. Since all deviations for
this interval are negative, the standard is satisfied.

In sum, the five combinations conform adequately to the standards in the first three degrees, -0,
-5, and -10; three of them conform adequately in
-15. The other two are not adequate, although they
provide relief of present congestion.

Judged on an over-all basis--by their total positive deviations over the four degrees--the five
combinations are ranked, within the two patterns, by
their order of appearance on Tables 61-65. The
first schedule, the one in the left column, has the
lowest total deviations in its pattern, and the lowest of the five. The second and third columns occupy these respective ranks within their pattern. The
fourth and fifth columns are first and second ranks
in the other pattern. The fifth column is also the
second lowest of the five.

The Other Intervals

Next, the other intervals--those preceding 7:40
and following 9:00--must be examined. Their computed counts are given in Table 64. The problem of
criteria for these intervals was discussed in Chapter 6. It was pointed out that there are no comfort
level criteria for them. Rather, they must be evaluated on the basis of their relationship to neigh-
boring intervals and by the contours of the cordon
count pattern to which they contribute.

The intervals preceding 7:40 create no problem
whatsoever, as Table 64 indicates. For every degree
of every combination, the counts rise progressively
from 6:20 onward. These ascending contours are
entirely satisfactory.

This is not altogether the case, however, in
the 9:00-9:20 interval. The counts for the first
three degrees, -0, -5, and -10, are satisfactory.
In the -0 and -5 degrees of all combinations, the

9:00-9:20 interval is well below the 8:40-9:00 interval. In the -10 degree, it is slightly below the 8:40-9:00 interval in three cases and slightly above in two. These are accepted as adequate in the belief that they will not exceed comfort level capacities during the interval. The -15 degree, however, exceeds all previous intervals in every combination with about 226,000 passengers. This is not a satisfactory count.

The Findings

It will prove helpful to summarize--and clarify --the findings of the examination just completed.

When the computed cordon counts of the five feasible combinations are compared with the standards, five intervals prove critical: from 7:40 to 9:20. For each interval there are four computed counts, one for each degree of change in arrival time practices. Thus, 100 computed numbers were evaluated for their conformity with standards.

The significant variable in the findings is the degree of arrival time practice. All the results for the intervals and combinations revolve around it. Hence the summary of the results can be stated in relation to this principal variable.

For two of the degrees, -0 and -5, the computed counts of all combinations conform adequately to the standards. For degree -10, the counts of three combinations are adequate. The other two combinations are less than adequate but not wholly unsatisfactory for the 8:40 interval. The -15 degree is unsatisfactory for all of the combinations in the 9:00-9:20 interval and for three of them in the 8:40-9:00 interval.

This leads to a summary finding of feasibility. None of the combinations is feasible if arrival time practices change by as much as 15 minutes. Three will be feasible if they change by less than 15 minutes. All five are feasible if the change is restricted to less than 10 minutes.

The Arrival Time Practice: Prospect

As a limiting factor to the feasibility of the
five combinations, the arrival time practices require further analysis. The results just reached
raise some questions. Do the limits imposed by the
arrival practice spoil the finding of feasibility?
Will the change in the practice fall within or exceed the maximum 10 or 15 minutes? What happens if
the limits are exceeded?

A closer examination of the arrival practice
produces some answers. The limits do not spoil the
findings. There are limits to the feasibility of
any work schedule. Whether or not the change will
fall within the 10- or 15-minute limits cannot be
said; but it is not likely to exceed the upper limit
because of the nature of the arrival practice. The
bases of these answers will be explained.

The four degrees of travel time practice are
four points along a continuum of changing behavior:
the reduction in early and late arrival. The range
of this continuum extends from-0--no change in be-
havior--to total elimination of early and late arrival, called in Chapter 6 the level of absolute demand. This continuum expresses the consummate or
average behavior of a total aggregate--all the people who work in the CBD and cross subway cordons to
and from work. Work staggering will set the stage
for a possible change in the behavior, but whether
it will actually occur, and if so by how much, cannot be known in advance. If work staggering is instituted, there will eventually emerge some over-all,
aggregate behavior, just as there is at present. It
will fall somewhere on the continuum between -0 and
absolute demand.

There is a relationship between this continuum
and a computed cordon count, given any CBD work
schedule. It is revealed by Table 64. For any combination, as the degrees increase, the cordon counts
also change. The change appears as a gradual lowering of the earlier and later counts, the emergence

of a peak at 9:00-9:20, and a raising of the counts
adjacent to the new peak. The mitigating or dis-
tributive effect of the arrival matrices is gradually diminished--as the higher degrees provide--and
the resultant cordon count comes more and more to
resemble the original work schedule. The relationship is this: As the degrees increase--as the
amount of early and late arrival time is reduced--
the cordon counts develop a peak corresponding to
the contours of the work schedule.

From this relationship, an important consequence follows. Given the work schedule, the amount
of change in arrival time will determine the shape
of the cordon count distribution and the height of
the peak. Given the amount of change in arrival
time, the work schedule will determine the shape of
the cordon count distribution and the location and
height of the peak. Either of two elements of the
system--the behavior or the work schedule--will determine the relevant characteristics of the third,
the cordon count.

This relationship and its consequence, considered in the light of the cordon count computations
shown in Table 64, yield a final observation. The
cordon counts of the five combinations, as seen in
Table 64, are very similar in magnitude and in contour. They are generally satisfactory, from the
viewpoint of congestion, through degree -10, and they
become excessive in the 9:00-9:20 interval at degree
-15. This common pattern is the result of the similarity in the total work schedules of the five combinations. In the language of the relationship
stated above, the work schedule is given, insofar as
the five combinations are concerned, and the resulting cordon counts are determined similarly for each
of them.

Thus, the five combinations are designed to relieve congestion for a range of aggregate travel behavior between -0 and -10 or a bit more, but not by
as much as -15 minutes. To produce combinations for
a range, say, of -10 to -20 minutes, a very different

work schedule would have to be given. It could undoubtedly be worked out, just as is the one which
provides relief for the -0 to -10 minute range. No
reasonable work schedule is capable of relieving
congestion for the whole range of possible change in
arrival times. The limits which the arrival behavior imposes upon the feasibility of the five combinations inheres in the systematic relationship of
work schedule, arrival behavior, and cordon count.
Any CBD work schedule will have such limited feasibility.

The question as to whether the change in the
practice will fall within the range of -0 to -10
minutes is unanswerable except speculatively.

The speculation turns on the determinants of
the arrival behavior. It was contended in Chapter 6
that the early and late arrival are caused in substantial part by congestion. The passengers overcome subway congestion by shifting their travel
times earlier or later than their work schedules require. Under any of the five combinations, congestion will begin to occur if the passengers reduce
their early and late arrival--on the over-all average
--by as much as 15 minutes. To avoid the congestion
the passengers may arrest their change in behavior
below the 15-minute level. The occurrence of congestion may be--as at present--a built-in barrier to
an excessive change in the practice.

If, despite the barrier, people reduce their
early and late arrival by 15 or more minutes, then
the subways will become congested. At 15 minutes
they will be less congested than now, and it will be
confined to one interval. The effectiveness of any
work staggering program, if it is otherwise sound,
will depend upon which of two options the subway
riders choose to take. They can have a more comfortable ride with some early and late arrival or
they can arrive more closely to their scheduled
start time and have a somewhat less comfortable
ride, but still better than at present. Ultimately,
this is the choice which governs the change in the

arrival behavior and which remains wholly unpredictable by present knowledge.

The Resulting CBD Schedules

The group schedules, as shown on Table 61, must also be examined with respect to their relationships to each other and to other CBD industries. Are the relationships viable? Can industries which must deal with each other actually carry out their dealings? These questions concern the schedule pattern which the five feasible combinations contain.

The scope of these questions has already been narrowed a great deal. Many aspects of interindustry relationships were taken care of by previous procedures. The matter of personal preference--by employers and employees--was taken into account, as fully as available data allow, by reducing the number of people who can be shifted in any industry to the proportion which, according to the sociological study, will tolerate the change in schedule. The specific percentages may over- or understate the proportion of people who will refuse to comply with a new schedule. But insofar as possible, by the best available data, their preferences and probable response have been included in the computations. This aspect of the suitability of schedules is not at issue here.

Further, the interindustry relations of particular firms arising from their unique business circumstances--insofar as they might prevent compliance with the new schedule--have also been taken into account. The expected response data, based upon the estimated tolerance of schedule change, are interpreted as covering noncompliance arising from this cause. Both this and the previous factor are discussed fully in Chapter 6.

Interindustry and labor market relationships were also taken into account when possible schedule alternatives were dropped from some of the groups, and others were tied into uniform schedule times.

These were done in order to eliminate starting times and schedule relationships which might place undue strain upon industries in dealing with other industries or in their access to the labor market. This served further to enhance the functionality and practicality of the final schedules.

Thus, in composing the five feasible schedules, a great deal of attention was given to the viability of the final results. Essential interbusiness relationships and access to the labor market ought to be fully possible under the new schedules. In certain respects, they may even be improved.

The schedule patterns are evident from Table 61. The production group occupies the 7:30 and 8:00 times. All the others are distributed among 8:30, 9:00, and 9:30. Eight-thirty is the starting time of banks or (part of) the wholesale trades, and by preference, government. For many wholesale trades, 8:30 is a very satisfactory time to start, particularly for those whose markets or customers are local. The 8:30 starting time for the banks will place them centrally among the large schedule subdivisions, a possible advantage to all. Nine-thirty will be the starting time of the administrative office group, the business professions and service industries, the insurance companies, and the investment and securities industries. This concentrates a large body of office employment at that time, but very substantial numbers will still remain at 8:30 and 9:00. Finally, the 9:00 starting time will continue to serve the no change groups, as well as many others not included among the modifiable ones.

The schedule pattern is a workable one for the CBD. Its principal changes are two. It separates the production from office industries and trades, which is generally a feasible change. And it distributes the offices and trades over the three times, 8:30, 9:00, and 9:30. This too is practical in respect to interbusiness relations and access to the local labor market.

The Amount of Change

In appraising the five feasible combinations, the numbers of people and the amount of change are matters of interest. Table 66 presents, for each of the five combinations, the numbers of people who would have to accept new starting times, by the number of minutes of change. The table also gives the same statistics as a per cent of the total CBD employment.

The table indicates that the differences among the five schedules, from this particular criterion, are very small. The number who would have to shift by 90 and 75 minutes earlier, and by 15, 30, 45, and 60 minutes later are the same for the five. All of their difference resides in the 60, 45, 30, and 15 minutes earlier change. Of these, 60 minutes is almost the same for all, thus leaving only three start times to account for their variations. The one time which shows some difference is 30 minutes earlier, but the amount is hardly worth any concern.

All of the five combinations require the same shifts to later starting times: 16.4 per cent of the total CBD employment, or 335,385 people. The shifts to earlier times require percentages ranging from a low of 10.8 per cent to a high of 12.1 per cent. In total, the range is from 27.2 per cent to 28.5 per cent, or from 556,400 to 583,400 people.

The principal shift is to 30 minutes later, with 12.7 per cent of the total CBD assigned to it. Next in size is 30 minutes earlier, which has between 5.6 per cent and 7.4 per cent of the CBD. Sixty minutes earlier, 45 minutes later, and 15 minutes earlier are the next three in order of size, and they range from about 1 per cent to 2 1/3 per cent of the total CBD.

THE STOP TIME SCHEDULES

To prove feasible, a work staggering program must also relieve subway congestion during the later

TABLE 66

The Numbers and Per Cents of People Whose Schedules are Changed Under Each of the Five Combinations, by Minutes of Change

Combination	Earlier						Later			
	90	75	60	45	30	15	15	30	45	60
1	7,505	2,606	48,038	13,149	146,829	29,857	13,633	259,143	42,508	20,101
2	7,505	2,606	47,843	13,104	133,295	19,366	13,633	259,143	42,508	20,101
3	7,505	2,606	47,901	12,888	125,606	21,183	13,633	259,143	42,508	20,101
4	7,505	2,606	47,495	14,330	151,801	20,605	13,633	259,143	42,508	20,101
5	7,505	2,606	47,486	12,813	115,009	35,505	13,633	259,143	42,508	20,101
1	.4	.1	2.4	.6	7.2	1.5	.7	12.7	2.1	1.0
2	.4	.1	2.3	.6	6.5	1.0	.7	12.7	2.1	1.0
3	.4	.1	2.3	.6	6.1	1.0	.7	12.7	2.1	1.0
4	.4	.1	2.3	.7	7.4	1.0	.7	12.7	2.1	1.0
5	.4	.1	2.3	.6	5.6	1.7	.7	12.7	2.1	1.0

afternoon peak periods, when people leave the CBD.
An acceptable schedule must reduce the cordon counts
leaving the CBD to the comfort level. The examination thus far has been confined to the mornings and
entering the CBD. It is now appropriate to evaluate
the five feasible combinations in respect to their
effects upon the afternoon rush.

The feasibility of the five combinations, insofar as the afternoon rush is concerned, will be determined by an examination of work schedules, not of
their consequent cordon counts. The numbers stopping work at each stop time under each of the five
combinations will be compared with their corresponding numbers at present. A judgment will then be
reached as to whether or not the new schedules make
a sufficient reduction in the concentration of numbers at the peak stop times.

This method is used in lieu of computing cordon
counts and evaluating them against comfort level
standards for leaving the CBD. It is considered
adequate to the kind of judgment which has to be
made. Enough is now known, from the intensive study
of the relationship between work schedule and cordon
count in the morning, to make it possible to detect
any significant danger points in the stop time schedules of the five combinations, if they exist.

The numbers of people scheduled to stop work
between 3:30 and 6:00 p.m., at present and under
each of the five combinations, is given in Table 63.
Figure 20 shows graphically the present stop time
schedule and the maximum and minimum numbers of the
five combinations at each time.

The effects discernible from Figure 20 are
clear. The new schedules bring down the 5:00 peak
from 761,100 to a range of 444,700 to 502,300, a reduction of between 258,800 to 316,400. The 5:30
numbers are raised by the new schedules from 207,800
to a range of 389,200 to 417,300, an increase of
from 181,400 to 209,500. There are also increases
at 4:00 and 5:45. The others are substantially the
same as at present.

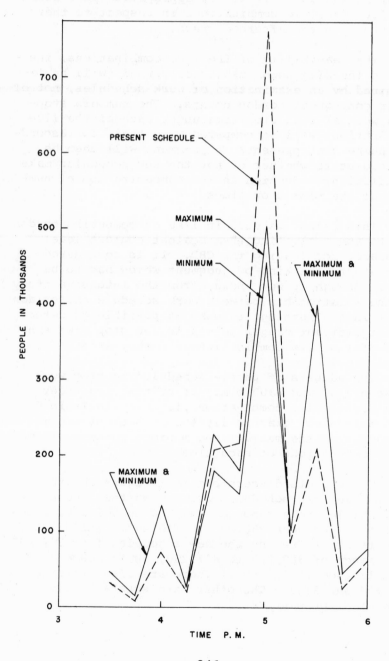

FIGURE 20

NUMBER OF PEOPLE SCHEDULED TO STOP WORK FROM 3:30 TO
6:00 P.M. AT PRESENT AND ACCORDING TO THE MAXIMUM AND
MINIMUM OF THE FIVE FEASIBLE COMBINATIONS

The question thus arises: Are the decreases at
5:00 and the increases at 5:30 sufficient? Will they
bring about an improvement in travel conditions?
Since no forecasting equation was developed for the
cordon counts out of the CBD, the answers to these
questions must remain as judgments, based upon related and contingent considerations.

There is reason to believe that the congestion
out of the CBD need not be as acute as the entering
congestion. Hence the reduction of the peaks can be
less during the afternoon and still provide adequate
relief. The belief rests upon a comparison of Figures 2 and 3, the cordon counts entering and leaving
the CBD. The morning rush hour is shorter and its
peak higher than the late afternoon one. The leaving cordon count has a blunter pinnacle, with two
intervals, 5:00-5:20 and 5:20-5:40, very similar.
In a general way, this suggests that the pressure of
traffic is less intense and more diffuse in the afternoon than in the morning.

Thus, the lesser reduction at 5:00 than at 9:00
and the lesser increase at 5:30 than at 9:30 do not
necessarily mean that the afternoon congestion will
now become worse than the morning. Rather, they are
different--and offsetting--changes to the slightly
different morning and afternoon patterns. The resulting patterns of the morning and afternoon schedules turn out to be quite similar. Figure 21 compares the start and stop times of the first of the
five combinations. It shows that the stop time pattern builds up slower than the start time, and
reaches a very slightly higher point at 5:00 and
5:30, a difference which is negligible. The other
combinations differ from this one in very minor ways.
It is concluded, therefore, that the resulting stop
schedules ought to be no more a source of subway congestion than the starting schedules.

This conclusion rests on two significant assumptions. First, it assumes that the travel time
practice leaving work has, in common with the arrival patterns, some power of diffusing the people over

FIGURE 21

NUMBER OF PEOPLE SCHEDULED TO START WORK
BETWEEN 7:30 AND 9:30 A.M. AND TO STOP WORK BETWEEN 3:30 AND
6 00 P.M., ACCORDING TO THE FIRST FEASIBLE COMBINATION

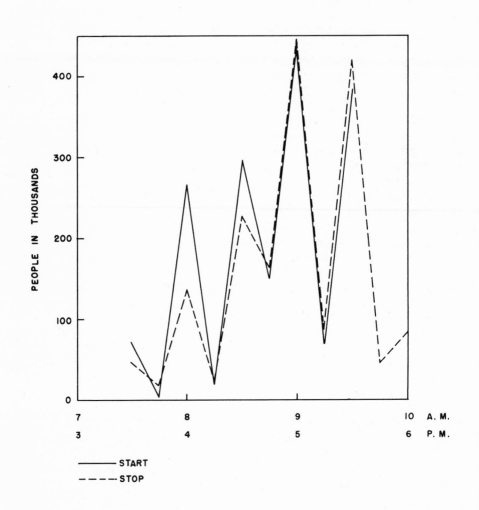

cordon count intervals, rather than concentrating
them at the interval adjacent to their stop times.
There is no direct evidence for this except that the
relationship between the numbers stopping work at
various times and the evening cordon counts looks
similar to the relationship of the entering cordon
counts and numbers starting work. This suggests
that there are practices which distribute the departing employees in a similar way, although the
substantive ingredients of the relationship have
not been investigated. The first assumption thus
has a certain amount of forceful but indirect support.

Second, it is assumed that the passengers during the peak afternoon intervals are primarily working people as in the morning intervals. This may
actually not be the case. The CBD has other origins
of subway passengers which become active in the late
afternoon and which may contribute to the cordon
counts. These passengers include shoppers, clients
of services, returning travelers from other areas,
people leaving places of entertainment, and others.
If they are a factor in the departing cordon counts,
they will inevitably complicate the relationship between the numbers stopping work and subway traffic.
There is one offsetting factor to this complication,
however. Again, the apparent relationship between
the numbers stopping work and the cordon counts do
not exhibit anything which differs markedly from the
entering counts in the morning. This may be because
the other people--not the CBD employees--do not constitute any appreciable number, or because the departing employees tend to diffuse even more in leaving work than in arriving. In either case, the assumption does not appear to be a damaging one.

On these grounds it is concluded that the five
combinations will provide sufficient relief during
the afternoon rush hour to warrant the judgment of
feasible. The changes they make in schedules are
large and in the desired direction. Accordingly,
they ought to provide substantial improvements in
subway traffic.

CONCLUSIONS

This chapter reaches conclusions which can be briefly summarized in four statements. Within the limitations imposed by the assumptions, conditions, constraints, and other restrictions originating in the phenomena and data describing them, it is concluded that:

1. Work staggering is a feasible way of relieving subway congestion into and out of Manhattan's CBD during the rush hours.

2. There are five different combinations of industry schedules by which to institute a work staggering program in the CBD.

3. These five combinations fall into two patterns of scheduling, of which one is clearly preferred.

4. The preferred pattern has three combinations, of which one is clearly the best.

CHAPTER **8** THE FEASIBILITY OF

WORK STAGGERING

One question remains for this study, the one
with which it began. Is work staggering in Manhattan's CBD a feasible way of relieving transit congestion during the rush hours? As a result of the
researches, analyses, and computations of the preceding chapters, an abundance of factual evidence is
now available by which to answer the question. But
above all else, it can now be raised concretely and
specifically as a result of the discoveries reported
in Chapter 7. These are five combinations of CBD
schedules which are capable--to a greater degree
than any other possible combinations--of relieving
rush hour congestion on the subways. Of them, it
may now be asked: Are they feasible--in the full
sense of the term--as ways of staggering the CBD's
work schedules?

The answer to this question will be a judgment,
not a product of precise calculations. There are no
quantitative methods for solving the final problem
of the study. The answer to the question of feasibility will arise out of an assessment of conse-
quences--insofar as they are now evident--of instituting any of the five combinations. To identify
the relevant consequences, to foresee their future
dimensions, to weigh them--balancing the favorable
against the unfavorable--is a work of analysis and
reason.

The judgment will rest upon the results of
three lines of inquiry to be presented in the remainder of this chapter. The first will consist of
an evaluation of the five schedule combinations in

respect to the criteria of work staggering established in Chapter 1. In applying these criteria,
the weaknesses as well as the strengths of the five
combinations will come to light. The determination
of feasibility requires, as its second support, an
assessment of the risks and potential damage which
might ensue if any of the five combinations is
adopted. These in turn give rise to the third part,
a search for safeguards by which to minimize the
risks. When these inquiries are finished and their
results become available, a final decision about the
feasibility of the five combinations will be made.

EVALUATION

A theory of work staggering was expounded in
Chapter 1 of this study. The theory provided a
framework for the entire inquiry. It was formulated
as a set of criteria by which to determine the feasibility of any proposal of work staggering. The
details of the theory are fully presented in Chapter
1 and need not be restated here. The criteria established there will now serve as the basis for
evaluating the five combinations.

By title, the criteria of feasibility are:
modifiability of work schedules, acceptability of
schedule change, relief of transit congestion, tolerance or resistance to work staggering, and durability. The five combinations--treated for this
purpose as a single proposal--will be examined for
conformity with each one of the criteria. Many aspects of the criteria were used earlier in the study,
to develop and test intermediate results of the inquiry. In this evaluation, all the criteria will be
brought to bear in a comprehensive assessment of the
five schedule combinations.

THE MODIFIABILITY OF WORK SCHEDULES

For work staggering to be feasible--indeed, for
it to occur at all--places of employment must be
able to modify their work schedules. The number of

such places, their locations, and the amount of
change which they must make depend upon the resultant flow of transit traffic. Enough of the people
who work in the CBD must be rescheduled by their
places of employment to reduce the peak hour traffic
to acceptable levels. By means of the industry
groupings and computations described in Chapter 7
and Appendix V, the required schedule changes are
specified in respect to industry, numbers of people,
and proposed start times. The first criterion of
feasibility thus raises the question: Can the
places of employment included in the five combinations actually modify their schedules as required of
them?

A final answer to this question can be provided
only by actual experience with work staggering, not
by studies or by the opinions of individual company
or industry representatives. The ability of places
of employment to modify their schedules as required
by any of the alternative staggering plans will depend not only upon their estimates of present capability, but even more crucially upon what the rest
of the CBD may be doing. Suppliers, competitors,
customers, banks, other business services and the
rest, by modifying their schedules, will alter the
circumstances of each individual place of employment
in ways it cannot foresee. Its own schedule determinants will change, and hence its ability to adopt
its proposed schedule. The over-all cumulative effect of work staggering will be to increase its feasibility.

Short of experience, the question of modifiability has to be answered by inquiry. The one undertaken by this study is presented in Chapters 4 and
5, and in the industry scheduling and sociological
reports. These sources disclose fully the grounds
upon which the schedules of the five combinations
are regarded as modifiable. They contain the theory
of work scheduling, the research evidence, and the
findings of modifiability. The theory and research
create a model of the circumstances which are expected to arise if work staggering is introduced.
The findings express a forecast of probable response

by the CBD's places of employment. They take into
consideration as many determining factors as such a
limited construction of future reality seemed capable of doing. The validity of the findings, as of
the actual modifiability of schedules, will ultimately be best resolved by experience.

Accordingly, it is reasonable to claim that the
studies furnish--in anticipation of actual experi-
ence--an acceptable forecast of the probable response of places of employment to any of the five
plans of work staggering. It is in this sense of a
forecast that the first criterion of feasibility may
be said to be satisfied. The industries included in
the five combinations appear capable, insofar as the
studies can show, of modifying their schedules by
the required amounts.

This claim gains strength from several other
factors worth mentioning. The studies of scheduling
disclosed that more industries are capable of modifying their schedules than were actually used in
constructing the five combinations. This means that
if the response of the included industries falls
short of expectations, there are available substi-
tutes to make up the deficit of people--a welcome
safety factor for work staggering. But more generally, it suggests that the ability to modify schedules within reasonable limits is fairly general and
widespread in the CBD, and not a drastic or unthinkable alteration in prevailing habits. Finally, in
making use of the findings as to modifiability, a
large margin has been allowed for noncompliance by
individual industries. This margin is introduced by
the use of the expected rather than the maximum response, as described in Chapter 7. Thus, the five
combinations do not require that all firms in the
included industries modify their schedules, but only
the proportion equal to the expected response. The
effect of these various factors is to increase the
likelihood that a sufficient number of places of
employment are capable of modifying their schedules
as required by work staggering, thereby strengthen-
ing the judgment that the first criterion will be
satisfied by experience.

THE ACCEPTABILITY OF SCHEDULE CHANGE

The second criterion of feasibility provides that work staggering must be acceptable to the people whose schedules are to be changed. In effect, this criterion is a part of the first one: The ability of places of employment to modify their schedules partly depends upon the acceptability of the new schedules to their employees. These two criteria were actually combined in the computations, as described in Chapters 5 and 7. To give emphasis to the requirements of the people whose schedules are to be changed--both employees and employers-- it is appropriate to evaluate the second criterion independently of its relationship to the first.

As a criterion of feasibility, the notion of acceptability signifies a responsiveness to the desires of people, a commitment to be guided by human and social--as distinguished from business and institutional--considerations in assessing staggered working hours. This notion gives rise to a general approach to the problem, defined in Chapter 6 as a problem of policy: Is the prevailing attitude toward schedule change sufficiently favorable, or ought the project be discontinued, as a matter of policy, on account of adverse opinion toward schedule change and work staggering?

The evidence of attitude and probable response of people to schedule change is given in Chapter 5 and in the report of the sociological study. It shows that attitudes vary, as might be expected. But it also reveals a preponderance of favorable opinion toward schedule change--tolerance, willingness, even preference for hours different from present ones. The sociological findings show that a sufficient number of people who work in the CBD--as a whole, and when analyzed by occupation, industry group, and other relevant socio-economic categories --will probably respond favorably to the schedule changes required to bring about work staggering. Thus, as a matter of policy, the general level of acceptability is sufficiently high to conclude that the second criterion of feasibility is satisfied.

Another, perhaps narrower, concept of acceptability inheres in the second criterion. It originates in the observation that attitudes toward
schedule change are bound to be distributed over the
entire range of possibilities, from enthusiastic approval to outright resistance. This range of response was in fact reported--and insofar as possible,
quantified--by the sociological study. The existence of such a range makes it difficult to apply
the first notion of acceptability in any operable
way. How satisfy the desires of people, when they
differ so widely? Such differences cannot be
weighted, evaluated, or reconciled by any "outside"
study. That is the responsibility of the available
political processes. A study of attitudes can at
best reveal the prevailing diversity of opinion and
preference, and perhaps the probable responses of
people to schedule change. This in turn ought to
shed light upon the decisions people will make, in
their various decision making capacities, when con-
fronted with the proposal to adopt a new work schedule.

According to this narrower notion, acceptability of schedule change means the decisions which
people will make--as individuals (employees or employers) or as members of decision making bodies
(unions, management, industry associations). Within
this setting, the welfare or paternalistic implications of the first notion of acceptability are replaced by the functions and prerogatives of the second. The problem of acceptability is thus no longer:
What proportion of favorable and unfavorable attitude will determine feasibility? It is replaced by
the more operable question: How will individuals
and their decision making organizations decide to
act? The responsibility of reconciling divergent
views is placed upon decision makers, including defining the adaptations available to their minorities.
The second criterion may thus be tested by assessing
the probable decisions and responses of people, responsibly made by themselves, rather than by super-
imposing an outside entity (a study, or a social
agency) to act on their behalf. The difference between the two notions is not simply one of style or

philosophy. It governs the nature of the inquiry
and the application of its findings.

The sociological findings, when analyzed by
categories of decision makers, yield the same conclusions. Employers, executives, managers, union
officials, and union members are as disposed to accept schedule change as the rest. Insofar as the
evidence permits a forecast of future decisions and
actions, there are adequate grounds for the conclusion that a sufficient number of firms, organizations, government agencies, institutions, industry
associations, and unions will decide in favor of
schedule change.

But what about the rest, the people who cannot
or prefer not to change their schedules but whose
places of employment--by decision of the employer,
or by agreement of employer and union--adopt a new
schedule? What happens to them, insofar as work and
schedules are concerned? They have only two possible courses if they are to continue to work in the
CBD: to accept the unacceptable schedules or to
find other jobs with suitable schedules. In this
particular circumstance, employers and employees encounter the obverse sides of the same problem. The
employees must find jobs with acceptable hours; the
employer must find employees to fill their places.
The acceptability of schedule change depends, at
least in part, upon such employers and employees
finding ways of adjusting to the change of schedules.

In a general way, the possibilities of adjustment are already evident. First, under staggering,
there will be a wide distribution of occupations--
perhaps even wider than at present--over the range
of starting times. In part, this inheres in the
five combinations, certainly for the office occupations which will be extended more widely than at
present. In part, there will undoubtedly be job
openings caused by people who cannot adopt the new
schedules. Second, the sociological study reveals
that large numbers of people prefer different hours
from the ones they now have. These two circumstances
open the way for possible readjustments by people to

their preferred times--either at the new schedules
of their present places of employment, or at the
present schedules of jobs vacated by people choosing
the newly available schedules. Obviously, this is
not to be taken as a mechanical adjustment process,
with people easily shifting from one job and time to
another. It means that adjustment to work staggering, by both people and places of employment which
cannot change schedules, will to some extent be
cushioned by these possibilities of maneuver. There
are even modest grounds for the belief that staggering may lead to a general increase in satisfaction
with work schedules by increasing the options now
available to firms and people.

                    RELIEF OF CONGESTION

     Above all else, work staggering must relieve
transit congestion during rush hours in order to
prove feasible. In general, this means reducing the
morning and evening traffic peaks to some acceptable
level--without creating new ones. Ideally, the relief should occur on all modes of passenger transportation serving the CBD.

     This study confined its analysis of the traffic
consequences of work staggering to the subway system. The assumption was made earlier that the findings about subway traffic--by far the largest of the
several modes--could be made applicable to the rest.
Accordingly, this evaluation will first deal with
subway traffic. Afterward it will examine the extent to which the assumption about the other modes
is supportable.

     With specific reference to the subway studies,
the criterion poses three principal topics for evaluation. They are: the standards of acceptable
traffic levels, the efficacy of the methods of computing traffic from work schedules, and the extent
to which the computed traffic conforms--or fails to
conform--to the standards. These make up the agenda
by which to apply the criterion of traffic relief to
the subway system.

The Traffic Standard

The criterion requires that traffic--in this case, the subways--be free of rush hour congestion after work staggering is instituted. To apply this criterion, a standard of subway traffic is required, one which will make the dividing line between a congested and an uncongested car or train. As presented in Chapter 2, the standard adopted by this study is the so-called comfort level. Its definition and mode of application are fully described in Chapter 2 and its appropriate appendixes.

If subway traffic were reduced to the comfort level, there would be no more rush hour congestion. The comfort level amounts to three fourths of the capacity now used for scheduling. During the peak periods, the cars are loaded well in excess of capacity. Removing more than 25 per cent of the passengers from the cars and trains could not fail to improve riding conditions substantially. Not everyone would have a seat, but there would be ample room for the standees to move about, read, manage small packages, and ride free of bodily contact with other passengers. The crowding that now occurs during the rush hours would no longer exist. As a standard, the comfort level would spell the end of rush hour congestion.

The question may be raised as to whether the amount of improvement introduced by the comfort level would prove sufficient. Might not the riders expect more? Will they consider the exchange of new work hours for comfort level conditions a fair one? There is no evidence on this point because the inquiry did not pursue it. It is reasonable to suppose, however, that the comfort level--if actually realized--will impress the riders as a significant gain in travel conditions, especially if it is made clear in advance that work staggering cannot provide seats for all riders. However, even though seats would not be available, standing conditions would be so markedly better that the response of the travelers ought to be favorable.

Accordingly, the comfort level is judged a satisfactory traffic standard for relieving subway congestion.

Work Schedules into Cordon Counts

The second issue posed for this evaluation is a technical one. The question which needs to be asked is: Are the forecasts of cordon counts resulting from work schedule changes reliable? If work schedules are changed, will the subway traffic turn out to be what the computations say they will? Here again, only experience can provide the test-- experience with the whole program of work staggering. But since neither experiment nor experience are possible, a substitute test must be devised. The only one which seems possible is to subject the computational method to a critical reexamination. Is the method by which the work schedules are translated in their resulting cordon counts dependable?

The method may be divided, for purposes of this evaluation, into three parts. They are: the forecasting equation, the input quantities (present and proposed work schedules, the reconstructed cordon counts), and the standards of traffic relief. Each of these has already been described in full detail elsewhere in the study. The forecasting equation is formulated in Chapter 6 and its mode of application explained in Chapter 7. The input statistics are presented, prepared, and evaluated throughout the study, especially in Chapters 2 and 3 and their appendixes, but also elsewhere. The appropriate traffic standard--the comfort level--is adopted in Chapter 2 (as described above) and it is made applicable to the tests of resulting cordon counts in Chapter 7. These sources not only formulate each of these components, they also search out and expose whatever shortcomings they possess.

Time and again, the evaluations, after carefully delineating the assumptions and limitations of each component element of the computational procedure, reach the conclusion that each one will prove adequate for the purposes of the study. There

appears to be no reason, as the study draws to its
end, to retreat from these individual conclusions
nor from their accumulated results. The forecasted
cordon counts of the five combinations are considered reasonable and acceptable.

Nevertheless, there are some additional things
to be said by way of final evaluation. They pertain
to aspects of the computational model which will
benefit from further investigation. They consist
of certain assumptions which had to be made in the
course of developing the model, and which seemed
reasonable to make at the time. The only alternative would have been to undertake additional field
research which would have interrupted the progress
of the study. As a result, the assumptions remain
operative, and the computations depend upon their
correctness. As will be shown, some of them are
open to modification on the basis of research findings. Once again it may be said: Such modifications will change the computational results, but
probably not enough to disturb the conclusions of
the study.

The computational model (the equations derived
in Chapter 6) is an abstraction from reality. It
attempts to describe in just a few terms, a segment
of customary behavior of 2,046,400 people who work
in the CBD. It receives, as its input, these
2,046,400 people according to their scheduled starting times, both their present ones and the new ones
under work staggering. It then performs a series of
operations or modifications on the numbers. It
first reduces them to the number who cross the subway cordons to work on any weekday, thereby eliminating all the people who live in the CBD or who
get there by other means of transport. It then redistributes the cordon crossers according to the
times they arrive at work (which may be different
from the times they are scheduled to start work).
Finally, it places these people back into their cordon stations according to the times they are supposed to cross them. Obviously, to perform such
calculations, the actual behaviors of 2,046,400

people have to be simplified and summarized in very
general ways.

The elements of the behavior which are picked
up by the model and generalized (abstracted) are
these: the numbers of people who take part in this
process, their habits with respect to arriving at
work early, on time, or late, and the timing of
their journey from cordon station to work. These
are fully explained in Chapter 6 and its appendixes.
It is appropriate, here in the final assessment, to
call attention to the vast reduction which had to be
made in order to compress the behaviors of 2,046,400
people into a single mathematical statement.

In pointing out this simplification of an in-
finitely complex reality, two things are intended.
One is to assert again that its inner structure appears valid, particularly after having analyzed
large numbers of its results. There appears to be
no reason to impeach either its component elements
or the particular quantities which make up its co-
efficients--the various adjustment tables. This is
not to say that they are true values--no such values
exist for a constantly fluctuating universe. Rather,
they give evidence, after repeated use and analysis
of results, of reliability. Further research will
undoubtedly refine both the model and its adjustment
tables, but up to the point, lacking more refined
statistics, the model continues serviceable and worthy of confidence.

The second intention in insisting upon the massive simplification of the model is to expose some
of its principal assumptions. The model could not
have been constructed without assumptions. The alternative would have been 2,046,400 models, one for
each person working in the CBD. Any attempt to reduce this number involves the making of assumptions.
To reach one model (perhaps four--one for each degree of change in travel practice), an uncountable
number of assumptions were required, most of them
without having actually been considered. In this
evaluation, a few will be mentioned, those which appear to the study to be the most sensitive.

Two sets of assumptions are discernible in the
forecasting equation. One relates to the travel
practices which it attributes to the people: their
numbers, their journey and its timing. The other
concerns the substitution of the total CBD for the
twenty individual cordon stations. The nature of
these assumptions and their implications will be
examined.

The first assumption--travel practice--may be
stated as follows. The forecast equation assumes
that the people who work in any given CBD industry,
who are now scheduled to start work at any given
time, will behave the same as people in any other
industry scheduled to start at the same time in respect to: (1) the percentage who will be present at
work on any given day; (2) the percentage who cross
subway cordons to work; (3) the percentages who arrive and start work early or late by given amounts
of time; and (4) the percentages who spend given
amounts of time traveling from cordon station to
place of employment.

The burden of this assumption is uniformity
among industries in respect to each of the enumerated behaviors. It does not mean that all the people in one industry behave like all those of another.
There is a second conditioning element--that the
people in one industry who are scheduled to start
work at the same time as the people in another will
act similarly. This constrains the range of uniformity to a smaller aggregate of people which is
defined by properties closely related to the behaviors in question.

The significance of this assumption can be
spelled out by an example. It says that employees
in factories scheduled to start, say, at 8:30 a.m.,
cross cordons in the same proportions and times as
the employees of the insurance industry scheduled at
the same time. Each will have the same percentage
who cross subway cordons, the same percentage of
early and late arrivals, and the same percentages
of travel times from cordon station to work. This

similarity of behavior will be expected to prevail
if they shifted to the same starting time.

The assumption of interindustry uniformity
rests upon many other assumptions as to residence,
location of employment in the CBD, practices of
places of employment, as well as behavior characteristics of employees. The validity of this assumption cannot be tested because essential data are
lacking. It is in fact impossible to get at how the
people of one industry might differ from those of
another in respect to any of these behaviors, or
even whether there are such differences. By tying
the behavior not only to industry but to starting
times, it is probable that the aggregates of employees at any given starting time are approximately described by the various tables employed as coefficients in the equations. But the differences,
if any, on an industry level which become significant in computing the effects of schedule change remain submerged in the assumption of uniformity.

Available evidence calls into question at least
two of these submerged assumptions; but problems of
data have thus far made it impossible to improve
upon the model. First, the assumption that people
in the various industry groups (not the smaller aggregates of industries) live in the four subway boroughs (Manhattan, Bronx, Queens, and Brooklyn), or
in outlying areas served by their subways in similar
proportions does not seem to be valid. There appear
to be differences in the percentages of people, by
industry group, living in these areas. This much is
indicated by available evidence. The statistics
have thus far not been judged sufficiently strong to
replace the assumption of uniform industry group percentages by residence area. It should also be noted
that the differences between the indicated actual
percentages and the assumption of uniformity do not
appear very large. Whether they are large enough to
make a difference to the final results cannot yet be
determined.

The second assumption implied in the model is
that the same proportion of people of each industry

cross cordon stations on their journey to work.
This proportion amounts to about two thirds, a statistic corroborated by other studies of traffic into
the CBD. As with the first, this assumption is
called into question by some of the available but
fragmentary evidence. There appear to be differences in the proportion of people of the various industry groups who cross cordons. This difference is
directly related to their residence. That is to say,
the percentages of people living in the four boroughs (or in their outlying areas) who cross cordons
show noticeable differences. Manhattan has a lower
than average proportion because it has more people
using buses, taxis, and cars, or walking to work,
and some live in the CBD. The other boroughs have
higher than average proportions crossing cordons.
Once again, the statistics have to be regarded as
indicative of conditions. They have not yet been
considered valid enough to replace the over-all assumption of uniformity.

The combined effect of these two inner assumptions finds expression in the general one of the
computational model: that the same proportions of
each industry group starting work at the same time
cross cordon stations. Insofar as the two inner assumptions are incorrect, this one too is weakened--
except as it limits its force to people in different
industries starting work at the same time. Uniformity of industry schedules offsets this shortcoming
to some extent. But after balancing these counter-
considerations, the conclusion emerges that the assumption in the model ought to be replaced by statistical evidence, if it becomes available.

Thus, the first of the two assumptions upon
which the forecasting equation is based--the one relating to industry uniformity of travel practices--
poses a crucial question. What may be said about
the conclusions depending upon this assumption? A
preliminary investigation has been made of this
question, using data which seemed suitable. By giving effect to variations in cordon crossing by industry, differences can be expected in the computed

cordon counts. It does not appear that these differences will change the final conclusions of the
study in any significant way. Changes in work
schedule affect cordon counts so intricately that
the modifications which might result from replacing
the assumption with statistics do not appear capable
of changing the ultimate results of the study.

The second of the two assumptions of the model
--use of total CBD instead of individual cordon sta-
tions--may be stated in the following language. The
equation assumes that the total number of people who
(according to the computations) are to pass through
subway cordon stations traveling to work during any
given 20-minute interval will be distributed among
the twenty cordon stations according to the per cent
of each station's cordon count to the total CBD
count for the interval.

The equation computes the total CBD cordon
count for each interval during the morning rush
hour. The assumption is made that these total
counts will be distributed among the twenty stations
according to their share of the total for the interval. This assumption enters into the procedure when
the cordon count standards for each interval are
computed and applied. (The net excess of each station is converted to its equivalent by dividing it
by the station's per cent of the total count for the
interval.)

This assumption had to be made--as explained in
Chapter 6--because information is not available by
which to formulate a forecasting equation for each
cordon station. To do so would require statistics
relating employment, work schedules, and the other
behavior to each cordon station individually, rather
than to the CBD as a whole. The resulting forecasting equations would also be somewhat different in
form from the one actually utilized. The assumption
accordingly was forced upon the study by circumstance, not necessarily by choice.

The validity of this assumption cannot be tested by reference to the conditions of industry and

cordon station which it implies. As a matter of
fact, the evidence presented in Chapter 2 shows that
the various stations have different cordon interval
patterns and accordingly different percentages of
the total CBD count during the rush hour interval.
This suggests a varying distribution of industry or
starting time by cordon station, a circumstance con-
tradicting the assumption. These differences are
not considered sufficient to affect materially the
findings of the study.

This appraisal of the computational model repeats the conclusion reached earlier in the study--
that it is adequate to the purposes at hand. The
model is a massive condensation and simplification
of an exceedingly complex phenomenon. It seeks to
reduce the route, timing, and other related practices
of the journey to work by 2,046,400 people to an expression involving only the few terms of the equation. Given the distance between the reality and
the model, the notion of accuracy is a difficult one
to apply. The test of validity of such a model can
ultimately be given only by experience. Short of
experience, the test consists of probing its structure and especially its assumptions. This final review discloses that many improvements can be made in
the computational model, but that this first effort
remains serviceable.

An Appraisal of the Computed
Cordon Counts

The final topic in this test of the third criterion raises the crucial question of feasibility.
The subway traffic standards, as argued above, appear suitable. The computational model seems capable, within reasonable limits of confidence, of producing reliable cordon counts from the projected
work schedules. The question then arises: Do the
computed counts conform to the standard? In short,
will work staggering relieve subway congestion?

The answer discovered by this study, and stated
as judiciously as possible, is: Work staggering can,

and probably would relieve subway congestion during
rush hours. The caution within this answer is dictated by all the limitations of data and assumptions
already described. But more immediately, it reflects a dispassionate view of the computed cordon
counts as compared with the comfort level standards.
These results are fully presented and discussed in
Chapter 7. By way of final evaluation, two things
remain to be emphasized.

First, no matter what the computations show or
how strong the statistical support of the study,
there is one behavioral condition affecting congestion which defies forecasting. It is the practice
of arriving at work earlier or later than required
by work schedules. This practice was shown to exist
and was given a quantitative description in Chapter
6. It was also contended that the practice is governed, at least to some extent, by the prevailing
congestion on the subways. The combined effects of
schedule change and relief of subway congestion can
and probably will bring about a change in this practice both by the people whose schedules are changed
and by the others who will also benefit from improved subway conditions. But the extent of such
change cannot even be guessed, much less estimated
by a reasoned forecast.

An attempt to deal with the probable change in
travel timing was introduced into the calculations
by modifying the tables depicting the present practices in a systematic (if mechanical) way--by reducing the practice of early and late arrival by 0, 5,
10, and 15 minutes for the CBD working population as
a whole. These are called the degrees of travel behavior: 0, -5, -10, and -15. All the computed cordon counts resulting from schedule changes are calculated according to each of the four degrees.

The existence of this unforeseeable but potential change in behavior makes it impossible to state
definitively that any given plan of work staggering
will or will not relieve congestion. It can relieve
congestion, depending upon how the behavior changes.

As a matter of fact, alternative work schedules can
be computed which will relieve congestion for any
amount of reduction in early and late arrival, down
to and including arrival exactly on time--the level
of absolute demand described in Chapter 6. Once an
assumption is made about change in the behavior, a
plan of work staggering can be made to fit it. But
in the nature of things, this assumption cannot be
made and as a consequence a definitive plan cannot
be devised. The ability of any program of schedule
change to relieve congestion must be made conditional upon changes which may occur in the timing of
travel.

     Accordingly, the five combinations must also be
received as conditionally feasible. They are capable of producing substantial relief of congestion
during the rush hours. They are also capable of re-
creating traffic peaks at the same time as at present or at different times. Whether congestion will
be relieved or reestablished will depend upon the
subway riders and the options they take up: change
in the timing of travel or improved conditions.
Fortunately, the choice is not an absolute one. The
five combinations actually permit the riders some of
each. They can, in aggregate, reduce their early or
late arrivals and still obtain significant improvements in riding comfort, but within limits.

     The limits of change in travel timing which ap-
ply to the five proposed combinations can be stated
explicitly. They are obtained by comparing the computed counts of each of the degrees in relation to
the comfort level standards. This was presented in
detail in Chapter 7. The general conclusion which
emerges from the comparison is that the five combinations will provide maximum relief if there is no
change in travel timing (degree -0), and that the
amount of relief will diminish as early and late arrivals are reduced (degree -5, -10, -15). The combinations vary in their reduction of relief as the
amount of travel time change increases. If the
change in timing reaches an average of fifteen minutes (degree -15), all five combinations show

congestion in one or more of the critical intervals.
But if the change is less than ten minutes, the
amount of relief provided by each of the five is
significant. As a general guideline, the limits of
change in early and late arrival may be set at a reduction of ten minutes and still allow for significant improvement in riding comfort in the subways.

It is tempting to ask: What are the chances
that the average change will be less than ten minutes? In a purely technical sense, it would require the same kind of information to answer this
question as to forecast the probable change in travel timing. Less technically, however, it is possible to offer some statements which may throw light
on the answer. A change of ten minutes is very
large, as an average for the whole CBD. Of the total number of people who work during the day, Monday
through Friday, the schedules of less than 30 per
cent are changed by the five combinations. If only
these people modify travel timing, they would have
to change by more than one half hour in order to
reduce the over-all average to ten minutes. Other
assumptions about who may change can also be made,
and the arithmetic of the ten minutes average performed. They lead to the same impression: An
average reduction for the whole CBD of ten minutes
is very large, and would require a great deal of
change by the people who actually modify their travel timing. Simply because it implies a substantial
change in practice, the chance of the average reduction reaching ten minutes is considered not very
great. It does not pose a serious risk to the conclusions reached by the study nor to implementing a
program of work staggering.

The second item of this appraisal pertains to
the results of the comparison of the computed cordon
counts and the comfort level standards. The details
of the comparison were set forth in Chapter 7, where
they were also interpreted. It now remains to emphasize the main findings of the comparison.

No matter which of the five plans, if any, is
adopted, and no matter how much travel timing may

(or may not) change, subway traffic cannot be
brought down to, or below the comfort level in all
of the four congested intervals. It was shown experimentally in Chapter 7 that the sheer arithmetic
of the computations made this impossible, given the
standards, the forecasting equation and its coefficients. The computed cordon counts could not fail
to exhibit the same characteristics: Some exceed,
others are less than the comfort level standards of
the individual intervals, but not by very large
amounts.

     This raises a very special kind of question,
ostensibly technical but actually a question of policy. If it were technical, a technical solution
could be sought. But as a policy question, it becomes a matter of judgment and decision on quite
other grounds. The question is: By how much may
the computed counts exceed the comfort level standard and still be regarded as acceptable within the
meaning of feasibility as employed in this study?
This is a question which turns on assessing the
amount of relief which the passengers are willing to
accept in exchange for modified work schedules.
Computed counts which are below the standard create
no difficulty so long as the differences are small.
From the viewpoint of riding conditions, a lower
count means that comfort in the car will be even
better than intended. If the computed count is much
below the standard, a question of cost or scheduling
might arise. But since the amounts of difference
are all small, the costs and scheduling aspects are
treated as negligible. Accordingly, only the deviations which exceed standard enter into the policy
problem.

     It proves useful to approach this policy prob-
lem in reverse: to determine first how much the
computed counts differ from the standards. These
differences identify the extent to which the standards must be relaxed in order to find the five combinations feasible--in general, a more realistic
approach to the problem. Once the issue is thus
made specific, the policy problem becomes more accessible.

WORK STAGGERING FOR TRAFFIC RELIEF

Table 67 shows how much of the congestion each
of the five combinations eliminates during each interval and for each degree of change in travel timing.* The numbers in Table 67 are the percentages
of excess passengers removed from each interval by
each combination, and by each degree. Obviously,
the higher the per cent, the greater the computed
riding comfort. The entry "all" means that zero or
negative deviations occur. That is, the computed
cordon count is equal to or less than the standard,
and hence the computed level is attained.

TABLE 67

Per Cent of Reduction in Congestion in Four
Intervals, by Each Schedule Combination and
by Degree of Change in Travel Timing

Degree	Interval	Combination				
		1	2	3	4	5
-0	7:40-8:00	all	all	all	all	all
	8:00-8:20	70	77	83	68	87
	8:20-8:40	all	95	93	99	94
	8:40-9:00	all	all	all	all	all
-5	7:40-8:00	all	all	all	all	all
	8:00-8:20	71	82	90	70	93
	8:20-8:40	99	95	92	98	94
	8:40-9:00	all	96	87	all	82
-10	7:40-8:00	all	all	all	all	all
	8:00-8:20	70	84	94	70	97
	8:20-8:40	98	93	91	96	94
	8:40-9:00	82	72	62	86	53
-15	7:40-8:00	all	all	all	all	all
	8:00-8:20	67	86	97	70	99
	8:20-8:40	97	91	90	94	93
	8:40-9:00	60	49	37	66	27

*This table was constructed by calculating the
required amount of reduction in each interval (the
reconstructed cordon count of Table 52 minus the
comfort level standard of Table 53) and by dividing
these amounts into the deviations given on Table 65.

It becomes clear from Table 67 that the policy problem cannot be resolved by establishing a single cut-off percentage and then judging any combination as unacceptable if it shows less than that amount of improvement in any interval. To assess the results responsibly, it is necessary to examine each combination's four intervals as a unit, and to assess their over-all reduction in congestion. For example, the first combination shows, at degree -0, that all congestion will be eliminated from three intervals and 70 per cent from the fourth. At first sight, the 70 per cent is disappointing; it means that 30 per cent of the congestion will remain. But this will not occur in all stations--only in the one or possibly two with the highest net excess of passengers. Viewed for the system as a whole, the 70 per cent is a remarkable improvement in riding comfort, especially when combined with the total reduction in the surrounding intervals. Similarly, the other combinations are arguably as good as the first one for degree -0. They are slightly lower in one or two intervals and higher in the other.

At degree -5, the percentages amount to about the same over-all degree of improvement as at degree -0. There is no single per cent as low as 68 per cent, but there is some slight lowering of the over-all average reduction in congestion. Once again, if congestion could be reduced according to the percentages shown for degree -5, there is no question but that the passengers would benefit from an enormous improvement in riding conditions, despite the few 70 and 80 per cents.

In degree -10, the amount by which congestion is reduced is slightly lower than for degree -5. But there is still a significant improvement in riding comfort. The only real departures from the percentages of the other degrees are to be found in combinations 3 and 5 for the 8:40-9:00 interval. They show reductions in congestion of 62 per cent and 53 per cent respectively. A priori, one might say that these are too low to be accepted as a return for work staggering. But when they are combined with the improvements in the other intervals

--well over 90 per cent--it is not reasonable to reject these two combinations at degree -10. It
should also be noted that these reductions would
eliminate the congestion from one or two of the
three stations which are congested during this interval.

Finally, at degree -15, percentages as low as
49 per cent, 37 per cent, and 27 per cent occur.
Again, coupled with the other per cents of the same
combinations, there is still a decided improvement
in riding comfort. But perhaps the line ought to be
drawn ahead of these percentages, or at least ahead
of 27 per cent and 37 per cent.

From the viewpoint of this study--as a policy
judgment not as a technical finding--any improvement
in a single interval by as much as 50 per cent (including the one case of 49 per cent), when occurring
in combination with substantial reductions of congestion in the other intervals, ought to be regarded
as an acceptable gain in riding comfort. While it
will not produce a comfort level ride, it will significantly reduce the amount of congestion. Even
more accurately, it will confine this residual
amount of congestion to one, possibly two stations
during a single interval.

Summary: The Subways

Will work staggering relieve subway congestion
during rush hours?

The available evidence says unequivocally: yes.
Any of the five combinations will bring the cordon
counts down to levels which will be dramatically more
comfortable than at present, according to the forecasts and computations.

OTHER MODES OF TRANSIT

Thus far, the study of congestion and its relief by work staggering has been confined to the subways. This was partly a matter of convenience and

partly the result of an assumption. It was assumed
that if changes in work schedule relieve congestion
on the subways, they will do the same for the other
modes of passenger transportation into and out of
the CBD. The assumption was based on the observation that peak hour congestion occurs similarly on
all modes of transit. Periodic studies by the Regional Planning Association show that this common
pattern prevails. The sociological study also reports that people who work in the CBD who use the
other modes of transit have the same characteristics
as the subway riders. It was therefore not an un-
reasonable course to treat the subways as the surro-
gates of the others.

At this juncture, when the results are undergoing evaluation, the assumption and its consequences
invite closer scrutiny. Can the schedule changes
which relieve subway congestion be expected to relieve congestion on the highways and streets into
and out of the CBD, the railroads, and the PATH
tubes? The answer to this question will be based on
an analysis of two factors. They are: the nature
of the traffic flows and the potential changes in
modes of travel. These furnish a basis for judging
whether the subway results may be applied to the
others.

Traffic Flow

Subway traffic is virtually a continuous flow.
During the rush hours, people enter the system in a
seemingly endless stream, and are transported continuously across the cordons and into (or out of)
the CBD. Of course it is not truly continuous, because the trains travel only at discrete intervals.
But for the purpose at hand, the system can be considered as such.

This means that changes in work schedule--dis-
regarding the travel timing problem--will be registered directly and uninterruptedly upon the subway's
traffic flow. If people are shifted earlier they
will flow to the system earlier, and will be transported earlier.

To apply the subway findings to the other modes
of transit, the relationship between work schedules
and traffic has to have the same property. Changes
in schedule must result in changes in the shape of
the traffic flow. This relationship depends, at
least in part, upon the flow characteristics of
other modes. If they are continuous, then they can
react immediately to changes in the flow of travelers into them. If they are not continuous, the flow
can be greatly disturbed--with resulting congestion
to the transit system and inconvenience to the travelers.

Most of the other modes of traffic have a continuous flow of traffic. The buses, cars, taxis,
and trucks enter and leave the CBD in a continuous
stream similar to the subway flow. Disregarding the
timing problem, the relationship between work schedule and cordon count for these other modes ought to
be as sensitive as in the case of the subways.

However, there is--or may be--a difference between some of the modes and the subways which can
affect the results of work staggering. It appears
that the other modes--the highways, streets, tunnels,
and bridges--carry more people who do not work in
the CBD than the subways during rush hours. These
include people in transit to other places, people
going to the CBD for reasons other than work, and
the like. It also includes freight carriers into
and across the CBD. These other people cannot fail
to schedule their travel, if possible, so as to
avoid the rush hours originating in work schedules.
Since the people who work in the CBD form only a
portion of the total, a shift in their travel times
may create a traffic bulge earlier or later than at
present, and to the same extent a traffic trough at
the present peak.

This is a relevant factor in applying the subway findings to the other modes. But, on balance,
it is not considered weighty enough to stand in the
way. If schedules are changed, people will flow to
these other modes according to their new work times.

There is even a good chance that traffic will quickly readjust to their changed times and that they
will encounter less congestion than at present--or
at least, not worse. Hence, with respect to these
modes of travel, the subway findings are regarded as
applicable. By changing CBD work schedules according to the five combinations, vehicular congestion
during rush hours stands a reasonable chance of
benefiting.

The railroads and intercity buses serving the
CBD pose a very different problem. They operate on
schedules which lack the essential characteristic of
continuous flow. Hence, people enter and leave them,
not in a continuous stream, but in distinct aggregates. Changing work schedules in the CBD may not--
perhaps will not--cause them to alter their operating schedules to handle the changed flow of passengers. In such a case, work staggering can create
greater congestion on these systems, an imbalance in
their schedules, and a great deal of inconvenience
to the people who travel on them.

This study did not investigate the ability of
the railroads and intercity buses to modify their
operating schedules to conform to the needs of work
staggering. Nor did it compute the changes in the
flow of people to these systems as a result of
schedule changes, as was done in the case of the
subways. Consequently, it is not possible to say
whether or not work staggering will relieve their
congestion or how it will affect their traffic--
other than that it will change the needs of their
passengers to some extent.

The effects of work staggering upon the railroads and intercity buses are a problem of implementation, not of feasibility. It may be reasonably
assumed that some portion of the railroad and bus
schedules will be adjustable to meet whatever
changes in demand arise from work staggering. The
unadjustable portion would hardly be sufficient to
stand in the way of work staggering if it proves
feasible on other grounds. This unadjustable portion, if it exists, will have to be assisted by

whatever means are available to meet the needs of
the passengers. This is typically the kind of problem which can best be taken care of during the period in which work staggering is under public review.
Only then will the program of schedule change actually emerge, and with it the new schedule needs for
railroads and intercity buses. The problems can
then be handled on the basis of concrete and realistic requirements. The effects of work staggering
upon the railroads and intercity buses must be kept
upon the agenda of work staggering because they are
extremely important to the economy of the CBD--and
hence to work staggering itself.

Changes in Travel Mode

One of the possible outcomes of work staggering
is a shift in transit mode by the people who travel
to and from the CBD. By changing the conditions of
travel, especially by relieving congestion in the
subways, people who now use other modes may find it
desirable to shift to the subway. This might be
accentuated by less favorable consequences on the
other modes. By the same token, if congestion is
reduced on the others, people may also change from
riding the subways to using cars, taxis, or buses.
Once a change is made in traffic conditions, shifts
of this kind are possible. And if they occur, the
forecasts of improvements will not be realized.

This possibility is noted for the record, not
because anything substantive can be said about it.
It was acknowledged as potential from the start of
the study, but it was not subjected to any inquiry.
This was primarily because the conditions of work
staggering, from which the shifts would emanate,
were unknown and hence could not be utilized as a
basis for formulating a suitable research.

In the absence of evidence, the assumption has
to be made that shifts in travel mode will not be
sufficient to distort the findings in the case of
the subways, nor their application to the other
modes of travel.

Summary

If work staggering proves capable of relieving
subway congestion during rush hours, there are ample
grounds for the belief that it will also benefit
other modes of passenger transportation into and out
of the CBD. Many of the other modes--city buses,
tubes, cars, and taxis using the city streets, and
possibly some intercity buses--have enough in common
with the subways, insofar as work staggering is concerned, to justify attributing the subway findings
to them. There are unquestionably some differences
between each of them and the subway system, and they
will undoubtedly sustain differing effects from work
staggering. But in the main, their present rush
hour congestion ought to be relieved by work staggering.

Some of the other modes--railroads, some intercity buses, the tunnels and bridges, and possibly
some city streets--are sufficiently different from
the subways to make the same attribution of findings
inadvisable. Work staggering may improve their rush
hour conditions, but there is far less strength in
such a judgment than in the case of the others. However, it is hard to see that work staggering can
worsen their conditions, certainly not after a period of adjustment to the new conditions. Some of the
uncertainty about these modes will be reduced by appropriate inquiries and assistance, if and when it
is decided to go forward with a program of work
staggering.

Conclusions

Will work staggering relieve traffic congestion
on all modes of transit?

To this question, a three-part answer must be
given. First, if work staggering relieves subway
congestion--as the computations indicate--it ought
also to relieve rush hour congestion on some of the
other modes of travel, those which have traffic
characteristics similar to the subways. Second,

those which are not relieved ought in any case not
be worsened. The streets serving buses and cars
should be better off over the earlier part of the
rush hour, but they might encounter heavy traffic in
the later part, after 9:00 a.m. Third, some of the
transportation modes will require special consideration in order to assist them to adjust their schedules to modified transit demands.

This much, however, seems reasonably clear. On
the whole, despite some special situations, work
staggering will relieve congestion. The areas which
remain uncertain do not seem significant enough, by
reason of their proportions of the total transit
traffic, to find staggering unfeasible on the
grounds of its traffic consequences.

TOLERANCE AND RESISTANCE

Any proposal for work staggering will inevitably meet with both approval and opposition. However
moderate the schedule changes, they are bound to
produce a wide range of effects in economic, social,
communal, and personal lives. Some of these effects
will be welcomed; others will stimulate opposition
because they are considered disadvantageous. If the
disadvantages prove capable of mobilizing a strong
enough resistance, work staggering can turn out to
be unfeasible, regardless of its benefits.

Feasibility requires, as a fourth condition,
that the community tolerate work staggering. This
refers to the people, firms, and institutions which
are not required to modify their own schedules but
which will be affected by work staggering within the
CBD. To be feasible, a proposal for work staggering
ought not to produce an effective resistance and opposition.

This criterion can best be tested after the
feasibility study is published but before work staggering is implemented. The community cannot be expected to react realistically to work staggering before the detailed proposals are published, since it

will not know just who will be affected and in what
respects. Once the proposals become public, the
community can be relied upon to generate its reactions and to make them known to the responsible public officials. To base an investigation of community attitude upon a general concept of work staggering, rather than upon definite proposals, is an unrewarding procedure. The response would be equally
general and hence not germane.

Another approach to this problem was developed
in the course of the study but it was not actually
pursued. In this approach, an investigation would
be made to try to identify the people, firms, and
institutions which would be affected by work staggering. The investigation would be expected to produce information about the identity of such people
and the nature of the effect they would sustain. In
this way, it might be possible to anticipate some of
the sources of community support as well as resistance.

This approach was not taken partly for the same
reason given above. It required fairly specific information about the actual proposals. Once these
become available it is just as well to make them
public and let the community respond as it chooses.

For these reasons, there is no direct evidence
as to whether or not this criterion is satisfied by
the five proposed schedule combinations. There is,
however, some indirect evidence which can be brought
to bear upon the problem. The sociological study
raised questions about opposition and resistance,
and also about the respondents' family and other social involvements. While the study was confined to
CBD employees, some of the material may be interpreted as reflecting the community at large.

The relevant findings were presented in considerable detail in Chapter 5. To sum up, they in-
dicate--at least as far as the universe of the respondents is concerned--that there are no danger
signals of resistance to work staggering. There
will be opposition and discontent, but the evidence

did not reveal any inclination to utilize available
instruments of resistance. Obviously, this does not
mean that it cannot happen. Under the pressure of a
real proposal, a genuine opposition may indeed develop.

As a program, work staggering enjoys substantial resources for approval by the community. The
changes embodied in the five combinations are actually quite modest. Their severest impact will probably fall upon the people directly affected, rather
than the others. Their effects on the others have
many favorable potentialities. These include the
benefits of reduced peak loads in other industries,
retail trades, services, and entertainment whose
clienteles will become available over longer time
periods.

With respect to the fourth criterion, this
study reaches two conclusions. On the basis of the
limited evidence arising from the sociological study,
there is no apparent reason for particular concern
that staggering will encounter organized resistance.
There are ample grounds for the belief that substantial sectors of the community will approve a program
of work staggering. Second, if there are any serious bases of objection or if significant opposition
develops, they can be ascertained upon publication
of the proposals, well in advance of implementation.
This ought to allow sufficient opportunity to assess
the opposition, to make appropriate adaptations in
the program, or to abandon it altogether if necessary.

DURABILITY

The final criterion of feasibility pertains to
the future, after work staggering is put into operation. It will take some time to implement a program
--to conduct the necessary public discussion, to obtain compliance from industries, and to allow the
adaptations by other industries and activities to
occur. As this process draws to a close, the period

of work staggering starts.   There ought to be some
assurance that the traffic improvements resulting
from the schedule changes and other adaptations will
endure, and not disappear in a short time.

This criterion can only be applied in a general
way, not rigorously.   There is no reasonable basis
for defining "short time," nor to set a minimum period for which the transit relief should "endure."
Even if such standards could be established, it is
not possible to forecast the future of work staggering with sufficient accuracy to apply them.   As an
alternative, the prospects of some of the factors
which will directly affect work staggering will be
examined.   From this, a reasonable judgment will
emerge.

During the course of the study, three phenomena
which significantly affect the future of work staggering were examined.   They are: the trends in
transit traffic, CBD employment, and hours of work.
Each was discussed in appropriate places in the preceding chapters.

The trend of cordon counts and transit has been
relatively stable in recent years with perhaps a
very slight tendency toward decline.   If this continues, a reappearance of congestion need not be
anticipated on account of an increase in subway
travel.   The trend in CBD employment has also ex-
hibited stability, again with a slight discernible
tendency toward decline.   Here too, if the trend
persists, no concern need be felt about an increase
in demand for travel to and from work.   There are
indications that the lengths of the working day in
the CBD is stabilizing at between seven and eight
hours.   Further reduction in hours of work seems to
be occurring in other ways than by shortening the
regular workdays.   The evidence, however, is not
altogether uniform because of the great disparity in
work hours among the various industries of the area.
But whether the workday remains stable or is shortened, the effects on transit need occasion no concern so long as the proposed starting times are

maintained. The present schedules of the CBD show a
great deal of irregularity of stopping times. If
the workday is shortened by moving the stopping
times earlier--so long as the numbers of people affected do not grow too large--there may even be an
improvement in transit conditions during the journey home from work.

The evidence that CBD employment, hours of work,
and transit traffic are stable, or diminishing
slightly, is reassuring to the future of transit
improvement resulting from work staggering. These
three factors are significant because they are determinants of the relationship of work schedules to
transit traffic, hence operationally connected with
the evolution of work staggering. Their stable
trends in recent years are also important because
these are inherently massive, slow-moving phenomena.
If they hold steady, the prospects of work staggering are very encouraging.

But there are also other things which inevitably govern the future of work staggering, such as
changes in population, economy, physical structure,
and transit systems of the CBD. Precisely because
work staggering is so intricately bound up with
these phenomena, anything which happens to them will
affect its future results. Each of these external
influences is dynamic, constantly undergoing change.
But the changes are generally slow, entailing long
periods before they come to fruition--periods which
are long enough to make work staggering, if otherwise feasible, a worthwhile endeavor. Short of cat-
astrophic events, the readings which can be made of
these environing determinants of work staggering do
not raise any danger signals.

There is enough reassurance in these large
scale indexes to warrant a favorable judgment about
the final criterion of feasibility. Certainly,
there are no indications from the more closely related phenomena that the conditions upon which staggering is formulated are about to change. Hence, in
a most general way, the conclusion is reached that

the beneficial effects of work staggering ought to
endure long enough to be worth the effort.

One final point about the future of work staggering remains to be made. Its durability can be
ensured by instituting an appropriate maintenance
program. Through continuing surveillance of work
schedules, transit traffic, employment, and hours,
it will be possible to introduce further modifications of work schedule in order to preserve the improvements in transit conditions. If a maintenance
program is not established, the program initially
put into operation will become obsolete more quickly
than it should.

WHAT IF . . .

The evaluation of the five schedule combinations on the basis of the criteria of work staggering, as established in Chapter 1, is now completed.
But before summing up its results and passing final
judgment on feasibility, an assessment will be made
of the risks and potential damage of work staggering, at least insofar as they are now visible. Some
safeguards which can reduce the risks and hence increase the likelihood of success will also be mentioned.

A lot of things can destroy a work staggering
program. Most of them are the kinds of things which
will also destroy other aspects of the community.
They include major changes in economic, social, political or cultural life, or some unforeseen catas-
trophe. As significant as they may be, they can be
left out of this inquiry as not directly relevant.
There are more immediate dangers which spring from
work staggering itself and from the economic and social processes upon which it depends.

To pursue the risks of work staggering, several
assumptions have to be made. It must be assumed,
first, that a policy is taken--by whoever is authorized to do so--that the proposal of work staggering

shall go forward. A second assumption then follows: that a full public discussion will ensue, and that the community--its people, institutions, and places of employment--will become fully and realistically informed about what is to happen to schedules and transit congestion. Third, as a result, there are no indications that compliance will be inadequate or that there will be an effective opposition. Fourth, if compliance promises to be sufficient and resistance fails to mobilize, a decision to implement work staggering is then made. Finally, it is assumed that the various transit bodies prove capable, both on economic and operating grounds, of modifying their schedules to carry the traffic. These assumptions carry the program, including any revisions in schedules which may arise during the period of preparation, from the completion of the study to the moment it is implemented.

The Transition

A period must be envisaged during which the change in work schedules is put into effect and the various transit agencies cope with the problems of their operating schedules. Even under the best circumstances, this period must be expected to produce its share of problems.

The places of employment whose schedules are to be changed will undoubtedly experience many difficulties of adjustment. Their personnel will have to reschedule their travel times. If past experience is a guide, people will experiment very carefully with all kinds of different travel arrangements, including a change of mode, route, timing, and others, which even the transit experts cannot foresee. This can produce increases in early arrival, lateness, and early or late departure. The places of employment will also encounter unexpected novelties in their relationships with suppliers and customers. They will have to learn their new schedules--when they will be available and when they won't. Every effort was made in formulating the program to minimize these time dislocations and inconveniences, but

they will occur, perhaps frequently, during the
transition period and until the people learn the new
CBD schedules. Finally, the places of employment
may also have to modify some of their other employment practices such as the timing of lunch hours.
There will undoubtedly be many other problems.

The people who work in the CBD--both in firms
changing schedules and in others--will meet up with
unaccustomed things. As mentioned above, they will
find new travel conditions: new schedules, new
street and highway traffic, new subway conditions,
and others. At the outset, these may be worse than
they are now. Lunch time will come either too soon
or too late, depending upon the change in starting
time and whether the lunch hour is rescheduled.
Restaurants will be more crowded for some, less for
others until the adjustments are completed. The
journey home can turn up even more complications because more kinds of travelers have to discover the
effects of the new schedules on traffic. Shopping
after work will also become easier for some and
harder for others at the beginning.

The places of employment whose schedules are
not changed by the work staggering proposals will
also encounter problems. Many will be similar to
the companies which change schedules--learning the
new timing of work in the CBD, the hours of their
suppliers and customers, absorbing the effects of
changed travel, lunch, and other conditions experienced by their employees, and making suitable adaptations to all these things. Some of these places
of employment will find it necessary to modify their
own schedules for business or personnel reasons.

Finally, the conditions in the transit system
can prove difficult during the transition period.
There can be crowding in stations, trains, highways,
streets, buses, sidewalks, and elevators. There may
be waiting lines at ticket counters, toll booths,
and other such places. There may be longer waits
for subways and trains. The journey to and from
work can actually become worse for some people. But
this should be temporary. The transit systems

cannot predict just how the new traffic will flow.
Nor will the passengers know just when, where, or
how to find the best ride to and from work. The
transit systems will adjust schedules to the new
traffic and the passengers will change their travel
day to day according to the conditions they actually
find. Each side can be expected to chase the other
until things settle down. All this will require
time and patience of everyone, and the utmost skill
on the part of the transit authorities.

If all goes well, these difficulties will iron
out, some quickly, others perhaps over a considerable period. The contingencies recited above should
prove only transitional. As much as possible, the
work staggering program makes provision for all of
them to disappear, given the necessary time to adjust.

The Risks

Transition is a luxury, to be identified and
enjoyed after it is over. The period will be transitional only if the problems are solved and the
difficulties are removed. Work staggering will then
emerge, perhaps gradually, into its full effectiveness. But may the transition never actually happen?
Can the difficulties prove unsolvable? Can problem
follow problem until the skills of the transit managers, the patience of the people, and the capabilities of the places of employment are exhausted?

Obviously these things can happen. It would be
most unrealistic to suppose that they cannot, for
all the reasons recited in many places in this study.
It does not follow that work staggering should
therefore be abandoned, but rather that the risks
be more realistically evaluated. How can work staggering fail? What damages can it cause? And what
are the possible protections against failure?

Failure means that the traffic forecast will
not be realized. The subway peaks will not be sufficiently reduced, or else will be shifted to other

times earlier or later than at present. It means
that the same will occur on the other modes of transit. There is even an intermediate possibility--
that some will be the same or better off than at
present, while others will be worse.

The way it appears now--after the study is completed but before it is issued or put into effect--
a failure of the traffic forecast would be traceable
to three possible sources: to compliance with the
schedule proposals, to the computations of the forecast, or to the timing of travel by the passengers.
If there are other sources, they are outside the
range of vision of the study.

The work staggering proposals are based upon
very specific schedule changes. They are identified
by industry, expected numbers of people, and starting times. The actual changes may be different:
Industries may shift more or less than the numbers
of people expected of them. It is considered unlikely that they will shift to other than the proposed starting times. Also, other industries not
included in the proposals may modify their schedules. Whichever happens, the results will be similar. Either more or fewer people than required will
be shifted to one or more of the four new starting
times.

The traffic forecasts were produced by means of
the computational procedure. Their accuracy depends
upon the equation and the data processed through it.
The data are the numbers of people whose schedules
are changed, which were just discussed. The equation is supposed to be a model of the journey and
its timing, with appropriate coefficients obtained
from the various studies. Assuming that the input
data are correct, the model may still produce inaccurate results because of some inherent defects.
The errors will consist of assigning too many people
to one or more cordon intervals and too few to
others.

The forecasts presuppose that the people who
work in the CBD will not modify their travel timing

by more than a 10-, possibly 15-, minute reduction
in early or late arrival.

If any one or a combination of these things occur, the forecasts will prove inaccurate. The likelihood of their occurring has already been discussed
several times in the study, most recently in the
preceding section of this chapter. It can be argued
that they are unlikely to occur; that insofar as
possible, all available precautions against them
were taken. If this is acceptable, then there is a
corresponding assurance that the forecasts will be
realized.

But they might occur, despite the precautions.
To be realistic, they probably will occur to some
degree, hopefully very small. It would be utterly
unthinkable for the forecasts to work out as the
computations say. None of the component elements
can possibly happen according to the quantities of
the equation or its results. But the question at
issue is whether the differences will be large or
small, and if large, enough to cause trouble.

Large or small, they all lead to the same consequence. More people than forecasted will pass
through the cordon stations during one or more intervals, and fewer during others. If the source
errors are small, the cordon counts will differ from
the forecasts by only small amounts; if large, by
large amounts. If by large amounts, the immediate
results will be crowding in one or more trains or
intervals, excessive waiting times at stations,
crowding in exit passages and stairways. People
will arrive at work late, and will reach home late.

At its worst, this kind of congestion cannot
be as bad as it now is. The five combinations
greatly flatten the distribution of people according
to the times they are scheduled to start work. They
reduce the persons scheduled at the peak interval to
about half of the present number. Accordingly, if
travel practices and timing do not change radically,
the sheer volume of congestion even under the most

adverse circumstances ought not to be as bad as conditions now are.

Safeguards

To minimize risk and damage during the imple-
mentation--arising either from computational errors
or from the normal difficulties of transition--cer-
tain safeguards emerge as a consequence of the
studies. As a matter of fact, the procedure of implementation deserves the most careful planning and
the suggested safeguards are intended only to contribute to a formulation of the procedure, not to
supplant it.

There ought to be an elaborate program of public information about the details of the work staggering plan. Mention has been made in previous
chapters of the specific definitions of industry and
the alternative schedules. To put these into effect,
the community must be informed very precisely as to
which industries are expected to change and which
are not included. As part of this program of public
information, a realistic estimate of the transit
consequences ought also to be disseminated. Such
expectations as seats for everyone during the rush
hours should be explicitly dispelled. The transition will be delicate enough without adding to its
difficulties the disappointment and frustration of
the riding public.

The work staggering program should be installed
by stages and according to a very definite sequence.
The shifts to 7:30 and 9:30 must take place first.
They are the only scheduled times that can now receive people without producing congestion. Shifts
to 8:30 depend upon prior ones to 7:30 and 9:30.
Accordingly, the industries scheduled to start at
8:30 cannot change their schedules until the others
have completed theirs. Similarly, the shift to 8:00
depends upon prior shifting to 7:30. The sequence
is dictated by these priorities.

To implement the sequence, a sufficient time
must be allowed after each change in order for

industries and people to adapt themselves to the new
schedule. These adaptations must be measured.
Schedule changes should be reported to some appropriate administrative office in order to keep a
check upon compliance. Cordon counts will have to
be made day by day to determine the consequences of
schedule change on subway traffic.

The results of these measurements will provide
guidance for each next step in the implementation
process. They will indicate when the next changes
may be made and whether the work staggering plan requires modification in the light of accumulating results.

These safeguards will provide the opportunity
to apply many parts of the criteria which were reserved for experience. The preliminary period of
public information will furnish the opportunity to
appraise the response of the community, both the industries whose schedules are to change, and the industries and people who will be affected by the
changes. Installation by stages will make it possible to test the validity of data, assumptions, and
computations, and will afford the opportunity to
make modifications in program on the basis of experience.

CONCLUSION

An answer is now available to the problem of
the study: Is work staggering in Manhattan's CBD a
feasible way of relieving transit congestion during
the morning and late afternoon rush hours? The answer is a judgment which is founded upon the researches, analyses, computations, and evaluation of
results as presented throughout this study, and it
incorporates all of the qualifications and conditions which were made during the course of the exposition. It applies only to the five schedule combinations developed and specified in Chapter 7.

The five schedule combinations were evaluated,
earlier in this chapter, in respect to their

conformity with each of the criteria of feasibility
established in Chapter 1. The evaluation yielded
conclusions for each of the criteria which, omitting
all of the qualifying conditions and suggested safeguards, may be formulated into the following summary
statements.

   1. The CBD industries whose schedules are modified by any of the five combinations appear capable,
in sufficient numbers, of adopting the new schedules
proposed for them.

   2. The people who work in the CBD appear favorably disposed to schedule change, and sufficient
numbers may be expected to accept the amounts of
change required by the five schedule combinations.

   3. There is reasonable assurance that any of
the five combinations will relieve rush hour congestion on subways and other modes of transit.

   4. There are no signs that work staggering
will provoke effective opposition in the community.

   5. There are no evident indications that work
staggering, once instituted, will not last for a
reasonable period of time.

   These conclusions are the basis for the judgment that work staggering in Manhattan's CBD, according to any one of the five combinations and subject to all stated conditions, is a feasible way of
relieving rush hour transit congestion.

   This judgment applies only to the feasibility
of work staggering. It does not claim, nor even imply, that work staggering is the only or the best
way of relieving rush hour congestion. This study
has not examined other ways of relieving congestion,
if any exist. In reaching a policy decision about
how the problem of rush hour traffic should be
solved, the community now has at least one feasible
method--staggered working hours.

APPENDIXES

LIST OF APPENDIX TABLES

Table   Page

1   Cordon Stations Entering the CBD, by
     Division, Lines, and Direction of
     Entry   410

2   Cordon Stations Leaving the CBD, by
     Division, Lines, and Direction of
     Leaving   411

3   Passengers in Trains at Cordon and Five
     Stations Before and After, as Per
     Cents of Cordon Station Number   413

4   The Numbers of Persons Entering the
     CBD Between 6:20 and 10:00 A.M., by
     Cordon Station and Interval,
     October, 1962   417

5   The Numbers of Persons Leaving the CBD
     Between 3:20 and 7:00 P.M., by
     Cordon Station and Interval, October,
     1962   418

6   Operating Efficiency During the 1962
     Cordon Count   420

7   Cordon Interval Patterns of Each
     Station, 6:20-10:00 A.M., Entering
     the CBD, 1958-63   423

8   Cordon Interval Patterns of Each
     Station, 3:20-7:00 P.M., Leaving
     the CBD, 1958-63   424

9   The Per Cent of Cars Reported at
     Scheduled Capacity, Entering the
     CBD, October, 1962   428

10   The Per Cent of Cars Reported at
     Scheduled Capacity, Leaving the
     CBD, October, 1962   429

397

Table   Page

11   The Truncation Adjustment for the
      October, 1962, Cordon Count, Entering
      the CBD   432

12   The Truncation Adjustment for the
      October, 1962, Cordon Count, Leaving
      the CBD   435

13   The October, 1962, Cordon Count Entering
      the CBD, Modified by the Truncation
      Adjustment   438

14   The October, 1962, Cordon Count Entering
      the CBD, Modified by the Cordon In-
      terval Pattern and the Truncation
      Adjustment   439

15   The October, 1962, Cordon Count Leaving
      the CBD, Modified by the Truncation
      Adjustment   440

16   The October, 1962, Cordon Count Leaving
      the CBD, Modified by the Cordon
      Interval Pattern and the Truncation
      Adjustment   441

17   Capacities of Subway Cars and Trains
      by Cordon Station, Line and Train   443

18   The Comfort Level Capacity per Interval,
      Entering the CBD, October, 1962,
      Based on the Actual Number of Cars   445

19   The Comfort Level Capacity per Interval,
      Leaving the CBD, October, 1962, Based
      on the Actual Number of Cars   446

20   88 Per Cent of the Comfort Level
      Capacity of Selected Stations per
      Interval, October, 1962, Entering
      the CBD, Based on the Actual Number
      of Cars   448

398

Table		Page
21	88 Per Cent of the Comfort Level Capacity of Selected Stations per Interval, October, 1962, Leaving the CBD, Based on the Actual Number of Cars	448
22	Passenger Capacity per 20-Minute Interval, per Cordon Station and Total CBD	450
23	Passengers, by Station and Interval, as Per Cents of Interval Totals	453
24	Excess Passengers by Cordon Station, Entering the CBD, October, 1962	455
25	Excess Space by Cordon Station, Entering the CBD, October, 1962	456
26	Excess Passengers by Cordon Station, Leaving the CBD, October, 1962	457
27	Excess Space by Cordon Station, Leaving the CBD, October, 1962	458
28	Excess Passengers Entering the CBD Through the Southeast Stations, October, 1962	459
29	Excess Space Entering the CBD Through the Southeast Stations, October, 1962	459
30	Excess Passengers Leaving the CBD Through the Southeast Stations, October, 1962	460
31	Excess Space Leaving the CBD Through the Southeast Stations, October, 1962	460
32	Net Excess Passengers Entering the CBD, by Cordon Station	461

Table   Page

33   The Contract Construction Industries and
     Employment in Manhattan's CBD,
     September, 1958   464

34   Selected Scheduled Starting-Stopping
     Times of Work, Regular Weekdays:
     Estimated Numbers of Employees of the
     Contract Construction Industries   465

35   Selected Scheduled Starting-Stopping
     Times of Work, Regular Weekdays:
     Estimated Per Cents of Employees of
     the Contract Construction Industries   466

36   Manufacturing Industries and Employment
     in Manhattan's Central Business
     District   467

37   Selected Scheduled Starting-Stopping
     Times of Work, Regular Weekdays:
     Estimated Numbers of Employees of the
     Manufacturing Industries   469

38   Selected Scheduled Starting-Stopping
     Times of Work, Regular Weekdays:
     Estimated Per Cents of Employees of
     the Manufacturing Industries   470

39   The Transportation, Communications, and
     Public Utilities Industries and
     Employment in Manhattan's CBD,
     September, 1958   471

40   Selected Scheduled Starting-Stopping
     Times of Work, Regular Weekdays:
     Estimated Numbers of Employees of
     the Transportation Industries   473

41   Selected Scheduled Starting-Stopping
     Times of Work, Regular Weekdays:
     Estimated Per Cents of Employees of
     the Transportation Industries   474

400

Table   Page

42   Selected Scheduled Starting-Stopping
      Times of Work, Regular Weekdays:
      Estimated Numbers of Employees of
      the Communications and Public
      Utilities Industries   475

43   Selected Scheduled Starting-Stopping
      Times of Work, Regular Weekdays:
      Estimated Per Cents of Employees of
      the Communications and Public
      Utilities Industries   476

44   The Wholesale Trades and Employment in
      Manhattan's CBD, September, 1958   477

45   Selected Scheduled Starting-Stopping
      Times of Work, Regular Weekdays:
      Estimated Numbers of Employees of
      the Wholesale Trades   479

46   Selected Scheduled Starting-Stopping
      Times of Work, Regular Weekdays:
      Estimated Per Cents of Employees
      of the Wholesale Trades   480

47   The Retail Trades and Employment in
      Manhattan's CBD, September, 1958   481

48   Selected Scheduled Starting-Stopping
      Times of Work, Regular Weekdays:
      Estimated Numbers of Employees of
      the Retail Trades   483

49   Selected Scheduled Starting-Stopping
      Times of Work, Regular Weekdays:
      Estimated Per Cents of Employees
      of the Retail Trades   484

50   The Finance, Insurance, and Real Estate
      Industries and Employment in Man-
      hattan's CBD, September, 1958   485

Table   Page

51   Selected Scheduled Starting-Stopping
        Times of Work, Regular Weekdays:
        Estimated Numbers of Employees of
        the Finance and Insurance Industries   487

52   Selected Scheduled Starting-Stopping
        Times of Work, Regular Weekdays:
        Estimated Per Cents of Employees of
        the Finance and Insurance Industries   488

53   Selected Scheduled Starting-Stopping
        Times of Work, Regular Weekdays:
        Estimated Numbers of Employees of
        the Real Estate Industry   489

54   Selected Scheduled Starting-Stopping
        Times of Work, Regular Weekdays:
        Estimated Per Cents of Employees
        of the Real Estate Industry   490

55   The Service Industries and Employment
        in Manhattan's CBD, September, 1958   491

56   Selected Scheduled Starting-Stopping
        Times of Work, Regular Weekdays:
        Estimated Numbers of Employees of
        the Services Division   493

57   Selected Scheduled Starting-Stopping
        Times of Work, Regular Weekdays:
        Estimated Per Cents of Employees
        of the Services Division   494

58   Total and Central Administrative Office
        Employment in Selected Major Industry
        Divisions in Manhattan's CBD   495

59   Selected Scheduled Starting-Stopping
        Times of Work, Regular Weekdays:
        Estimated Numbers of Employees of
        the Central Administrative Offices   496

402

Table		Page
60	Selected Scheduled Starting-Stopping Times of Work, Regular Weekdays: Estimated Per Cents of Employees of the Central Administrative Offices	497
61	Government Employment in Manhattan's CBD, September, 1958	498
62	Selected Scheduled Starting-Stopping Times of Work, Regular Weekdays: Estimated Numbers of Employees of Governments	500
63	Selected Scheduled Starting-Stopping Times of Work, Regular Weekdays: Estimated Per Cents of Employees of Governments	501
64	Functionally Feasible Alternative Starting Times for Industries in Manhattan's Central Business District	502
65	Total and Modifiable Employment in the Production Industries Group	515
66	Employment in the Transportation Company Offices	522
67	Employment in Radio, Television, and Motion Picture Companies and Organizations	523
68	Employment in Other Administrative Offices	525
69	Employment in Business Professions and Services	528
70	Employment in the Wholesale Trades	531
71	Total and Modifiable Employment in the Financial Industries	534

Table   Page

72   Total and Modifiable Employment of
       Insurance Carriers   539

73   Total and Modifiable Employment in
       Government   540

74   Per Cents of People Scheduled to Start
       and Actually Starting Work   544

75   Comparison: Scheduled and Actual Start-
       ing Per Cents, by Interval and
       Cumulatively   546

76   Lateness Adjustment Matrix, 8:30 A.M.
       Origin: From Scheduled to Actual
       Start   555

77   Lateness Adjustment Matrix, 8:00 A.M.
       Origin: From Scheduled to Actual
       Start   556

78   Subway Riders as Per Cents of Total CBD
       Employees, by Actual Start Work Time   559

79   Adjustment Matrix: Per Cents of CBD
       Employees Who Cross Subway Cordons   560

80   Estimated Per Cents of People: Who Work
       in the CBD and Who Travel Through Sub-
       way Cordons to Work--Who Actually
       Start Work at Selected Times, by the
       Times They Arrive at Work   566

81   Estimated Per Cents of People: Who Work
       in the CBD and Who Travel Through Sub-
       way Cordons to Work--Who Actually Start
       Work at Selected Times, by the Times
       They Arrive at Work or Eat Breakfast in
       the CBD, Whichever Occurs Earlier   567

82   Per Cent of Respondents Reporting Early
       Arrival by Varying Intervals   569

404

Table   Page

83   Adjustment Matrix: From Actual Start
         to Arrival Time in Per Cents   570

84   Travel Time Ranges Between Arrival and
         Cordon Count Time Intervals   576

85   Per Cent of Sample, by Cordon Station,
         Having Specified Travel Time Ranges   579

86   Travel Time Ranges and Per Cent of
         Passengers, CBD   580

87   Per Cent of Passengers, by Arrival Time
         and Cordon Interval Time, on 5-Minute
         (1/3) Intervals, for the Total CBD   582

88   Arrival-Cordon Interval Assignment
         Table, CBD   584

89   Computed Cordon Counts, Based upon
         Various Adjustment Factors   588

90   Arrival-Cordon Interval Assignment Table,
         Extended to 6:30-10:30 A.M.   596

91   Arrival Adjustment Table, Extended to
         6:30-11:45 A.M.   598

92   Lateness Adjustment Table, Extended to
         6:30-11:45 A.M.   599

93   Computation: Numbers Actually Starting
         Work and Crossing Cordons, 6:30-7:15 A.M.   606

94   Computation: Numbers Arriving at Work,
         6:30-7:15 A.M.   606

95   Computation: Numbers Actually Starting
         Work and Crossing Cordons, 9:45-
         11:45 A.M.   608

96   Computation: Numbers Arriving at Work,
         8:30-10:30 A.M.   609

405

Table   Page

97   Computation: Arrivals During 8:30-
      10:30 A.M. as Per Cents of Actual
      Starts During 9:45-11:45 A.M.   610

98   Computation: Numbers of People in
      Cordon Intervals, 6:20-7:20 A.M.   612

99   Computation: Numbers of People in
      Cordon Intervals, 9:00-10:00 A.M.   613

100   Degrees of Adjustment: Lateness   617

101   Degrees of Adjustment: Early Arrival   618

102   Equivalent Net Excess Passengers,
      Corrected   623

103   Computation of Correction Factor   624

104   Equivalent Net Excess Passengers,
      Corrected, by Size   625

105   Estimates of Required Total CBD Cordon
      Counts to Eliminate Net Excess
      Passengers   627

106   A Comparison of Comfort Level Standards
      Based on Adjusted and Reconstructed
      Cordon Counts   629

107   The Net Numbers of People in the Pro-
      duction Industries, by Start and Stop
      Times, Whose Schedules Would Change,
      According to Maximum and Expected
      Responses   632

108   The Net Numbers of People of Central
      Administrative Offices, by Start
      and Stop Times, Whose Schedules
      Would Change, According to Maximum
      and Expected Responses   633

Table   Page

109   The Net Numbers of People in the Trans-
       portation Company Offices, by Start
       and Stop Times, Whose Schedules Would
       Change, According to Maximum and Ex-
       pected Responses   634

110   The Net Numbers of People in Radio,
       Television, and Motion Picture Com-
       panies and Organizations, by Start
       and Stop Times, Whose Schedules Would
       Change, According to Maximum and Ex-
       pected Responses   635

111   The Net Numbers of People in Other Ad-
       ministrative Offices, by Start and
       Stop Times, Whose Schedules Would
       Change, According to Maximum and
       Expected Responses   636

112   The Net Numbers of People in the Business
       Professions and Services, by Start and
       Stop Times, Whose Schedules Would
       Change, According to Maximum and Ex-
       pected Responses   637

113   The Net Numbers of People in the Earlier
       Wholesale Trades, by Start and Stop
       Times, Whose Schedules Would Change,
       According to Maximum and Expected
       Responses   638

114   The Net Numbers of People in the Later
       Wholesale Trades, by Start and Stop
       Times, Whose Schedules Would Change,
       According to Maximum and Expected
       Responses   639

115   The Net Numbers of People in Commercial
       Banks, by Start and Stop Times, Whose
       Schedules Would Change, Under Various
       Alternatives, According to Maximum
       Response   640

Table   Page

116   The Net Numbers of People in Commercial Banks, by Start and Stop Times, Whose Schedules Would Change, Under Various Alternatives, According to Expected Response   641

117   The Net Numbers of People in Business Credit Institutions, by Start and Stop Times, Whose Schedules Would Change, According to Maximum and Expected Responses   642

118   The Net Numbers of People in Security Brokers, Dealers, and Flotation Companies, by Start and Stop Times, Whose Schedules Would Change, According to Maximum and Expected Responses   643

119   The Net Numbers of People in Life Insurance Companies, by Start and Stop Times, Whose Schedules Would Change, According to Maximum and Expected Responses   644

120   The Net Numbers of People in Fire, Marine, and Casualty Insurance Companies, by Start and Stop Times, Whose Schedules Would Change, According to Maximum and Expected Responses   645

121   The Net Numbers of People in Government, by Start and Stop Times, Whose Schedules Would Change, According to Maximum and Expected Responses   646

APPENDIX A THE
CORDON
STATIONS

The Transit Authority designates as cordon stations the last stations at which trains stop before
entering the central business district, and the last
stations at which trains stop before leaving the
central business district. There are twenty cordon
stations entering and twenty cordon stations leaving
the CBD.

Appendix Tables 1 and 2 present respectively
the entering and leaving cordon stations. They are
arranged on these tables by division, by line, and
then by the direction of origin of entering trains
and by direction of destination of trains leaving
the CBD.

Appendix Table 2 gives the cordon station of
the Lexington Avenue Express as Grand Central. This
has been changed to 59th Street since the opening of
the express station there. Grand Central is shown
on the table because it was the cordon station for
all the data used in this study.

TABLE 1

Cordon Stations Entering the CBD, by Division, Lines, and Direction of Entry

Division	Line	Cordon Station (by Direction of Entry)			
		North	North-East	East	South-East
IRT	Lexington Ave. Express	86th & Lexington			Borough Hall
	Lexington Ave. Local	68th & Lexington			
	7th Avenue Express	72nd & Broadway			Clark Street
	Broadway Local	66th & Broadway			
	Flushing Line		Vernon-Jackson		
IND	A	125th & St.Nicholas		High Street	
	D	125th & St.Nicholas			York Street
	AA, BB, CC	72nd and C.P.W.			
	E		23rd and Ely	High Street	
	F		23rd and Ely		
BMT	Brighton Express				Canal Street[a]*
	Brighton Local				Court Street[b]
	Sea Beach Express		Queensboro Plaza		Canal Street[a]*
	West End Express		Queensboro Plaza		Canal Street[a]*
	West End Local (Nassau)				Court Street[b]
	West End (Special)				Pacific Street[a]
	4th Avenue Local		Queens Plaza		Court Street[b]
	14th St.--Canarsie			Bedford Ave.	
	Jamaica--Express & Local			Marcy Ave.**	
	Broadway-Brooklyn Local			Marcy Ave.	
	Myrtle Express--Chambers			Marcy Ave.	

*Cordon counts made as train enters the station.
**No stop, counts made as train passes through the station.
[a]Via tunnel.
[b]Via bridge.

410

TABLE 2

Cordon Stations Leaving the CBD, by Division, Lines, and Direction of Leaving

Division	Line	Cordon Station (by Direction of Leaving)			
		North	North-East	East	South-East
IRT	Lexington Ave. Express	Grand Central*			Bowling Green
	Lexington Ave. Local	59th & Lexington			
	7th Avenue Express	Times Square			Wall and William
	Broadway Local	59th & Broadway			
	Flushing Line		Grand Central		
IND	A	59th & Broadway		Broadway-Nassau	
	D	59th & Broadway			
	AA, BB, CC	59th & Broadway			
	E		53rd & Lexington	Broadway-Nassau	
	F		53rd & Lexington		East Broadway
BMT	Brighton Express		60th & Lexington		Canal Street[a]
	Brighton Local				Whitehall[b]
	Sea Beach Express		60th & Lexington		Canal Street[a]
	West End Express				Canal Street[a]
	West End Local (Nassau)		60th & Lexington		Broad Street[b]
	West End (Special)				Chambers Street[a]
	4th Avenue Local		60th & Lexington		Whitehall[b]
	14th St.--Canarsie			First Avenue	
	Jamaica--Express & Local			Essex Street	
	Broadway--Brooklyn Local			Essex Street	
	Myrtle Express--Chambers			Essex Street	

*Now 59th Street and Lexington Avenue.

a via tunnel.
b via bridge.

411

B

As a train proceeds along its route, the number of passengers it carries changes. Traveling through origin areas--residential areas in the morning and employment areas in the late afternoon--a train receives more passengers than it discharges. Its load thus increases until it reaches destination areas-- business and employment areas in the morning and residential neighborhoods in the late afternoon-- where it discharges more passengers than it receives. Its load thus increases as it proceeds through origin areas and decreases in destination areas. The changing passenger load gives shape to the flow of passengers along a route.

This appendix will present the dimensions of subway traffic flows into the CBD. Four such flows will be described, one from each origin area.

Appendix Table 3 presents an analysis of the material gathered in this study. It divides the data into four groups, each representing an origin area. The numbers in the table are the per cents of passengers in the observed cars at each of five stations before and after the cordon station. The number at the cordon station serves as the base of the percentages, and appears on the table as 100 per cent. All the percentages are weighted by the proportion of passengers traveling through each cordon station, as determined from the October, 1962, cordon count.

In constructing this table the cordon station is used as the center and each station of the

individual lines is enumerated in sequence before
and after the cordon. The numbers obtained from the
studies were distributed according to these numbered
stations. This produces a certain degree of imbalance in the results. For example, from the north on
the Lexington Avenue line, the express cordon is
86th Street. This same station is the second before
the cordon on the local. The same station thus
turns up on two different columns of the same summary. Another factor affecting the table arises
from special characteristics of some of the stations. There may be important junctions at, shortly
before, or after the cordon. Where passengers shift
from one train to another, sometimes to different
cordon stations, the result is a change in volume of
traffic of both trains. Perhaps the distribution of
the numbers ought to be made so as to reflect some
of these linkages of stations. However, there are
not enough data to permit such a detailed analysis.
Finally, it should be noted that the table arbitrarily examines five stations before and after the cordon. These are located at very different distances
from the cordon station and may be serving different
kinds of areas and passengers at the extremes. Some
of this will be briefly noted below.

TABLE 3

Passengers in Trains at Cordon and Five Stations
Before and After, as Per Cents of
Cordon Station Number

	5	4	3	2	1	0	1	2	3	4	5
North	56	64	72	89	94	100	86	76	72	55	38
Northeast	59	70	76	94	97	100	73	68	44	36	40
East	68	69	72	80	87	100	95	96	59	39	14
Southeast	65	71	79	80	114	100	87	64	27	10	13
Total (Weighted)	61	68	75	87	100	100	84	73	51	36	29

Within these limitations, the table shows the
dimensions of traffic flow from the origin areas into the CBD. The material for the north, northeast,
and east may be considered representative of the
lines serving these areas. The southeast is restricted to the BMT division. However, the critical
first station before the cordon falls in the same
area served by the other southeast stations and by
the E and F trains.

Three main observations may be made about the
traffic flow as depicted on Appendix Table 3.
First, the cordon station is the maximum station for
three areas. Second, the flow increases regularly
from the first station shown on the table to the
maximum station and thereafter it decreases. To
this regular pattern there are only three small exceptions, each occurring within the CBD. Trains
from the east increase slightly after the second CBD
station. These trains encounter residential areas
at their second stations. Trains from the northeast
show an increase at their fifth station in the CBD.
It is likely that a much larger exchange of passengers occurs on these trains than the table actually
discloses. As these trains proceed through the CBD
they become important means of internal transport
and they begin to pick up passengers for the trips
to their opposite terminals. A similar shift occurs
in the fifth station of the southeast BMT trains.
These minor exceptions notwithstanding, the table
discloses regularity in the expansion and contraction of the flow for all the areas.

Third, while the cordon station for the southeast trains is not the maximum station, it occupies
a definable position in the flow. For this area, it
can be treated as the 88 per cent, not the 100 per
cent station. This applies explicitly to the BMT
trains, and may be extended to the other southeast
trains as well as the E and F trains which enter
through the High Street Cordon Station. These cordon stations--and the stations preceding them--lie
in a high employment area. The area has large numbers of governmental, trade, manufacturing, and

service establishments. It is therefore an important destination of a.m. rush hour riders, and an
origin area in the p.m. Hence, in the absence of
statistics for the other cordon stations, it is
reasonable to apply the same 88 per cent to them.

APPENDIX C THE OCTOBER, 1962,

CORDON COUNT

The cordon counts of October, 1962, are given on the accompanying Appendix Tables 4 and 5. Table 4 contains the counts of people entering the CBD, by station and time interval, from 6:20 to 10:00 a.m. Table 5 contains the number leaving the CBD in the late afternoon from 3:20 to 7:00 p.m.

On both tables the time intervals are expressed as full 20-minute amounts, thus showing an overlap between the end of one interval and the beginning of the next. This is merely a convenience. Actually, each interval begins with the time shown, and goes to but does not include the time of the end of each interval. Thus, 6:20-6:40 contains passengers from 6:20 to 6:39$\frac{1}{2}$.

TABLE 4

The Numbers of Persons Entering the CBD Between 6:20 and 10:00 A.M., by Cordon Station and Interval, October, 1962

Stations	6:20 6:40	6:40 7:00	7:00 7:20	7:20 7:40	7:40 8:00	8:00 8:20	8:20 8:40	8:40 9:00	9:00 9:20	9:20 9:40	9:40 10:00
86 & Lexington	2,800	4,200	8,710	12,550	13,340	13,180	12,810	8,190	6,460	5,680	2,810
68 & Lexington	1,500	2,090	6,190	11,140	7,940	8,800	14,460	13,370	7,330	4,140	2,560
72 & Broadway	2,530	3,650	6,060	8,830	10,780	10,940	13,490	9,320	6,290	3,750	2,860
66 & Broadway	1,530	1,700	2,420	4,960	6,460	8,330	10,040	9,410	3,470	3,420	2,310
125 & St. Nicholas	2,760	3,900	7,730	12,580	17,750	21,470	19,170	13,940	7,000	4,650	3,740
72 & Central Park West	780	690	2,110	5,010	3,900	7,210	7,770	9,200	3,340	1,610	810
Borough Hall	1,110	1,910	2,790	4,140	6,270	11,160	10,880	8,010	4,060	2,660	1,370
Clark St.	880	1,070	1,980	5,870	6,890	9,480	9,850	7,050	4,040	2,310	1,040
High St.	2,240	3,530	4,850	8,440	9,920	16,550	19,050	14,140	3,990	3,120	2,580
York St.	560	1,110	2,600	4,490	5,030	6,180	6,330	3,730	2,160	1,390	1,140
Court St. (Btn., 4 Ave. Lcl.)	660	1,390	840	1,190	1,490	7,500	9,540	6,960	4,430	1,740	1,220
Court St. (West End, Nassau)		100	80		260	2,220	1,810	5,720	1,580	340	770
Bedford Ave.	980	2,230	3,220	3,110	5,830	5,150	6,700	4,650	1,780	1,340	1,240
Manhattan Br. (Btn., WE, SB Exp.)	1,590	5,490	6,890	8,910	13,330	14,810	16,660	16,550	8,850	6,180	3,960
Manhattan Br. (WE Special)					830	1,220	3,440	920			
Williamsburg Br. (Jam.-Myrt.)	1,210	2,180	4,210	5,300	5,960	11,360	7,680	6,140	3,080	1,530	1,380
23 & Ely	2,240	2,630	5,190	9,570	17,670	18,070	22,410	18,130	13,630	6,220	5,000
Vernon-Jackson	950	2,060	3,790	8,360	9,320	14,020	15,040	13,160	9,780	2,350	2,270
Queensboro Plaza (Btn. Lcl., WE)	810	2,250	1,890	4,820	7,400	7,600	7,650	4,830	2,520	2,220	1,050
Queens Plaza (4 Ave. Lcl.)		490	1,270	2,940	3,550	4,130	7,720	3,540	2,240	1,100	1,060
Total CBD	25,130	42,670	72,820	122,210	153,920	199,380	222,500	176,960	96,030	55,750	39,170

TABLE 5

The Numbers of Persons Leaving the CBD Between 3:20 and 7:00 P.M., by Cordon Station and Interval, October, 1962

Stations	3:20 3:40	3:40 4:00	4:00 4:20	4:20 4:40	4:40 5:00	5:00 5:20	5:20 5:40	5:40 6:00	6:00 6:20	6:20 6:40	6:40 7:00
Grand Central (Lex. Ave. Exp.)	3,770	4,820	5,550	6,550	10,660	13,890	12,390	10,270	5,880	6,620	3,700
59 & Lexington (Lex. Ave. Lcl.)	3,490	5,080	6,350	6,650	12,590	13,920	13,970	12,960	8,100	4,290	3,010
Times Square (7 Ave. Exp.)	2,730	2,300	5,230	5,120	9,990	10,330	13,040	9,700	8,150	5,500	4,020
59 & Broadway (Bway Lcl.)	2,170	2,210	2,740	3,340	7,800	10,780	11,960	9,080	5,650	3,770	3,070
59 & Broadway (A, D)	5,410	6,180	7,410	8,100	14,850	21,100	20,840	16,160	12,550	8,190	6,690
59 & Broadway (AA, BB, CC)	1,050	1,090	1,350	2,520	4,620	8,720	10,130	6,640	4,140	2,980	1,940
Bowling Green	1,770	1,810	1,920	3,820	8,810	11,200	9,940	8,400	3,920	2,990	2,420
Wall & William	1,650	1,850	2,570	4,580	9,560	8,800	9,620	5,270	3,410	3,120	1,980
Broadway-Nassau	2,200	2,910	3,980	6,250	10,730	14,180	17,240	10,280	6,370	3,860	2,620
East Broadway	1,220	1,400	2,220	1,970	3,170	3,930	8,000	4,610	3,240	1,980	1,590
Whitehall St.	1,440	1,620	3,610	5,610	10,520	8,910	6,930	7,000	3,820	2,400	1,480
Broad St.	170	350	860	420	3,270	6,280	2,180	720	490	140	
1st Ave.	1,640	2,360	1,740	2,550	5,300	7,770	7,480	3,990	2,590	2,160	1,730
Manhattan Br. (Btn., SB, WE Exp.)	3,570	4,550	4,810	5,610	6,840	11,090	10,710	11,790	11,660	8,610	5,600
Manhattan Br. (WE Special)						1,420	600				
Williamsburg Br. (Jam.-Myrt.)	860	1,650	2,810	3,520	5,140	10,210	8,150	5,780	3,140	3,140	1,380
Lexington & 53	5,490	4,860	5,190	9,290	15,260	20,260	18,440	16,360	12,830	9,540	4,480
Grand Central (Flushing)	2,780	3,110	4,320	6,340	11,140	16,790	15,170	12,170	6,540	4,220	2,900
Lexington & 60 (Btn. Lcl., WE)	2,320	2,020	2,330	2,780	4,910	6,640	6,630	6,950	3,190	2,180	1,570
Lexington & 60 (4th Ave. Lcl.)	1,490	970	1,020	1,910	2,660	5,980	3,770	3,860	1,450	1,590	960
Total CBD	45,220	51,140	66,010	86,930	157,820	212,200	207,190	161,990	107,120	77,280	51,140

APPENDIX   D   OPERATIONS DURING
                 THE OCTOBER, 1962,
                 CORDON COUNT

The operating efficiency of the system during
the cordon count period of October, 1962, may be
measured by a ratio of actual to scheduled operations. The cordon counts report the number of
trains and cars passing through the cordon stations
during each time interval. Information on schedules
was obtained from the Transit Authority. The ratio
(x 100) of actual to scheduled number of trains is
a measure of operating efficiency.

Appendix Table 6 presents the operating data
and efficiency during the October, 1962, cordon
count for the intervals 6:20-9:40 a.m. (entering the
CBD) and 3:20-6:20 p.m. (leaving the CBD). The table gives the information both by interval and
cumulatively.

For each of the total periods, three hours and
twenty minutes in the morning and three hours in the
late afternoon, the system operates at 99 per cent
efficiency as measured by the number of trains passing through the stations. However, the efficiencies
over these long intervals obscure the actual operating conditions within the periods. The long periods
enable the system to catch up on delays which occur
in preceding intervals. In the morning, the 20-
minute efficiencies range from 93 per cent to 99 per
cent over the period 6:20-8:40. Thereafter the efficiency climbs to 101 per cent, 113 per cent, and
112 per cent, as the delayed trains make their runs.
In the afternoon, the general level of efficiency is
slightly higher. It ranges from 96 to 99 per cent,
except for two recovery periods during which it rose
to 105 and 107 per cent.

TABLE 6

Operating Efficiency During the 1962 Cordon Count

	By Interval			Cumulative		
Entering	Scheduled Trains	Actual Trains	Actual Scheduled	Scheduled Trains	Actual Trains	Actual Scheduled
6:20-6:40	55	51	93	55	51	93
6:40-7:00	78	74	95	133	125	94
7:00-7:20	93	92	99	226	217	96
7:20-7:40	120	115	96	346	332	96
7:40-8:00	140	130	93	486	462	95
8:00-8:20	154	147	95	640	609	95
8:20-8:40	155	153	99	795	762	96
8:40-9:00	143	145	101	938	907	97
9:00-9:20	111	126	113	1,049	1,033	98
9:20-9:40	85	94	112	1,134	1,127	99
Leaving						
3:20-3:40	81	78	96	81	78	96
3:40-4:00	88	85	97	169	163	96
4:00-4:20	97	102	105	266	265	100
4:20-4:40	115	113	98	381	378	99
4:40-5:00	136	130	96	517	508	98
5:00-5:20	151	145	96	668	653	98
5:20-5:40	146	142	97	814	795	98
5:40-6:00	134	132	99	948	927	98
6:00-6:20	116	124	107	1,064	1,051	99

The cumulative efficiencies in the right-hand column of Appendix Table 6 show a gradual rise from 6:20 to 7:40, a slight fall back during the rush period, and then a recovery to 9:40. In the afternoon, the cumulative efficiency, after an early lapse, remains at 99 and 98 per cent.

Operating efficiency as measured by number of trains will always appear somewhat better than efficiency as measured by passenger capacity. Some of the trains passing through the system have fewer than the required number of cars. This would lower the actual capacity even further than the number of trains would indicate. The difference, however, is not important for present purposes.

APPENDIX   E

Cordon interval pattern is the name applied to
the shape of the distribution of cordon counts, interval by interval. The eleven intervals used in
this study show a progression from a low count in
the first interval to a maximum count at the peak
and then a decline to the final interval. This distribution, expressed as the percentage of each interval to the total, is called the cordon interval
pattern.

A pattern was calculated for each cordon station for the eleven intervals entering and the elev-
en leaving the CBD. The pattern is each interval
average for the five years of 1959-63. These averages are then turned into percentages of the sum of
the averages of each station.

The cordon interval patterns are presented in
Appendix Tables 7 and 8. The first applies to the
entering stations during the morning and the second
to the leaving stations during the late afternoon
and early evening.

These tables may be used to convert the actual
data of any year into cordon counts which reflect
this five-year pattern. This is done by multiplying
the total count for the eleven intervals by each
percentage. This redistributes the total according
to the stations' five-year patterns.

The tables are of interest quite apart from
their use as an adjustment device. They disclose,

TABLE 7

Cordon Interval Patterns of Each Station, 6:20-10:00 A.M.,
Entering the CBD, 1958-63

Stations	6:20 6:40	6:40 7:00	7:00 7:20	7:20 7:40	7:40 8:00	8:00 8:20	8:20 8:40	8:40 9:00	9:00 9:20	9:20 9:40	9:40 10:00
86 & Lexington	3.0	5.8	9.2	14.5	15.2	14.5	15.0	10.4	5.8	4.0	2.6
68 & Lexington	2.1	3.0	6.3	10.6	13.6	14.5	17.4	15.6	8.7	4.8	3.3
72 & Broadway	2.7	4.4	7.3	10.9	15.2	15.4	14.6	13.3	8.0	5.0	3.3
66 & Broadway	2.3	2.6	4.9	9.0	13.2	17.1	18.1	17.0	7.1	5.0	3.7
125 & St. Nicholas	2.5	4.1	8.1	11.5	14.9	16.7	16.8	11.8	6.2	4.2	3.4
72 & Central Park West	1.6	1.7	4.8	12.7	11.1	16.1	21.0	18.2	7.7	3.1	2.2
Borough Hall	2.2	3.2	5.6	7.9	9.8	18.2	21.2	16.1	7.5	5.7	2.6
Clark St.	2.0	2.7	4.5	9.2	12.0	17.6	18.6	16.7	9.2	4.9	2.5
High St.	1.8	3.1	5.9	9.8	12.5	16.7	20.2	16.9	7.0	3.6	2.6
York St.	1.5	3.6	6.9	11.8	14.2	18.6	16.7	13.8	6.1	3.6	3.3
Court St. (Btn., 4 Ave. Lcl.)	2.0	3.3	4.6	6.8	9.7	16.5	21.1	17.7	10.2	4.8	3.4
Court St. (West End, Nassau)	0.0	0.9	1.6	4.4	5.8	15.2	21.2	29.5	13.2	4.6	3.5
Bedford Ave.	2.9	5.6	6.7	10.2	14.0	16.9	19.7	11.9	5.4	4.0	2.8
Manhattan Br. (Btn., WE, SB Exp.)	2.4	4.8	6.4	9.5	12.0	15.7	16.6	15.2	8.4	4.9	4.1
Manhattan Br. (WE Special)	0.0	0.0	0.0	0.0	2.6	21.0	45.2	27.9	3.3	0.0	0.0
Williamsburg Br. (Jam.-Myrt.)	2.7	4.7	6.7	11.1	14.3	18.6	18.3	12.9	5.9	2.6	2.2
23 & Ely	2.0	2.7	5.4	8.2	12.8	15.2	18.2	16.9	9.8	5.4	3.5
Vernon-Jackson	1.2	2.6	4.3	8.1	10.0	16.8	19.2	20.1	10.6	4.6	2.5
Queensboro Plaza (Btn. Lcl., WE)	2.3	4.7	7.0	9.8	15.3	16.5	18.1	12.3	6.0	4.7	3.3
Queens Plaza (4 Ave. Lcl.)	0.0	3.3	5.3	9.3	12.1	15.7	22.5	15.3	7.6	5.1	3.9
Total CBD	2.1	3.7	6.2	10.1	12.9	16.3	18.2	15.2	7.8	4.5	3.1

TABLE 8

Cordon Interval Patterns of Each Station, 3:20-7:00 P.M., Leaving the CBD, 1958-63

Stations	3:20 3:40	3:40 4:00	4:00 4:20	4:20 4:40	4:40 5:00	5:00 5:20	5:20 5:40	5:40 6:00	6:00 6:20	6:20 6:40	6:40 7:00
Grand Central (Lex. Ave. Exp.)	4.1	5.1	5.9	8.0	13.3	15.3	16.0	12.9	8.7	6.5	4.3
59 & Lexington (Lex. Ave. Lcl.)	5.9	7.5	7.4	6.6	10.8	12.2	13.8	14.8	10.5	6.3	4.1
Times Square (7 Ave. Exp.)	3.4	4.0	6.0	7.3	12.1	14.8	16.5	12.8	10.8	7.4	4.9
59 & Broadway (Bway Lcl.)	3.9	3.6	4.6	6.3	11.3	15.6	17.0	13.7	10.0	7.1	5.0
59 & Broadway (A, D)	3.9	4.4	5.3	6.3	11.7	15.6	17.0	13.7	10.0	7.1	5.0
59 & Broadway (AA, BB, CC)	2.4	2.5	3.1	5.6	10.3	16.9	21.8	15.6	10.4	7.9	3.6
Bowling Green	3.0	3.4	4.3	6.6	12.6	19.4	18.9	13.8	7.7	6.5	3.8
Wall & William	3.3	3.7	5.0	8.1	15.4	19.4	16.8	11.4	6.5	6.4	4.1
Broadway-Nassau	2.6	3.2	4.8	7.0	12.9	21.2	17.5	12.5	7.8	6.3	4.3
East Broadway	3.6	5.0	5.5	7.1	9.9	13.0	20.1	13.1	10.1	8.2	4.7
Whitehall St.	2.7	3.1	5.1	7.5	13.3	21.3	17.7	12.1	8.0	5.9	3.4
Broad St.	1.8	3.4	5.0	9.6	23.2	29.8	14.8	7.7	3.8	1.0	0.0
1st Ave.	4.0	5.7	4.9	6.9	13.6	17.4	17.6	12.5	7.4	6.1	3.4
Manhattan Br. (Btn., SB, WE Exp.)	3.8	5.0	5.7	6.3	10.2	14.8	15.3	13.5	11.2	8.0	6.2
Manhattan Br. (WE Special)	0.0	0.0	0.0	0.0	0.0	67.0	33.0	0.0	0.0	0.0	0.0
Williamsburg Br. (Jam.-Myrt.)	2.3	3.7	5.2	6.7	12.0	21.1	19.6	10.6	8.2	7.3	3.3
Lexington & 53	3.6	4.1	4.7	6.7	10.7	15.3	17.8	15.2	10.5	7.2	4.3
Grand Central (Flushing)	3.3	3.8	4.9	6.6	14.2	19.7	19.1	12.5	7.2	5.3	3.3
Lexington & 60 (Btn. Lcl., WE)	4.7	5.0	5.8	7.5	10.1	17.2	17.0	13.4	8.5	6.3	4.5
Lexington & 60 (4th Ave. Lcl.)	4.5	4.6	3.7	7.5	11.8	20.0	14.1	16.7	7.2	5.5	4.5
Total CBD	3.6	4.3	5.2	6.9	12.1	17.1	17.4	13.3	9.1	6.7	4.3

on a comparable percentage basis, the differences in
interval pattern among the stations. These differences occur in the peak period and in some aspects
of the contours of the distributions. The tables
show the relative height of the peaks of the stations and the relative position of each of their
cordon intervals. There is a great deal of diversity in the interval patterns of the individual
stations.

F

The truncation adjustment is a device for offsetting the downward bias in cordon counts caused by
truncated estimates. This appendix will describe
the adjustment and the method by which it was developed. The adjustment table to be presented here applies specifically to the October, 1962, count but it
can be computed for other recent counts.

The cordon counts underestimate the number of
people in the subways because of the practice of
truncating the estimates. They never report more
passengers in any car than its stated "capacity."
For each type of car in the system there is a
"capacity" number which is actually about 85-90 per
cent of its estimated maximum capacity. Accordingly, more people can--and do--ride in cars than are
reported in the count. This procedure produces truncated estimates which impart a systematic downward
bias to the results. The underestimate is even more
pronounced during the peak periods when many cars
are crowded to capacity.

The practice of truncating the estimates may
also affect the reports about cars having fewer than
the "capacity" number. Once introduced, the practice of underestimating can conceivably become a generalized tendency and affect the observer's judgment
of the loading of other cars, especially those almost full. This possible additional cause of underestimate is not accepted by the personnel of the
Transit Authority.

The observation sheets which the checkers fill
out give their estimates of the number of passengers
in each car of a train. It is thus possible to count

the number of cars estimated at or above capacity on each train and for any interval of interest. Appendix Tables 9 and 10 show the per cent of cars reported at capacity in each 20-minute interval, entering and leaving the CBD. In some instances there were none or very few such cars, but in a number of stations the percentage of capacity cars rises to substantial levels. These are the ones which are underestimated and for which an adjustment is required if the cordon counts are to be corrected.

It has not been possible to establish definitively the extent to which the cordon counts underestimate the actual number of passengers. The only data having any bearing on this subject were collected in a private study made in 1957. The purpose was to determine as accurately as possible the actual number of passengers in a single car of each train passing through each cordon station during the period of observation. Forty such studies were made, covering every entering cordon station. It was a meritorious effort and the results shed some light on the present problem. The material has been made available and will be used to develop a truncation adjustment.

The study records the time of each train, its number of cars, and the estimated number of passengers in one car, usually a car at or close to the middle of the train. In making this study the observer used the procedures of the Transit Authority but removed the limitation of the capacity number. He was thus able to report more people in cars than the cordon counts permit.

The sample can hardly be considered adequate for present purposes. The observations were made only on a few days. Hence, they do not reflect possible differences arising from seasonal variations in travel. Since only a single car of each train was reported, variations in the number of people per car in different positions of the train were not picked up by the study. More observations, extended over longer periods, would have provided a more complete picture of car loading.

TABLE 9

The Per Cent of Cars Reported at Scheduled Capacity, Entering the CBD, October, 1962

Stations	7:00 7:20	7:20 7:40	7:40 8:00	8:00 8:20	8:20 8:40	8:40 9:00	9:00 9:20
86 & Lexington	6	25	9	49	26	36	
68 & Lexington		2	13	26	16	9	3
72 & Broadway		17	21	52	32	54	2
66 & Broadway							8
125 & St. Nicholas			19	13	51	5	
72 & Central Park West							
Borough Hall			2	21	6		
Clark St.				21	8		
High St.			5		15	5	
York St.						5	
Court St. (Btn., 4 Ave. Lcl.)					13	5	
Court St. (West End, Nassau)					33		
Bedford Ave.							
Manhattan Br. (Btn.,WE,SB Exp.)		3			1		
Manhattan Br. (WE Special)							
Williamsburg Br. (Jam-Myrt.)		5					
23 & Ely				14	10	18	
Vernon-Jackson					29	24	
Queensboro Plaza (Btn. Lcl., WE)	8	17	2	4	17	23	4
Queens Plaza (4 Ave. Lcl.)					5		

428

TABLE 10

The Per Cent of Cars Reported at Scheduled Capacity,
Leaving the CBD, October, 1962

Stations	3:20 4:20	4:20 4:40	4:40 5:00	5:00 5:20	5:20 5:40	5:40 6:00	6:00 6:20
Grand Central (Lex. Ave. Exp.)		12	27	64	25	4	
59 & Lexington (Lex. Ave. Lcl.)		2	28	63	58	33	
Times Square (7 Ave. Exp.)		2	14	51	54	13	
59 & Broadway (Bway.Lcl.)				8	26	6	
59 & Broadway (A, D)			24	56	53	1	
59 & Broadway (AA, BB, CC)				3			
Bowling Green			16	36	52	4	
Wall & William			35	54	14		
Broadway-Nassau			6	39	27		
East Broadway							
Whitehall St.			6	14	2		
Broad St.			36	11			
1st Ave.							
Manhattan Br. (Btn.,SB,WE Exp.)			12	79	73	16	
Manhattan Br. (WE Special)							
Williamsburg Br. (Jam.-Myrt.)							
Lexington & 53		3	7	36	37	3	
Grand Central (Flushing)			43	60	28		
Lexington & 60 (Btn. Lcl., WE)						3	
Lexington & 60 (4th Ave. Lcl.)						3	

429

It is by no means to the discredit of the in-
vestigator that the data are insufficient for the
purposes to which this study desires to put them.
Their use here will unquestionably be somewhat over-
extended. Even so, the results will be less detailed than desired. However, they produce a partial adjustment which improves the October, 1962,
cordon counts.

PROCEDURE

The data of the study produce a useful statistic. They show how many people were in the cars
which the cordon count would report at capacity. By
summarizing the data for a single cordon station, it
becomes possible to construct a distribution showing
the number of cars at capacity, at capacity plus ten
passengers, plus twenty passengers, etc. Thus, an
initial statement can be made to the effect that: Of
the cars which the cordon count would report at capacity, ___ per cent actually had the capacity number,
___ per cent had ten more, ___ per cent twenty more,
etc. This distribution can be simplified, depending upon
the purpose, to an average, as follows. Of the cars
which the cordon count would report at capacity, the
average number of passengers was ___, or ___ per
cent of capacity.

An analysis was made, by cordon station and by
20-minute time interval, of the cars with capacity
or more passengers. The exact number of cars and
their passengers were noted. From this information,
an average was computed of the number of passengers
in these cars. This was done initially for each station and for each 20-minute interval, insofar as the
available data permitted. The results were a set of
averages by 20-minute intervals for all stations in
which the underreported cars were observed.

Upon examination, this first set of averages
proved unsatisfactory. There appeared to be an insufficient relationship between the averages and the
percentage of capacity cars during each interval in

the 1962 count. One would have expected that the
average would be higher when the percentage of capacity cars reported in the 1962 count was greater.
There were simply too many departures from this kind
of regularity to accept the first results.

The reasons for the inadequate relationship between these two sets of data are severalfold. First,
the sample study is admittedly too small for an
analysis of the desired degree of detail. Many of
the cordon stations had only a single study and all
their observations pertain to one day only. Second,
the number of persons in excess of capacity would be
affected at any given time by schedules, operating
conditions in the subway, weather, and other factors
which influence the volume and timing of transit
traffic. These irregularities become magnified in
the results of a small sample.

Accordingly, it became necessary to group the
original data so as to offset some of the distortions. On the basis of a variety of trials, it was
found that by abandoning the 20-minute interval
breakdown, acceptable results by cordon station
could be obtained. Accordingly, a single average
was computed for each station with capacity cars.
These were then converted into percentages in excess
of capacity.

Averages and percentages were found for most of
the larger stations. These were then applied in
various ways to the stations which did not have adequate representation in the study. The outcome was
a percentage for each cordon station. It represents
the per cent by which the cars reported at capacity
by the cordon count exceed the capacity number of
passengers. These percentages are the truncation
adjustment factors. They tie in directly to the cordon counts.

The first column of Appendix Table 11 shows the
adjustment factor for each cordon station. Thus,
the first cordon station has an adjustment factor of
112 per cent. These adjustment factors, combined

TABLE 11

The Truncation Adjustment for the October, 1962,
Cordon Count, Entering the CBD

Stations	Adjustment Factor	7:00 7:20	7:20 7:40	7:40 8:00	8:00 8:20	8:20 8:40	8:40 9:00
86 & Lexington	112	101	103	101	106	103	104
68 & Lexington	105			101	101	101	
72 & Broadway	107		101	101	104	102	104
66 & Broadway							
125 & St. Nicholas	126			105	103	113	101
72 & Central Park West							
Borough Hall	104				101		
Clark St.	(a) 104				101		
High St.	(b) 118			101		103	101
York St.							
Court St. (Btn., 4 Ave. Lcl.)	(c) 108					101	
Court St. (West End, Nassau)	(c) 108					103	
Bedford Ave.							
Manhattan Br. (Btn.,WE,SB Exp.)	(c) 108						
Manhattan Br. (WE Special)							
Williamsburg Br. (Jam.-Myrt.)	(b) 118		101				
23 & Ely	117					102	103
Vernon-Jackson	105				102	105	104
Queensboro Plaza (Btn. Lcl.,WE)	102					101	101
Queens Plaza (4 Ave. Lcl.)							

432

(a) This is the adjustment factor of the Borough Hall station. The available data did not permit an adjustment factor to be calculated for Clark Street. The Borough Hall factor is used because both stations serve local IRT trains which have cars of 180 capacity.

(b) This percentage is computed from the combined data of the 125th Street and St. Nicholas, and 23rd and Ely Street stations. Neither of them alone had sufficient observations to compute acceptable factors. The combination was considered possible because the stations serve Independent Express trains whose cars have 220 capacity. The factor is also applied to other Independent stations with cars of this capacity.

(c) This is a combined average of BMT trains whose cordon stations are Court Street, Bedford Avenue, and Canal Street. The capacity of their cars is 260.

433

with the per cent of cars reported at capacity during the October, 1962, cordon count as shown on
Appendix Table 9, produce the truncation adjustment
which is given in the remaining columns of Appendix
Table 11. The equation by which the truncation adjustment is calculated from the data is as follows:
The truncation adjustment (X 100) = the adjustment
factor X the per cent of cars reported at capacity +
100 X the per cent of cars reported at less than
capacity.

The remaining columns of Appendix Table 11 contain the truncation adjustment table. Referring to
the first cordon station, it indicates that the October, 1962, count can be corrected for truncation by
increasing the 7:00-7:20 interval count by 1 per
cent, the 7:20-7:40 interval by 3 per cent, the
7:40-8:00 interval by 1 per cent, and so forth.

The percentages of Appendix Table 11 are applicable only to the 1962 count. Similar adjustment
can be computed for other counts by using the adjustment factors applied to the percentages of cars reported at capacity in the other years.

Appendix Table 12 gives the same results for
the p.m. cordon counts, leaving the CBD. It uses
the same adjustment factors as the a.m. table. They
are applied to Appendix Table 10 to produce Appendix
Table 12.

EVALUATION

The truncation adjustment table provides a systematic way of increasing the cordon counts. It
cannot be said with any assurance that the adjustment factors correct the counts to a satisfactory
degree. The extent to which the adjusted cordon
counts deviate from accuracy must inevitably remain
unknown. In evaluating this truncation adjustment
it seems reasonable to assert that it does not overstate the required amount of correction. If anything, it still falls short of producing estimates
of the actual numbers of people passing through the
cordon stations, particularly during the rush hour.

TABLE 12

The Truncation Adjustment for the October, 1962,
Cordon Count, Leaving the CBD

Stations	Adjustment Factor	3:20 4:20	4:20 4:40	4:40 5:00	5:00 5:20	5:20 5:40	5:40 6:00	6:00 6:20
Grand Central (Lex. Ave. Exp.)	112		101	103	108	103	100	
59 & Lexington (Lex. Ave. Lcl.)	105		100	101	103	103	102	
Times Square (7 Ave. Exp.)	107		100	101	104	104	101	
59 & Broadway (Bway.Lcl.)	105				100	101	100	
59 & Broadway (A, D)	126			106	115	114	100	
59 & Broadway (AA, BB, CC)	105				100			
Bowling Green	104			101	101	102	100	
Wall & William	104			101	102	101		
Broadway-Nassau	118			101	107	105		
East Broadway								
Whitehall St.	108			100	101	100		
Broad St.	108			103	101			
1st Ave.								
Manhattan Br. (Btn.,SB,WE Exp.)	108			101	106	106	101	
Manhattan Br. (WE Special)	118							
Williamsburg Br. (Jam.-Myrt.)	117		100					
Lexington & 53	105			101	106	106	101	
Grand Central (Flushing)				102	103	101		
Lexington & 60 (Btn. Lcl., WE)	102						100	
Lexington & 60 (4th Ave. Lcl.)	102						100	

APPENDIX G THE ADJUSTED
CORDON
COUNTS

This appendix will present two sets of adjusted
cordon counts. Both are based on the data of October, 1962. In the first, the actual counts are modified by the truncation adjustment. They are intended
to correct the actual data for the underestimates
arising from the truncation procedure. The second
set of counts consists of the October, 1962, data
modified: first, by the cordon interval patterns;
and then, by the truncation adjustment.

In computing these tables one problem had to be
resolved. This was whether to apply the truncation
adjustment before or after the data were modified by
the cordon interval pattern. The decision was to apply the truncation adjustment last, and was based
substantially on practical considerations. In order
to give effect to the truncation correction before
the data were modified, the cordon counts of all
five years would have had to be corrected before calculating the cordon interval patterns. Otherwise,
if it were applied only to October, 1962, its effect
would have been lost among the uncorrected other
four years. But to correct all five years, it would
have been necessary to calculate the per cent of
cars exceeding capacity for each interval of each of
the years. This was not possible because the required observation sheets of the other years were
not available. Accordingly, as a practical matter,
the truncation adjustment was used after the original
data had been modified by the cordon interval pattern.

The effect of this reverse procedure is considered inconsequential. It involves a slight illogi-
cality but the distortion in the results probably

436

does not exceed the limitations of the adjustment
itself.

Appendix Tables 13 and 15 give the a.m. and
p.m. actual counts, modified by the truncation adjustment. Appendix Tables 14 and 16 give the a.m.
and p.m. counts with the double modification: first,
by the cordon interval pattern, then by the truncation adjustment.

TABLE 13

The October, 1962, Cordon Count Entering the CBD, Modified by the Truncation Adjustment

Stations	6:20 6:40	6:40 7:00	7:00 7:20	7:20 7:40	7:40 8:00	8:00 8:20	8:20 8:40	8:40 9:00	9:00 9:20	9:20 9:40	9:40 10:00
86 & Lexington	2,800	4,200	8,797	12,927	13,473	13,971	13,194	8,518	6,460	5,680	2,810
68 & Lexington	1,500	2,090	6,190	11,140	8,019	8,888	14,605	13,370	7,338	4,140	2,560
72 & Broadway	2,530	3,650	6,060	8,918	10,888	11,378	13,760	9,693	6,290	3,750	2,860
66 & Broadway	1,530	1,700	2,420	4,960	6,460	9,330	10,040	9,410	3,470	3,420	2,310
125 & St. Nicholas	2,760	3,900	7,730	12,580	18,638	22,114	21,662	14,079	7,000	4,650	3,740
72 & Central Park West	780	690	2,110	5,010	3,900	7,210	7,770	9,200	3,340	1,610	810
Borough Hall	1,110	1,910	2,790	4,140	6,270	11,272	10,880	8,010	4,060	2,660	1,370
Clark St.	880	1,070	1,980	5,870	6,890	9,575	9,850	7,050	4,040	2,310	1,040
High St.	2,240	3,530	4,850	8,440	10,019	16,550	19,622	14,281	3,990	3,120	2,580
York St.	560	1,110	2,600	4,490	5,030	6,180	6,330	3,730	2,160	1,390	1,140
Court St. (Btn., 4 Ave. Lcl.)	660	1,390	840	1,190	1,490	7,510	9,635	6,960	4,430	1,740	1,220
Court St. (West End, Nassau)	-	100	80	-	260	2,220	1,864	5,720	1,580	340	770
Bedford Ave.	980	2,230	3,220	3,110	5,830	4,150	6,700	4,650	1,780	1,340	1,240
Manhattan Br. (Btn., WE,SB Exp.)	1,590	5,490	6,890	8,910	13,330	14,810	16,660	16,550	8,850	6,180	3,968
Manhattan Br. (WE Special)	-	-	-	-	830	1,220	3,440	920	-	-	-
Williamsburg Br. (Jam.-Myrt.)	1,210	2,180	4,210	5,353	5,960	11,360	7,834	6,324	3,080	1,530	1,380
23 & Ely	2,240	2,630	5,190	9,570	17,670	18,431	23,531	18,855	13,630	6,220	5,000
Vernon-Jackson	950	2,060	3,790	8,360	9,320	14,020	15,190	13,292	9,780	2,350	2,270
Queensboro Plaza Btn. Lcl., WE)	810	2,250	1,890	4,820	7,400	7,600	7,650	4,830	2,520	2,220	1,050
Queens Plaza (4 Ave. Lcl.)	-	490	1,270	2,940	3,550	4,130	7,720	3,540	2,240	1,100	1,060
Total CBD	25,130	42,670	72,907	122,728	155,227	201,709	227,937	178,982	96,030	55,750	39,170

TABLE 14

The October, 1962, Cordon Count Entering the CBD, Modified by the Cordon Interval Pattern and the Truncation Adjustment

Stations	6:20 6:40	6:40 7:00	7:00 7:20	7:20 7:40	7:40 8:00	8:00 8:20	8:20 8:40	8:40 9:00	9:00 9:20	9:20 9:40	9:40 10:00
86 & Lexington	2,753	5,268	8,422	13,576	13,948	13,905	13,993	9,842	5,273	3,620	2,320
68 & Lexington	1,692	2,343	5,037	8,423	10,921	11,681	14,002	12,431	6,928	3,807	2,617
72 & Broadway	2,126	3,457	5,720	8,628	12,056	12,560	11,700	10,889	6,254	3,898	2,551
66 & Broadway	1,256	1,403	2,665	4,851	7,145	9,256	9,760	9,167	3,820	2,714	2,014
125 & St. Nicholas	2,905	4,665	9,239	13,163	17,883	19,727	21,733	13,697	7,076	4,779	3,887
72 & Central Park West	668	736	2,028	5,383	4,711	6,824	8,886	7,716	3,247	1,306	923
Borough Hall	1,168	1,756	3,040	4,296	5,314	10,017	11,541	8,750	4,081	3,089	1,408
Clark St.	1,015	1,385	2,265	4,650	6,065	8,960	9,369	8,447	4,630	2,489	1,276
High St.	1,572	2,695	5,253	8,699	11,153	14,758	18,366	15,076	6,205	3,142	2,286
York St.	525	1,249	2,385	4,089	4,925	6,467	5,808	4,781	2,119	1,239	1,133
Court St. (Btn., 4 Ave. Lcl.)	751	1,127	1,681	2,529	3,583	6,082	7,868	6,546	3,750	1,764	1,252
Court St. (West End, Nassau)	-	119	210	572	745	1,952	2,816	3,793	1,705	598	453
Bedford Ave.	1,041	2,019	2,430	3,678	5,074	6,119	7,120	4,308	1,949	1,465	1,026
Manhattan Br. (Btn., WE,SB Exp.)	2,463	4,996	6,641	9,838	12,341	16,181	17,150	15,668	8,702	5,055	4,185
Manhattan Br. (WE Special)	-	-	-	-	166	1,344	2,896	1,791	213	-	-
Williamsburg Br. (Jam.-Myrt.)	1,334	2,360	3,345	5,602	7,154	9,310	9,355	6,658	2,935	1,292	1,117
23 & Ely	2,410	3,230	6,495	9,952	15,414	18,662	23,056	21,245	11,787	6,550	4,238
Vernon-Jackson	963	2,116	3,478	6,526	8,111	13,631	15,757	16,424	8,612	2,745	2,055
Queensboro Plaza (Btn. Lcl., WE)	940	2,040	3,019	4,234	6,593	7,090	7,769	5,313	2,569	2,023	1,401
Queens Plaza (4 Ave. Lcl.)	-	931	1,491	2,594	3,387	4,407	6,303	4,282	2,127	1,417	1,101
Total CBD	25,582	43,895	74,844	121,283	156,689	198,934	225,249	186,824	93,982	52,992	37,249

TABLE 15

The October, 1962, Cordon Count Leaving the CBD, Modified by the Truncation Adjustment

Stations	3:20 3:40	3:40 4:00	4:00 4:20	4:20 4:40	4:40 5:00	5:00 5:20	5:20 5:40	5:40 6:00	6:00 6:20	6:20 6:40	6:40 7:00
Grand Central (Lex. Ave. Exp.)	3,770	4,820	5,550	6,616	10,980	15,001	12,762	10,770	5,880	6,620	3,700
59 & Lexington (Lex. Ave. Lcl.)	3,490	5,080	6,350	6,650	12,716	14,338	14,389	13,219	8,100	4,290	3,010
Times Square (7 Ave. Exp.)	2,730	2,300	5,230	5,120	10,090	10,743	13,562	9,797	8,150	5,500	4,020
59 & Broadway (Bway.Lcl.)	2,170	2,210	2,740	3,340	7,800	10,780	12,080	9,080	5,650	3,770	3,070
59 & Broadway (A, D)	5,410	6,180	7,410	8,100	15,741	24,265	23,758	16,160	12,550	8,190	6,690
59 & Broadway (AA, BB, CC)	1,050	1,090	1,350	2,520	4,620	8,720	10,130	6,640	4,140	2,980	1,940
Bowling Green	1,770	1,810	1,920	3,820	8,898	11,312	10,138	8,400	3,920	2,990	2,420
Wall & William	1,650	1,850	2,570	4,580	9,656	8,976	9,620	5,270	3,410	3,120	1,980
Broadway-Nassau	2,200	2,910	3,980	6,250	10,837	15,173	18,102	10,280	6,370	3,860	2,620
East Broadway	1,220	1,400	2,200	1,970	3,170	3,930	8,000	4,610	3,240	1,980	1,590
Whitehall St.	1,440	1,620	3,610	5,610	10,520	8,999	6,930	7,000	3,820	2,900	1,480
Broad St.	170	350	860	420	3,368	6,343	2,180	720	490	140	-
1st Ave.	1,640	2,360	1,740	2,550	5,300	7,770	7,480	3,990	2,590	2,160	1,730
Manhattan Br. (Btn., SB, WE Exp.)	3,570	4,550	4,810	5,610	6,908	11,755	11,353	11,908	11,660	8,610	5,600
Manhattan Br. (WE Special)	-	-	-	-	-	1,420	600	-	-	-	-
Williamsburg Br. (Jam.-Myrt.)	860	1,650	2,810	3,520	5,140	10,210	8,150	5,780	3,140	3,140	1,380
Lexington & 53	5,490	4,860	5,190	9,290	15,413	21,476	19,546	16,524	12,830	9,540	4,480
Grand Central Flushing	2,780	3,110	4,320	6,390	11,363	17,294	15,322	12,170	6,540	4,220	2,900
Lexington & 60 (Btn. Lcl., WE)	2,320	2,020	2,330	2,780	4,910	6,640	6,630	6,950	3,190	2,180	1,570
Lexington & 60 (4th Ave. Lcl.)	1,490	970	1,020	1,910	2,660	5,980	3,770	3,860	1,450	1,590	960
Total CBD	45,220	51,140	65,990	86,996	160,090	221,125	214,502	162,628	107,120	77,290	51,140

TABLE 16

The October, 1962, Cordon Count Leaving the CBD, Modified by the Cordon
Interval Pattern and the Truncation Adjustment

Stations	3:20 3:40	3:40 4:00	4:00 4:20	4:20 4:40	4:40 5:00	5:00 5:20	5:20 5:40	5:40 6:00	6:00 6:20	6:20 6:40	6:40 7:00
Grand Central (Lex. Ave. Exp.)	3,434	4,251	4,927	6,783	11,518	13,914	13,825	10,871	7,324	5,500	3,590
59 & Lexington (Lex. Ave. Lcl.)	5,301	6,805	6,710	5,962	9,861	11,394	12,830	13,650	9,522	5,705	3,743
Times Square (7 Ave. Exp.)	2,587	3,016	4,580	5,567	9,333	11,720	13,073	9,842	8,190	5,642	3,703
59 & Broadway (Bway. Lcl.)	2,461	2,278	2,863	3,951	7,042	9,993	12,369	8,722	5,605	4,371	3,037
59 & Broadway (A, D)	4,961	5,582	6,787	8,061	15,737	22,922	24,755	17,499	12,685	8,988	6,424
59 & Broadway (AA, BB, CC)	1,062	1,132	1,393	2,534	4,632	7,696	9,830	7,058	4,681	3,587	1,623
Bowling Green	1,712	1,924	2,458	3,774	7,227	11,184	11,003	7,873	4,391	3,674	2,179
Wall & William	1,702	1,944	2,637	4,220	8,176	10,351	8,893	5,949	3,380	3,361	2,168
Broadway-Nassau	2,112	2,577	3,836	5,678	10,497	18,264	14,808	10,062	6,270	5,063	3,458
East Broadway	1,210	1,620	1,816	2,367	3,298	4,321	6,688	4,356	3,368	2,731	1,555
Whitehall St.	1,422	1,674	2,727	4,011	7,076	11,482	9,431	6,463	4,241	3,125	1,802
Broad St.	265	501	739	1,429	3,557	4,472	2,205	1,146	561	154	-
1st Ave.	1,572	2,243	1,935	2,691	5,338	6,838	6,928	4,919	2,923	2,396	1,527
Manhattan Br. (Btn., SB, WE Exp.)	3,245	4,264	4,838	5,348	8,700	13,320	13,743	11,551	9,507	6,819	5,236
Manhattan Br. (WE Special)	-	-	-	-	-	1,353	667	-	-	-	-
Williamsburg Br. (Jam.-Myrt.)	1,064	1,680	2,373	3,081	5,512	9,672	8,963	4,828	3,757	3,346	1,502
Lexington & 53	4,325	5,055	5,674	8,113	13,148	19,791	23,012	18,764	12,837	8,796	5,223
Grand Central (Flushing)	2,807	3,227	4,208	5,664	12,341	17,375	16,524	10,716	6,126	4,559	2,844
Lexington & 60 (Btn. Lcl., WE)	1,948	2,091	2,411	3,102	4,175	7,160	7,062	5,567	3,527	2,601	1,876
Lexington & 60 (4th Ave. Lcl.)	1,144	1,169	938	1,924	3,037	5,122	3,625	4,287	1,836	1,422	1,155
Total CBD	44,334	53,033	63,850	84,260	150,205	218,294	220,234	164,123	110,731	81,840	52,645

APPENDIX H CAPACITY

Appendix Table 17 presents the passenger capacity of each type of car passing through the forty cordon stations. It gives the number of seats per car, the car capacities, the scheduled number of cars per train, and the train capacities. These data were obtained from the Transit Authority.

The order of the table corresponds to the order of the cordon stations, both entering and leaving, which have been used elsewhere in this study. However, because this table deals with specific cars which occur in both the entering and leaving stations, the order of presentation is denoted by the line and train rather than the station name. The station names can be identified from the other tables or from the presentation of cordon stations in Appendix Tables 1 and 2, where the lines and trains of the stations are specified.

There are three kinds of capacity applied to the cars of the subway system. There is a maximum capacity of each car which was estimated by engineering methods. There is the capacity shown on the table which is designated as schedule capacity. This runs about 10 to 15 per cent below the maximum and is used by the Transit Authority as the capacity number for fixing train schedules. Finally there is the comfort level capacity which is also shown on the table, and it is 75 to 80 per cent of the schedule capacity.

COMFORT LEVEL CAPACITY

The comfort level capacity was established by the Transit Authority engineers on the basis of

TABLE 17

Capacities of Subway Cars and Trains by Cordon Station, Line, and Train

Line and Train	Division	Seats per Car	Car Capacities			Scheduled Cars per Train	Train Capacities		
			Maximum	Schedule	Comfort		Maximum	Schedule	Comfort
Lex. Ave. Exp.	IRT	40	200	180	140	10	2,000	1,800	1,400
Lex. Ave. Local	IRT	40	200	180	140	9	1,800	1,620	1,260
7th Ave. Exp.	IRT	40	200	180	140	9	1,800	1,620	1,260
Broadway Local	IRT	40	200	180	140	8	1,600	1,440	1,120
A & D Expresses	IND	60	250	220	170	10	2,500	2,200	1,700
AA, BB, CC Locals	IND	60	250	220	170	8	2,000	1,760	1,360
Lex. Ave. Exp.	IRT	40	200	180	140	10	2,000	1,800	1,400
7th Ave. Exp.	IRT	40	200	180	140	9	1,800	1,620	1,260
A & E Expresses	IND	60	250	220	170	10	2,500	2,200	1,700
D Exp.	IND	60	250	220	170	10	2,500	2,200	1,700
Brighton Local	BMT	50	280	250	180	Var. 6/8	1,680 / 2,240	1,500 / 2,000	1,080 / 1,440
4th Ave. Line	BMT	50	280	250	180	8	2,240	2,000	1,440
West End-Nassau	BMT	50 / 80	280 / 300	250 / 260	180* / 200	Var. 6/7	1,800 / 2,100	1,560 / 1,820	1,200 / 1,400
14th St.-Canarsie	BMT	80	300	260	200	6	1,800	1,560	1,200
Sea Beach	BMT	60	220	200	150	12	2,640	2,400	1,800
West End Exp.	BMT	80	300	260	200	Var. 6/8	1,800 / 2,400	1,560 / 2,080	1,200 / 1,600
Brighton Exp.	BMT	60	220	200	150	8	1,760	1,600	1,200
West End-Nassau	BMT	50	280	250	180	AM-8 PM-6	1,680 / 2,240	1,500 / 2,000	1,080 / 1,440
Myrtle Chambers	BMT	80	300	260	200	6	1,800	1,560	1,200
Jamaica	BMT	60	250	220	170	Var. 6/8	1,500 / 2,000	1,320 / 1,760	1,020 / 1,360
Bway. Short Line	BMT	60	250	220	170	Var. 5/6	1,250 / 1,500	1,100 / 1,320	850 / 1,020
E & F Expresses	IND	60	250	220	170	10	2,500	2,200	1,700
Flushing Line	IRT	40	200	180	140	9	1,800	1,620	1,260
Brighton Local	BMT	50	280	250	180	Var. 6/8	1,680 / 2,240	1,500 / 2,000	1,080 / 1,440
West End Exp.	BMT	80	300	260	200	Var. 6/8	1,800 / 2,400	1,560 / 2,080	1,200 / 1,600
4th Ave. Line	BMT	50	280	250	180	8	2,240	2,000	1,440

*This type of car used only during a.m. rush hours.

studies of each type of car used in the system. The
criteria and procedures of these studies are described in the text of the chapter. The results are
given in the column of comfort level capacities
shown on Appendix Table 17.

The procedures employed by the Transit Authority engineers were briefly reviewed and the following
conclusions were reached. First, the ellipse of
2 X 1 1/2 feet is an adequate amount of space for
the standing passengers. It exceeds the measurement
data provided in the Handbook of Human Engineering.
Second, the review indicated that this individual
standard was applied in such a way as to maximize
the utilization of car space. This resulted in comfort level standards per car which are higher than
might be obtained with a more liberal application of
the standard. For example, the IRT car is assigned
a comfort level capacity of 140 passengers, of whom
44 occupy seats. In examining the Authority's floor
plan of the car with its inscribed ellipses, a
slightly different conclusion was reached. The
Authority's engineers find that the car could hold
98 standees. Together with the 44 seated passengers,
they make a total of 142. The Authority's engineers
rounded this to 140 for the comfort level. The review by this study suggests that 91 or 92 would be
able to stand comfortably. The Authority's number
includes a certain amount of overlap of the ellipses
and some double counting. Instead of a comfort
level of 142 (rounded to 140), it ought to be 135 or
136, a reduction of 4 or 5 per cent.

A question might also be raised, in placing the
ellipses on the floor plan, as to whether the standees
would have adequate devices such as poles or straps
for supporting themselves during the ride. This appears not to be the case from the drawings. If the
availability of such devices were required, the
standard would probably be reduced a bit further.

Comfort Level Capacity, October, 1962

Appendix Tables 18 and 19 give the comfort level
capacities of the actual trains (for the actual

TABLE 18

The Comfort Level Capacity per Interval, Entering the CBD,
October, 1962, Based on the Actual Number of Cars

Stations	6:20 6:40	6:40 7:00	7:00 7:20	7:20 7:40	7:40 8:00	8:00 8:20	8:20 8:40	8:40 9:00	9:00 9:20	9:20 9:40
86 & Lexington	5,600	9,800	11,200	12,460	13,720	11,200	11,200	7,000	12,460	11,200
68 & Lexington	3,780	3,780	10,080	11,340	8,820	7,560	12,600	12,600	8,820	5,040
72 & Broadway	6,300	8,820	8,820	8,820	10,080	8,820	11,340	7,560	6,300	6,300
66 & Broadway	4,480	3,360	5,600	7,840	8,960	10,080	11,200	11,200	5,600	5,600
125 & St. Nicholas	6,800	8,160	11,900	15,300	17,000	18,700	15,300	17,000	17,000	10,200
72 & Central Park West	2,040	2,040	4,420	11,220	7,140	10,540	14,620	16,320	10,200	6,120
Borough Hall	4,200	4,200	7,000	8,400	8,400	9,800	9,800	11,200	12,460	11,200
Clark St.	3,780	3,780	5,040	7,560	8,820	8,820	8,820	10,080	7,560	7,560
High St.	3,060	3,400	5,100	10,200	10,200	20,400	18,700	17,000	10,200	6,800
York St.	1,360	2,720	6,120	8,500	8,330	8,160	8,330	8,500	6,800	5,100
Court St. (Btn., 4 Ave. Lcl.)	2,880	6,480	4,320	4,320	3,960	10,080	8,640	7,200	6,840	4,320
Court St. (West End, Nassau)	-	2,880	1,400	-	1,400	4,400	2,600	6,440	2,880	1,400
Bedford Ave.	2,400	3,600	3,600	3,600	7,200	6,000	7,200	7,200	4,800	3,600
Manhattan Br. (Btn., WE, SB Exp.)	4,840	11,840	11,400	15,000	15,600	15,000	15,200	16,480	16,000	14,200
Manhattan Br. (WE Special)	-	-	-	-	1,440	1,440	2,700	1,080	-	-
Williamsburg Br. (Jam.-Myrt.)	5,120	5,630	7,840	6,480	7,500	11,750	9,040	10,050	8,530	3,740
23 & Ely	5,440	6,800	9,520	11,900	18,700	15,300	18,700	15,300	15,980	8,160
Vernon-Jackson	2,520	5,040	7,560	8,820	11,340	15,120	13,860	11,340	11,340	5,040
Queensboro Plaza (Btn. Lcl., WE)	4,480	6,080	2,280	4,560	8,280	9,000	10,720	7,520	7,440	9,280
Queens Plaza (4 Ave. Lcl.)	-	1,440	2,880	3,600	3,600	4,320	7,200	4,320	3,240	2,520

TABLE 19

The Comfort Level Capacity per Interval, Leaving the CBD,
October, 1962, Based on the Actual Number of Cars

Stations	3:20 3:40	3:40 4:00	4:00 4:20	4:20 4:40	4:40 5:00	5:00 5:20	5:20 5:40	5:40 6:00	6:00 6:20
Grand Central (Lex. Ave. Exp.)	5,600	7,000	8,400	7,000	9,800	11,200	11,200	11,200	11,200
59 & Lexington (Lex. Ave. Lcl.)	6,300	6,300	8,820	8,820	11,340	11,340	11,340	11,340	8,820
Times Square (7 Ave. Exp.)	5,040	6,300	10,080	8,820	10,080	8,820	11,340	8,820	8,820
59 & Broadway (Bway.Lcl.)	5,600	5,600	5,600	7,840	11,200	11,200	10,080	8,960	7,840
59 & Broadway (A, D)	10,200	10,200	13,600	15,300	15,300	17,000	17,000	17,000	15,300
59 & Broadway (AA, BB, CC)	2,040	2,720	2,720	7,480	9,520	12,240	16,660	12,240	10,880
Bowling Green	8,400	8,400	7,000	11,200	11,200	9,800	8,400	9,800	7,000
Wall & William	6,300	8,820	8,820	8,680	8,820	7,560	10,080	7,560	5,040
Broadway-Nassau	3,400	5,100	5,100	8,500	15,300	15,300	17,000	13,260	11,900
East Broadway	5,100	5,100	6,480	5,100	8,500	6,800	10,200	6,800	8,500
Whitehall St.	4,680	4,320	6,480	6,480	10,080	10,080	8,640	8,640	10,080
Broad St.	1,200	2,400	2,400	1,200	2,800	5,800	2,400	2,600	2,400
1st Ave.	3,600	4,800	3,600	4,800	6,000	8,400	7,200	4,800	6,000
Manhattan Br. (Btn., SB, WE Exp.)	8,800	11,200	11,000	10,400	9,000	8,800	8,400	12,000	16,480
Manhattan Br. (WE Special)						2,160	1,080	–	–
Williamsburg Br. (Jam.-Myrt.)	3,060	4,760	7,820	7,500	7,160	10,900	8,520	8,520	7,500
Lexington & 53	6,800	6,800	8,160	10,880	15,300	17,000	15,300	15,300	15,300
Grand Central (Flushing)	6,300	5,040	8,820	8,820	10,080	13,860	13,860	12,600	10,080
Lexington & 60 (Btn. Lcl., WE)	5,760	5,680	7,680	7,520	9,120	9,120	9,120	9,360	6,840
Lexington & 60 (4th Ave. Lcl.)	3,960	2,880	2,880	4,320	2,880	5,760	4,320	5,400	2,160

number of cars) passing through each cordon station
in each of the eleven intervals during the October,
1962, count, entering and leaving the CBD. The numbers of cars and trains were obtained from the reports of the cordon count. The types of car passing
through these stations are recorded on the observation sheets and confirmed by other information provided by the Transit Authority. These numbers of
cars, multiplied by the comfort capacity data as
given in Appendix Table 17, produced the comfort
level capacities shown on Appendix Tables 18 and 19.

Appendix Tables 20 and 21 give the comfort
level capacity reduced to 88 per cent for the cordon
stations located in the area served by the southeast
trains. It was shown in Appendix B (Table 3) that
the maximum stations for trains from the southeast
occur before the first cordon station, and that, on
the average, the cordon stations have 88 per cent of
the maximum passenger loads. In order to evaluate
traffic and to assure that the comfort level is not
exceeded along the southeast lines, the standard of
these cordon stations must be fixed at 88 per cent
of the comfort level. The cordon stations to which
this restriction applies are the ones situated in
the area through which the southeast trains pass.
These include all of the southeast trains and the Independent D train which, although not a southeast
train, actually passes through the area of the southeast cordon stations.

A Partial Maximum Comfort
Level Capacity

A partial maximum comfort level capacity of subway traffic during a 20-minute cordon interval will
now be defined and quantified. It is a partial maximum capacity because it uses two different bases for
assigning comfort level capacity to the individual
stations. For those stations whose traffic volume
equals or exceeds maximum capacity, the comfort
level is designated as the maximum which the station
can provide. For those stations whose traffic is
less than the maximum, the comfort level is set at

TABLE 20

88 Per Cent of the Comfort Level Capacity of Selected Stations per Interval, October, 1962, Entering the CBD, Based on the Actual Number of Cars

Stations	6:20 6:40	6:40 7:00	7:00 7:20	7:20 7:40	7:40 8:00	8:00 8:20	8:20 8:40	8:40 9:00	9:00 9:20	9:20 9:40
Borough Hall	3,696	3,696	6,160	7,392	7,392	8,624	8,624	9,856	10,964	9,856
Clark St.	3,326	3,326	4,435	6,653	7,762	7,762	7,762	9,504	6,653	6,653
York St.	1,197	2,394	5,386	7,480	7,330	7,180	7,330	7,480	5,984	4,488
Court St. (Btn., 4 Ave. Lcl.)	2,534	5,702	3,802	3,802	3,485	9,504	7,603	6,336	6,019	3,802
Court St. (West End, Nassau)	-	2,534	1,232		1,232	3,872	2,288	5,667	2,534	1,232
Manhattan Br. (Btn., WE, SB Exp.)	4,259	10,419	10,032	13,200	13,728	13,200	13,376	14,502	14,080	12,496
Manhattan Br. (WE Special)	-	-	-	-	1,267	1,267	2,376	950	-	-

TABLE 21

88 Per Cent of the Comfort Level Capacity of Selected Stations per Interval, October, 1962, Leaving the CBD, Based on the Actual Number of Cars

Stations	3:20 3:40	3:40 4:00	4:00 4:20	4:20 4:40	4:40 5:00	5:00 5:20	5:20 5:40	5:40 6:00	6:00 6:20
Bowling Green	7,392	7,392	6,160	9,856	9,856	8,624	7,392	8,624	6,160
Wall & William	5,544	7,762	7,762	7,638	7,762	6,653	8,870	6,653	4,435
East Broadway	4,488	4,488	5,984	4,488	7,480	5,984	8,976	5,984	7,480
Whitehall St.	4,118	3,802	5,702	5,702	8,870	8,870	7,603	7,603	8,870
Broad St.	1,056	2,112	2,112	1,056	2,464	5,104	2,112	2,288	2,112
Manhattan Br. (Btn., SB, WE Exp.)	7,744	9,856	9,680	9,152	7,920	7,744	7,392	10,560	14,502
Manhattan Br. (WE Special)	-	-	-	-	-	1,901	950	-	-

448

their actual requirements. The CBD total is therefore not the absolute maximum capacity of the system.
It is the capacity which the system is capable of
providing to meet its peak demand.

Appendix Table 22 presents the partial maximum
comfort level capacity for the CBD and its forty stations. For the whole system during a 20-minute interval, this specially defined capacity is now
239,480 passengers. After the planned increase in
train size, it will rise to 242,200. When the
trains serving the southeast area are adjusted to 88
per cent of their capacity, the special comfort
level capacity becomes 233,734.

There are some things about the preparation of
the table which now must be explained.

Train Size and Headway

The first numerical column of the table gives
the train size--the number of cars per train for
each of the stations. With certain exceptions to be
noted, they are taken directly from Appendix Table
17, and they are the present maximum sizes. Some
stations, as indicated by Appendix Table 17, have
mixed lines, cars, and train sizes. These were
handled as follows. The Court Street stations are
combined into a single station with capacity as provided by the Transit Authority on the basis of prospects and plans for the lines serving these stations.
The Manhattan Bridge station serving the three BMT
express trains has at least three train sizes and
three types of car. The present comfort level capacity was determined by taking the highest number observed in any interval during the October, 1962, cordon count. This may in fact exceed the operating
capacity of the station.

The present maximum train size is given for the
West Side IRT stations. However, as the table shows,
special computations of their capacity are shown for
after their planned increase in cars per train.

TABLE 22

Passenger Capacity per 20-Minute Interval, per Cordon Station and Total CBD

Entering Cordon Station	Cars per Train	Trains per 20-Minutes	Maximum	Schedule	Passenger Capacities — Comfort Level Present	After Car/Train Increase	S.E. 88%	Leaving Cordon Station
86 & Lexington	10	10	20,000	18,000	14,000			Grand Central (Lex. Ave. Exp.)
68 & Lexington	9	10	18,000	16,200	12,600			59 & Lexington (Lex. Ave. Lcl.)
72 & Broadway	9	10	18,000	16,200	12,600	14,000		Times Square (7 Ave. Exp.)
66 & Broadway	8	10	16,000	14,400	11,200	14,000		59 & Broadway (Bway.Lcl.)
125 & St. Nicholas	10	10	25,000	22,000	17,000			59 & Broadway (A, D)
72 & Central Park West	9	10	22,500	19,800	15,300			59 & Broadway (AA,BB,CC)
Borough Hall	10	10	20,000	18,000	14,000		12,320	Bowling Green
Clark St.	9	10	18,000	16,200	12,600	14,000	12,320	Wall & William
High St.	10	10	25,000	22,000	17,000			Broadway-Nassau
York St.	10	5	12,500	11,000	8,500		7,480	East Broadway
Court St. (Btn., 4 Ave. Lcl.)	8	10	22,400	20,000	14,400		12,672	Whitehall St.
Court St. (West End, Nassau)								Broad St.
Bedford Ave.	6	6	10,800	9,360	7,200			1st Ave.
Manhattan Br. (Btn., WE, SB Exp.)	6-12	10			16,480		14,502	Manhattan Br. (Btn., SB, WE Exp.)
Manhattan Br. (WE Special)	8	3	6,720	6,000	4,320		3,802	Manhattan Br. (WE Special)
Williamsburg Br. (Jam.-Myrt.)	8	9	18,000	15,840	12,240			Williamsburg Br. (Jam.-Myrt.)
23 & Ely	10	10	24,000	22,000	17,000			Lexington & 53
Vernon-Jackson	9	12	21,600	19,440	15,120			Grand Central (Flushing)
Queensboro Plaza (Btn. Lcl., WE)	8	7	16,800	15,160	11,200			Lexington & 60 (Btn. Lcl., WE)
Queens Plaza (4 Ave. Lcl.)	8	5	11,200	10,000	7,200			Lexington & 60 (4 Ave. Lcl.)
Total			354,720	314,200	239,480			
Total, incorporating car increases						242,200		
Total, incorporating 88%							233,734	

450

The second column of the table gives the number of trains per 20 minutes which were used for computing the comfort levels. For most of the stations the capacity headway was used. For the Vernon-Jackson station this is 12 trains per 20 minutes and for most of the others it is 10 trains per 20 minutes. The remaining stations showing less than 10 trains per 20 minutes are fixed at the maximum which their traffic requires. In one case, the West End Special train at the Manhattan Bridge cordon, the schedule was increased from 2 to 3 trains per 20 minutes.

Capacities

The capacities were determined by extending the data of the preceding columns. The maximum and schedule capacities are given for the purpose of comparison. The comfort level capacities are given on three bases. For all stations the present level is shown. For the three West Side IRT stations the prospective level after the increase of train size is given. The final column gives 88 per cent of the comfort level which is applicable to the stations serving the southeast area.

The total rows give the capacities of the entire system at 100 per cent operating efficiency on the three bases: at present capacity, after the increase in train size, and after incorporating the 88 per cent level for the southeast stations.

APPENDIX | PER CENTS OF PASSENGERS,
BY CORDON STATION
AND INTERVAL

Appendix Table 23 presents the passengers traveling through each interval of each station as per
cents of the total interval count. (The column sums
are 100 per cent.) The table was calculated from
Appendix Table 14, which contains the October, 1962,
cordon count modified by the cordon interval pattern
and the truncation adjustment.

452

TABLE 23

Passengers, by Station and Interval, as Per Cents* of Interval Totals**

Stations	6:20 6:40	6:40 7:00	7:00 7:20	7:20 7:40	7:40 8:00	8:00 8:20	8:20 8:40	8:40 9:00	9:00 9:20	9:20 9:40	9:40 10:00
Grand Central (Lex. Ave. Exp.)	10.8	12.0	11.3	11.2	8.9	7.0	6.2	5.3	5.6	6.8	6.2
59 & Lexington (Lex. Ave. Lcl.)	6.6	5.3	6.7	6.9	7.0	5.9	6.2	6.7	7.4	7.2	7.0
Times Square (7 Ave. Exp.)	8.3	7.9	7.6	7.1	7.7	6.3	5.2	5.8	6.7	7.4	6.9
59 & Broadway (Bway. Lcl.)	5.0	3.2	3.6	4.0	4.6	4.7	4.3	4.9	4.1	5.1	5.4
59 & Broadway (A, D)	11.4	10.6	12.3	10.9	11.4	9.9	9.7	6.3	7.5	9.0	10.4
59 & Broadway (AA, BB, CC)	2.6	1.7	2.7	4.4	3.0	3.4	3.9	4.1	3.5	2.5	2.5
Bowling Green	4.6	4.0	4.1	3.5	3.4	5.0	5.1	4.7	4.3	5.8	3.4
Wall & William	4.0	3.2	3.0	3.8	3.9	4.5	4.2	4.5	4.9	4.7	3.4
Broadway-Nassau	6.1	6.1	7.0	7.2	7.1	7.4	8.2	8.1	6.6	5.9	6.1
East Broadway	2.1	2.9	3.2	3.4	3.1	3.3	2.6	2.6	2.3	2.3	3.0
Whitehall St.	2.9	2.6	2.3	2.1	2.3	3.1	3.5	3.5	4.0	3.3	3.4
Broad St.	.0	.3	.3	.5	.5	1.0	1.3	2.0	1.8	1.1	1.2
1st Ave.	4.1	4.6	3.3	3.0	3.2	3.1	3.2	2.3	2.1	2.8	2.8
Manhattan Br. (Btn., SB, WE Exp.)	9.6	11.4	8.9	8.1	7.9	8.1	7.6	8.4	9.3	9.5	11.2
Manhattan Br. (WE Special)	.0	.0	.0	.0	.1	.7	1.3	1.0	.2	.0	.0
Williamsburg Br. (Jam.-Myrt.)	5.2	5.4	4.5	4.6	4.6	4.7	4.2	3.6	3.1	2.4	3.0
Lexington & 53	9.4	7.4	8.7	8.2	9.8	9.4	10.2	11.4	12.5	12.4	11.4
Grand Central (Flushing)	3.8	4.8	4.7	5.4	5.2	6.9	7.0	8.8	9.2	5.2	5.5
Lexington & 60 (Btn. Lcl., WE)	3.7	4.7	4.0	3.5	4.2	3.6	3.5	2.8	2.7	3.8	3.8
Lexington & 60 (4th Ave. Lcl.)	.0	2.1	2.0	2.1	2.2	2.2	2.8	2.3	2.3	2.7	3.0

*Column sums = 100 per cent.

**Based on Appendix Table 14: the October, 1962, cordon count modified by the cordon interval pattern and the truncation adjustment.

APPENDIX   J   EXCESS
                   PASSENGERS
                   AND SPACE

This appendix will present tables showing the
numbers of persons above and below the comfort level,
by cordon station and interval, both entering and
leaving the CBD during the October, 1962, cordon
count. It will also give an estimate of the next ex-
cess--the irreducible number, under prevailing condi-
tions--of passengers entering the CBD during the
morning peak periods. The tables were computed by
subtracting the comfort level capacity of each interval from the actual number of passengers reported by
the cordon count. A supplementary set of tables will
also be given for the stations in the neighborhood
served by trains originating in the southeast.

The data from which the tables in this appendix
were constructed were obtained from Appendixes G and
H. The numbers of passengers are taken from Appendix Tables 13 and 15, the actual October, 1962, cordon counts as modified by the truncation adjustment.
The comfort level capacities were obtained from
Appendix Tables 18 and 19; for the southeast stations from Appendix Tables 20 and 21; and for the
net excess, from Appendix Table 22. The comfort
level capacity data are on a 20-minute interval
basis and the computations of excess passengers and
space were made for 20-minute intervals.

Appendix Tables 24 and 26 give the excess number of passengers respectively for entering and leaving the CBD. Appendix Tables 25 and 27 give the excess space in trains entering and leaving the CBD
respectively. Appendix Tables 28, 29, 30, and 31
give similar information for the cordon stations
serving the southeastern areas.

454

TABLE 24

Excess Passengers by Cordon Station, Entering the CBD, October, 1962

Stations	6:20 6:40	6:40 7:00	7:00 7:20	7:20 7:40	7:40 8:00	8:00 8:20	8:20 8:40	8:40 9:00	9:00 9:40
86 & Lexington				467		2,771	2,793	1,518	
68 & Lexington						1,328	2,005	770	
72 & Broadway				98	808	2,558	2,920	2,133	
66 & Broadway									
125 & St. Nicholas					1,638	3,414	6,362		
72 & Central Park West									
Borough Hall						1,472	1,080		
Clark St.						755	1,030		
High St.		130					922		
York St.									
Court St. (Btn., 4 Ave. Lcl.)							995		
Court St. (West End, Nassau)									
Bedford Ave.									
Manhattan Br. (Btn., WE, SB Exp.)							1,460	70	
Manhattan Br. (WE Special)							740		
Williamsburg Br. (Jam.-Myrt.)									
23 & Ely						3,131	4,831	3,555	
Vernon-Jackson							1,330	1,952	
Queensboro Plaza (Btn. Lcl., WE)				260					
Queens Plaza (4 Ave. Lcl.)							520		

TABLE 25

Excess Space by Cordon Station, Entering the CBD, October, 1962

Stations	6:20 6:40	6:40 7:00	7:00 7:20	7:20 7:40	7:40 8:00	8:00 8:20	8:20 8:40	8:40 9:00	9:00 9:20	9:20 9:40
86 & Lexington	2,800	5,600	2,403						6,000	5,520
68 & Lexington	2,280	1,690	3,890	200	801				1,490	900
72 & Broadway	3,770	5,170	2,760						10	2,550
66 & Broadway	2,950	1,660	3,180	2,880	2,500	1,750	1,160	1,790	2,130	2,180
125 & St. Nicholas	4,040	4,260	4,170	2,720				2,921	10,000	5,550
72 & Central Park West	1,260	1,350	2,310	6,210	3,240	3,330	6,850	7,120	6,800	4,510
Borough Hall	3,090	2,290	4,210	4,260	2,130			3,190	8,400	8,540
Clark St.	2,900	2,710	3,060	1,690	1,930			3,030	3,520	5,250
High St.	820		250	1,760	181	3,850		2,719	6,210	3,680
York St.	800	1,610	3,520	4,010	3,300	1,980	2,000	4,770	4,640	3,710
Court St. (Btn., 4 Ave. Lcl.)	2,220	5,090	3,480	3,130	2,470	7,580		240	2,410	2,580
Court St. (West End, Nassau)		2,780	1,320		1,140	2,180	736	720	1,300	1,060
Bedford Ave.	1,420	1,370	380	490	1,370	850	500	2,550	3,020	2,260
Manhattan Br. (Btn., WE, SB Exp.)	3,250	6,350	4,510	6,090	2,270	190			7,150	8,020
Manhattan Br. (WE Special)					610	220		160		
Williamsburg Br. (Jam.-Myrt.)	3,910	3,450	3,630	1,127	1,540	390	1,206	3,726	5,450	2,210
23 & Ely	3,200	4,170	4,330	2,330	1,030				2,350	1,940
Vernon-Jackson	1,570	2,980	3,770	460	2,020	1,100			1,560	2,690
Queensboro Plaza (Btn. Lcl., WE)	3,670	3,830	390		880	1,400	3,070	2,690	4,920	7,060
Queens Plaza (4 Ave. Lcl.)		950	1,610	660	50	190		780	1,000	1,420

TABLE 26

Excess Passengers by Cordon Station, Leaving the CBD, October, 1962

Stations	3:20 4:40	4:40 5:00	5:00 5:20	5:20 5:40	5:40 6:00	6:00 6:20
Grand Central (Lex. Ave. Exp.)		1,180	3,801	1,562		
59 & Lexington (Lex. Ave. Lcl.)		1,376	2,998	3,049	1,879	
Times Square (7 Ave. Exp.)		10	1,923	2,722	977	
59 & Broadway (Bway. Lcl.)				2,000	120	
59 & Broadway (A, D)		441	7,265	6,758		
59 & Broadway (AA, BB, CC)						
Bowling Green			1,512	1,738		
Wall & William		836	1,416			
Broadway-Nassau				1,102		
East Broadway						
Whitehall St.		440				
Broad St.		568	543			
1st Ave.				280		
Manhattan Br. (Btn., SB, WE Exp.)			2,955	2,953		
Manhattan Br. (WE Special)						
Williamsburg Br. (Jam.-Myrt.)						
Lexington & 53		113	4,476	4,246	1,224	
Grand Central (Flushing)		1,283	3,434	1,462		
Lexington & 60 (Btn. Lcl., WE)						
Lexington & 60 (4th Ave. Lcl.)			220			

457

TABLE 27

Excess Space by Cordon Station, Leaving the CBD, October, 1962

Stations	3:20 3:40	3:40 4:00	4:00 4:20	4:20 4:40	4:40 5:00	5:00 5:20	5:20 5:40	5:40 6:00	6:00 6:20
Grand Central (Lex. Ave. Exp.)	1,830	2,180	2,850	384				930	5,320
59 & Lexington (Lex. Ave. Lcl.)	2,810	1,220	2,470	2,170					720
Times Square (7 Ave. Exp.)	2,310	4,000	4,850	3,700					670
59 & Broadway (Bway. Lcl.)	3,430	3,390	2,860	4,500	3,400	420			2,190
59 & Broadway (A, D)	4,790	4,020	6,190	7,200				840	2,750
59 & Broadway (AA, BB, CC)	990	1,630	1,370	4,960	4,900	3,520	6,530	5,600	6,740
Bowling Green	6,630	6,590	5,080	7,380	2,302			1,400	3,080
Wall & William	4,650	6,970	6,250	4,100			460	2,290	1,630
Broadway-Nassau	1,200	2,190	1,120	2,750	4,463	127		2,980	5,530
East Broadway	3,880	3,700	4,600	3,130	5,330	2,870	2,200	2,190	5,260
Whitehall St.	3,240	2,700	2,870	870		1,081	1,710	1,640	6,260
Broad St.	1,030	2,050	1,540	780			220	1,880	1,910
1st Ave.	1,960	2,440	1,860	2,250	700	630		810	3,410
Manhattan Br. (Btn., SB, WE Exp.)	5,230	6,650	6,190	4,790	2,092			92	4,820
Manhattan Br. (WE Special)						740	480		
Williamsburg Br. (Jam.-Myrt.)	2,200	3,110	5,010	3,980	2,020	690	370	2,740	4,360
Lexington & 53	1,310	1,940	2,970	1,590					2,470
Grand Central (Flushing)	3,520	1,930	4,500	2,480				430	3,540
Lexington & 60 (Btn. Lcl., WE)	3,440	3,660	5,350	4,740	4,210	2,480	2,490	2,410	3,650
Lexington & 60 (4th Ave. Lcl.)	2,470	1,910	1,860	2,410	220		550	1,540	710

458

TABLE 28

Excess Passengers Entering the CBD Through the Southeast Stations, October, 1962

Stations	6:20 6:40	6:40 7:00	7:00 7:20	7:20 7:40	7:40 8:00	8:00 8:20	8:20 8:40	8:40 9:00	9:00 9:20	9:20 9:40
Borough Hall						2,648	2,256			
Clark St.						1,813	2,088			
York St.										
Court St. (Btn., 4 Ave. Lcl.)							2,032	624		
Court St. (West End, Nassau)										
Manhattan Br. (Btn., WE, SB Exp.)						1,610	3,284	2,048		
Manhattan Br. (WE Special)							1,064			

TABLE 29

Excess Space Entering the CBD Through the Southeast Stations, October, 1962

Stations	6:20 6:40	6:40 7:00	7:00 7:20	7:20 7:40	7:40 8:00	8:00 8:20	8:20 8:40	8:40 9:00	9:00 9:20	9:20 9:40
Borough Hall	2,586	1,786	3,370	1,522	502			2,806	6,924	7,546
Clark St.	2,446	2,256	2,455	783	872			2,454	2,613	4,343
York St.	637	1,284	2,786	2,990	2,300	1,000	1,000	3,750	3,824	3,098
Court St. (Btn., 4 Ave. Lcl.)	1,874	4,312	2,962	2,612	1,995	2,004			1,589	2,062
Court St. (West End, Nassau)		2,434	1,152		972	1,652	424	53	954	462
Manhattan Br. (Btn., WE, SB Exp.)	2,669	4,929	3,142	4,290	398	1,000			5,230	6,316
Manhattan Br. (WE Special)					437	47		30		

TABLE 30

Excess Passengers Leaving the CBD Through the Southeast Stations, October, 1962

Stations	3:20 3:40	3:40 4:00	4:00 4:20	4:20 4:40	4:40 5:00	5:00 5:20	5:20 5:40	5:40 6:00	6:00 6:20
Bowling Green						2,688	2,746		
Wall & William					1,894	2,323	750		
East Broadway									
Whitehall St.					1,650	129			
Broad St.					904	1,239	68		
Manhattan Br. (Btn., SB, WE Exp.)						4,011	3,961	1,348	
Manhattan Br. (WE Special)									

TABLE 31

Excess Space Leaving the CBD Through the Southeast Stations, October, 1962

Stations	3:20 3:40	3:40 4:00	4:00 4:20	4:20 4:40	4:40 5:00	5:00 5:20	5:20 5:40	5:40 6:00	6:00 6:20
Bowling Green	5,622	5,582	4,240	6,036	958			224	2,240
Wall & William	3,894	5,912	5,192	3,058				1,383	1,025
East Broadway	3,268	3,088	3,784	2,518	4,310	2,054	976	1,374	4,240
Whitehall St.	2,678	2,182	2,092	92			673	603	5,050
Broad St.	886	1,762	1,252	636				1,568	1,622
Manhattan Br. (Btn., SB, WE Exp.)	4,174	5,306	4,870	3,542	1,012				2,842
Manhattan Br. (WE Special)						481	350		

THE NET EXCESS

A special computation of excess passengers entering the CBD is given in Appendix Table 32. It is considered the irreducible estimate of excess passengers after adjustment for maximum comfort level capacity and off-schedule operations. Its construction will be briefly described.

TABLE 32

Net Excess Passengers Entering the CBD,
by Cordon Station

Stations	7:40 8:00	8:00 8:20	8:20 8:40	8:40 9:00
68 & Lexington			2,005	770
125 & St. Nicholas	1,134	3,549	6,583	
High Street			2,622	
Court St. (Btn., 4 Ave. Lcl.)	)			)
Court St. (West End, Nassau)	)			) 8
Manhattan Br. (Btn., WE, SB Exp.)		308	2,158	2,048
23 & Ely		3,399	4,567	1,855
Vernon-Jackson			70	
Queens Plaza (4 Ave. Lcl.)			520	

The cordon count employed in the table is from October, 1962, adjusted for truncation, as given in Appendix Table 13.

Several revisions in cordon counts were made for the purpose of this computation. The counts at 125th Street and St. Nicholas Avenue and at 23rd and Ely were distorted because of very minor deviations from operating schedule. To correct for these distortions the following changes were made. At the

125th and St. Nicholas count, the first train of
each of the four intervals from 7:40 to 9:00 was
shifted back to the preceding interval. These
shifts bring the actual operations into conformity
with the schedule. They involve very small modifications in the train time, usually of one-half to
one minute. In the 23rd and Ely cordon count, the
first train of the 7:40-8:00 interval was shifted
back to 7:20-7:40, and the first train of the 8:20-
8:40 interval was shifted back to 8:00-8:20. These
changes made the actual operations conform to schedule. The effect in both cases makes no difference
to the total number of excess passengers, but they do
offer a more accurate picture of the time during
which the excesses occur.

To determine the excess, the special maximum
comfort level capacities as given in Appendix Table
22 were employed. These capacities are the largest
possible ones during 20-minute intervals for all stations whose counts are equal to or greater than
these amounts. For all other stations, they are the
least full train size capable of providing comfort
level transportation. These comfort level capacities also include appropriate modifications for the
southeast stations and for the planned increases in
the West Side IRT trains.

Thus, the excess passengers calculated on this
basis give an irreducible estimate, the net excess.

To be useful in this study, the employment and
work schedule data, presented in the first part of
Chapter 3 for the total CBD, must be reduced to
smaller aggregates. The extent of the reduction depends ultimately upon each particular need. The statistics are available for several levels of industry
classification. The total CBD statistics are sub-
divided--actually composed of--the statistics of
large industry aggregates called major industry divisions. These in turn are further subdivided into
three succeeding levels, the 2-, 3-, and 4-digit
classifications. At various places in the study and
in the computations, the statistics are required at
all available levels.

This appendix will present the major industry
divisions of the CBD. The agriculture, forestry, and
fisheries division will be excluded because it has
only 300 employees. The mining division is incorporated in the central administrative offices and
therefore will not appear as a separate group. Each
of the others will be taken up in succession.

In general, each division will be presented
with a table showing its component industrial subdivisions, the employment in each group, and the
total employment for the aggregate. A map then follows, depicting the location of employment of the
major division in the CBD. Finally, a set of two
tables, giving the numbers and per cents, respectively, is set forth showing the present work schedules
of the employees of the division.

Two industry divisions have no map. They are

463

the contract construction industry and the central
administrative offices. The former is a relatively
small group and its offices are principally located
in the area surrounding Grand Central Station.
There are no location statistics for the latter
group.

Two other major divisions present their work
schedules in two sets of two tables each. The first,
the transportation, communications, and public utilities division, splits up into the two groups of:
(1) transportation and (2) communications and public utilities. The second, the finance, insurance,
and real estate division, has the two groups of:
(1) finance and insurance and (2) real estate. Because of the variety of schedules in the aggregates
as a whole, it was deemed better to divide them, for
the sake of clarity, according to schedule groupings.

THE CONTRACT CONSTRUCTION DIVISION

TABLE 33

The Contract Construction Industries and
Employment in Manhattan's CBD, September, 1958

SIC	Industry	Employment
15	General building construction	9,803
16	Construction other than building construction--general con-tractors	4,914
17	Construction--special trades contractors	20,641
	Total	35,358

TABLE 34

Selected Scheduled Starting-Stopping Times of Work, Regular Weekdays: Estimated Numbers of Employees of the Contract Construction Industries

Start \ Stop	3:30	3:45	4:00	4:15	4:30	4:45	5:00	5:15	5:30	5:45	6:00	Other	Total
7:30												186	186
7:45													
8:00	12,571		2,890	94	1,382		1,116					5,996	24,049
8:15													
8:30			47		323		197	383	279				1,227
8:45						149			9				158
9:00					17		5,923	1,375	604		93	1	8,013
9:15							9	9					17
9:30							17				385	241	643
Other			46		81		16		465			457	1,065
Total	12,571		2,983	94	1,803	149	7,278	1,767	1,357		478	6,878	35,358

465

TABLE 35

Selected Scheduled Starting-Stopping Times of Work, Regular Weekdays:
Estimated Per Cents of Employees of the Contract Construction Industries

Start \ Stop	3:30	3:45	4:00	4:15	4:30	4:45	5:00	5:15	5:30	5:45	6:00	Other	Total
7:30												1.2	1.2
7:45													
8:00	1.2		1.0	.6	9.2		7.4					5.6	25.0
8:15													
8:30			.3		2.2		1.3	2.6	1.9				8.2
8:45						1.0			.1				1.1
9:00					.1		39.5	9.2	4.0		.6		53.4
9:15							.1	.1					.1
9:30							.1				2.6	1.6	4.3
Other			.3		.5		.1		3.1			2.7	6.7
Total	1.2		1.6	.6	12.0	1.0	48.5	11.8	9.1		3.2	11.0	100.0

466

TABLE 36

Manufacturing Industries and Employment in
Manhattan's Central Business District

SIC	Industry	Number of Employees*
19	Ordnance and accessories	80
20	Food and kindred products	11,099
21	Tobacco manufactures	290
22	Textile mill products	11,637
23	Apparel and other finished products made from fabrics and similar materials	201,583
24	Lumber and wood products, except furniture	1,128
25	Furniture and fixtures	3,729
26	Paper and allied products	7,303
27	Printing, publishing, and allied industries	49,782**
28	Chemicals and allied products	8,883
29	Petroleum refining and related industries	60
30	Rubber and miscellaneous plastics products	2,112
31	Leather and leather products	18,296
32	Stone, clay, and glass products	1,525
33	Primary metal industries	693
34	Fabricated metal products, except ordnance, machinery, and transportation equipment	5,507
35	Machinery, except electrical	5,353
36	Electrical machinery, equipment and supplies	7,572
37	Transportation equipment	570
38	Professional, scientific, and controlling instruments; photographic and optical goods; watches and clocks	5,643
39	Miscellaneous manufacturing industries	37,756
Less:	Additional central administrative offices	15,601
	Total	365,000

 * Excludes central administrative office employment.
** Excludes 56,885 employees in publishing.
Source: New York State Department of Labor, New York
         City Planning Commission, and the Staggered
         Working Hours Project of the City of New York.

467

FIGURE 22
LOCATION OF FACTORY EMPLOYMENT

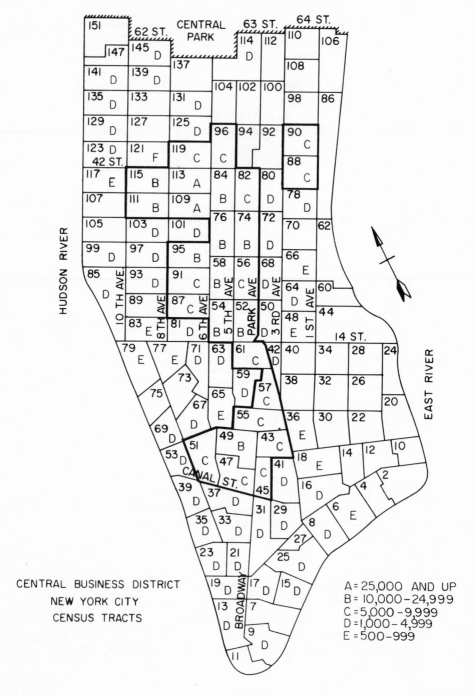

CENTRAL BUSINESS DISTRICT
NEW YORK CITY
CENSUS TRACTS

A= 25,000 AND UP
B= 10,000-24,999
C= 5,000-9,999
D= 1,000-4,999
E= 500-999

468

TABLE 37

Selected Scheduled Starting-Stopping Times of Work, Regular Weekdays:
Estimated Numbers of Employees of the Manufacturing Industries

Start \ Stop	3:30	3:45	4:00	4:15	4:30	4:45	5:00	5:15	5:30	5:45	6:00	Other	Total
7:30	327		413		831							472	2,043
7:45	96	17		260	472	32						11	888
8:00	3,070	5,351	7,557	1,781	24,697	11,211	14,199					3,703	71,569
8:15			2,303	1,548	2,534	6,182	6,823					3,965	23,355
8:30			2,486	16,084	51,794	5,780	27,771	10,882	9,141			1,668	125,606
8:45				130	6,727	12,309	939	769	635	59		100	21,668
9:00					3,202	3,609	92,518	1,849	17,708		2,872	1,550	123,308
9:15						36	36	3,908	62			82	4,124
9:30							132	32	4,641		642	1,238	6,685
Other	958	1,740	2,472	63	1,133	15	400	2,152	1,431	103	6,688	24,361	41,516
Total	4,451	7,108	15,231	19,866	91,390	39,174	142,818	19,592	33,618	162	10,202	37,150	420,762

TABLE 38

Selected Scheduled Starting-Stopping Times of Work, Regular Weekdays:
Estimated Per Cents of Employees of the Manufacturing Industries

Stop / Start	3:30	3:45	4:00	4:15	4:30	4:45	5:00	5:15	5:30	5:45	6:00	Other	Total
7:30	0.1		0.1		.2							.1	.5
7:45				0.1	.1								.2
8:00	.7	1.3	1.8	.4	5.9	2.7	3.4					.8	17.0
8:15			.5	.4	.6	1.5	1.6					1.0	5.6
8:30			.6	3.8	12.3	1.4	6.6	2.6	2.2			.4	29.9
8:45					1.6	2.9	.2	.2	.1				5.1
9:00					.7	.9	22.0	.4	4.2		.7	.4	29.3
9:15								.9					1.0
9:30					.3				1.1		.2	.3	1.6
Other	.2	.4	.6				.1	.5	.3		1.6	5.9	9.9
Total	1.0	1.7	3.6	4.7	21.7	9.4	33.9	4.6	8.0		2.5	8.8	100.0

TABLE 39

The Transportation, Communications, and Public
Utilities Industries and Employment in
Manhattan's CBD, September, 1958

SIC	Industry	Employment
40	Railroad transportation	9
41	Local and suburban transit and interurban passenger transportation	20,957
42	Major freight transportation and warehousing	20,894
44	Water transportation	33,900
45	Transportation by air	9,219
46	Pipe line transportation	104
47	Transportation services	15,807
48	Communication	48,100
49	Electric, gas, and sanitary services	11,499
	Total	160,489

FIGURE 23
LOCATION OF EMPLOYMENT OF THE TRANSPORTATION,
COMMUNICATIONS, AND PUBLIC UTILITIES DIVISION

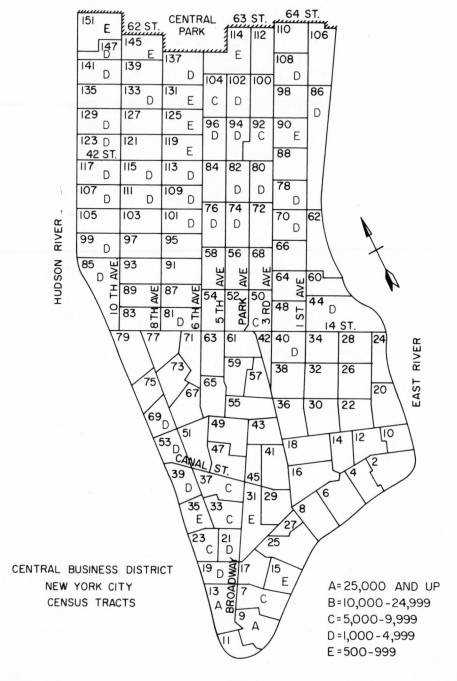

CENTRAL BUSINESS DISTRICT
NEW YORK CITY
CENSUS TRACTS

A = 25,000 AND UP
B = 10,000 - 24,999
C = 5,000 - 9,999
D = 1,000 - 4,999
E = 500 - 999

472

TABLE 40

Selected Scheduled Starting-Stopping Times of Work, Regular Weekdays:
Estimated Numbers of Employees of the Transportation Industries

Stop / Start	3:30	3:45	4:00	4:15	4:30	4:45	5:00	5:15	5:30	5:45	6:00	Other	Total
7:30	160	6	35	6	171							352	730
7:45				6		6						7	19
8:00			14,555		561	118	11,039					2,324	28,507
8:15						6						40	46
8:30					94		1,368	423	230			12	2,127
8:45							3,802	57					3,859
9:00					99		31,344	4,536	4,713	100	3,659	94	44,545
9:15							133						133
9:30							70	29	190		6	51	346
Other	152	124	1,394	25	175	44	54	5	159	6	2,251	14,877	19,266
Total	312	130	15,984	37	1,100	174	47,810	5,050	5,292	106	5,916	17,757	99,668

TABLE 41

Selected Scheduled Starting-Stopping Times of Work, Regular Weekdays: Estimated Per Cents of Employees of the Transportation Industries

Stop / Start	3:30	3:45	4:00	4:15	4:30	4:45	5:00	5:15	5:30	5:45	6:00	Other	Total
7:30	.2				.2							.3	.7
7:45													
8:00			14.6		.6	.1	11.1					2.3	28.7
8:15												.1	.1
8:30					.1		1.4	.4	.2				2.1
8:45							3.8	.1					3.9
9:00					.1		31.5	4.5	4.7	.1	3.7	.1	44.7
9:15							.1						.1
9:30							.1		.2			.1	.4
Other	.1	.1	1.4		.1	.1		.1	.2		2.2	15.0	19.3
Total	.3	.1	16.0		1.1	.2	48.0	5.1	5.3	.1	5.9	17.9	100.0

474

TABLE 42

Selected Scheduled Starting-Stopping Times of Work, Regular Weekdays: Estimated Numbers of Employees of the Communications and Public Utilities Industries

Stop / Start	3:30	3:45	4:00	4:15	4:30	4:45	5:00	5:15	5:30	5:45	6:00	Other	Total
7:30	39		40		38							1	118
7:45		2		59	16	27							103
8:00			1,000		184	686	3,419					22	5,311
8:15			5	14		65						31	110
8:30					2,426		338	10,631	265			40	13,705
8:45						3,081				73		4	3,158
9:00						4,305	15,654	30	352	8	643	215	21,207
9:15								1,485		25		27	1,537
9:30									2,834		156	143	3,133
Other	113		289	2	2	22	12	28		99	2,171	8,384	11,122
Total	152	2	1,334	75	2,666	8,186	19,423	12,174	3,451	205	2,970	8,866	59,504

TABLE 43

Selected Scheduled Starting-Stopping Times of Work, Regular Weekdays: Estimated Per Cents of Employees of the Communications and Public Utilities Industries

Start \ Stop	3:30	3:45	4:00	4:15	4:30	4:45	5:00	5:15	5:30	5:45	6:00	Other	Total
7:30	.1		.1		.1								.2
7:45				.1								.1	.2
8:00			1.7		.3	1.2	5.7						8.9
8:15						.1						.1	.2
8:30					4.1		.6	17.9	.4				23.0
8:45						5.2				.1			5.3
9:00						7.2	26.3	.1	.6		1.1	.3	35.6
9:15								2.5				.1	2.6
9:30									4.8		.3	.2	5.3
Other	.2		.4			.1				.2	3.6	14.2	18.7
Total	.3		2.2	.1	4.5	13.8	32.6	20.5	5.8	.3	5.0	14.9	100.0

476

TABLE 44

The Wholesale Trades and Employment in
Manhattan's CBD, September, 1958

SIC	Trade	Employment
501	Motor vehicles and other auto- motive equipment	4,117
502	Drugs, chemicals, and allied products	14,458
503	Dry goods and apparel	54,311
504	Groceries and related products	17,722
505	Farm products--raw materials	2,854
506	Electrical goods	12,200
507	Hardware, and plumbing and heating equipment and supplies	6,855
508	Machinery, equipment, and supplies	31,636
509	Miscellaneous wholesalers	82,578
	Total	226,731
	Less: Central administrative offices	13,755
	Total	212,976

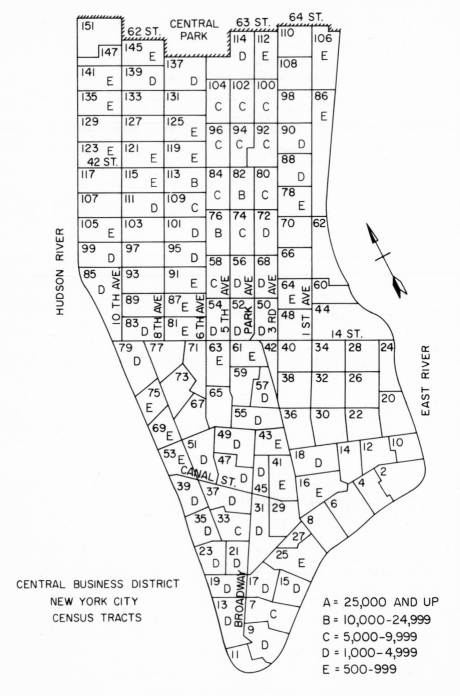

FIGURE 24

LOCATION OF EMPLOYMENT OF THE WHOLESALE TRADES

CENTRAL BUSINESS DISTRICT
NEW YORK CITY
CENSUS TRACTS

A = 25,000 AND UP
B = 10,000-24,999
C = 5,000-9,999
D = 1,000-4,999
E = 500-999

478

TABLE 45

Selected Scheduled Starting-Stopping Times of Work, Regular Weekdays:
Estimated Numbers of Employees of the Wholesale Trades

Start \ Stop	3:30	3:45	4:00	4:15	4:30	4:45	5:00	5:15	5:30	5:45	6:00	Other	Total
7:30			3		9							20	32
7:45												20	20
8:00			519		2,792		6,025					416	9,752
8:15						243	420					4	667
8:30				20	3,302	13,239	9,948	239	2,377			507	29,632
8:45					32	10,494	30,000	267	773			43	41,609
9:00					493	1,055	58,067	3,273	48,233	181	3,645	1,756	116,703
9:15								3,098	121			24	3,243
9:30							229	126	338	20	480	227	1,420
Other	493		2,494		126	131	303	265	298		521	19,022	23,653
Total	493		3,016	20	6,754	25,162	104,992	7,268	52,140	201	4,646	22,039	226,731

479

TABLE 46

Selected Scheduled Starting-Stopping Times of Work, Regular Weekdays: Estimated Per Cents of Employees of the Wholesale Trades

Start \ Stop	3:30	3:45	4:00	4:15	4:30	4:45	5:00	5:15	5:30	5:45	6:00	Other	Total
7:30													
7:45													
8:00			.2		1.2		2.7					.2	4.3
8:15						.1	.2						.3
8:30					1.5	5.8	4.4	.1	1.0			.3	13.1
8:45						4.6	13.2	.1	.3			.2	18.4
9:00					.2	.5	25.6	1.4	21.3	.1	1.6	.8	51.5
9:15								1.4					1.4
9:30					.1		.1	.1	.3		.2	.1	.6
Other	.2		1.1					.1			.2	8.3	10.4
Total	.2		1.3		3.0	11.1	46.3	3.2	23.0	.1	2.0	9.7	100.0

480

TABLE 47

The Retail Trades and Employment in
Manhattan's CBD, September, 1958

SIC	Trades	Employment
52	Building materials, hardware, and farm equipment	1,989
53	General merchandise	41,835
54	Food	11,745
55	Automotive dealers and gasoline stations	2,788
56	Apparel and accessories	41,108
57	Furniture, home furnishings, and equipment	6,683
58	Eating and drinking places	68,035
59	Miscellaneous retail stores	19,003
	Total	193,186
	Less: Central administrative offices	22,152
	Total	171,034

FIGURE 25

LOCATION OF EMPLOYMENT OF THE RETAIL TRADES

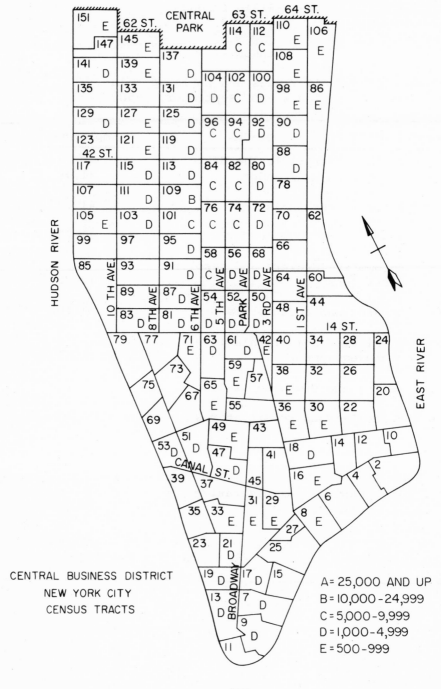

CENTRAL BUSINESS DISTRICT
NEW YORK CITY
CENSUS TRACTS

A = 25,000 AND UP
B = 10,000 - 24,999
C = 5,000 - 9,999
D = 1,000 - 4,999
E = 500 - 999

482

TABLE 48

Selected Scheduled Starting-Stopping Times of Work, Regular Weekdays: Estimated Numbers of Employees of the Retail Trades

Start \ Stop	3:30	3:45	4:00	4:15	4:30	4:45	5:00	5:15	5:30	5:45	6:00	Other	Total
7:30	1,061		30		971							1,178	3,240
7:45													
8:00	42		103		2,584		6,129					4,318	13,176
8:15												126	126
8:30			152		2,260	61	395		4,547			293	7,708
8:45						1,968	104	1,038					3,110
9:00					174		8,442		7,024		16,805	807	33,252
9:15								1,346	13,485	24,576		11,163	50,570
9:30							100	20	1,013		1,558	1,210	3,901
Other	7,197		3,064		373	1	1,345	213	2,666	87	4,081	59,076	78,103
Total	8,300		3,349		6,362	2,030	16,515	2,617	28,735	24,663	22,444	78,171	193,186

TABLE 49

Selected Scheduled Starting-Stopping Times of Work, Regular Weekdays:
Estimated Per Cents of Employees of the Retail Trades

Start \ Stop	3:30	3:45	4:00	4:15	4:30	4:45	5:00	5:15	5:30	5:45	6:00	Other	Total
7:30	.6				.5							.6	1.7
7:45													
8:00			.1		1.3		3.2					2.2	6.8
8:15												.1	.1
8:30			.1		1.2		.2		2.4			.1	4.0
8:45						1.0	.1	.5					1.6
9:00					.1		4.4		3.6		8.7	.4	17.2
9:15								.7	7.0	12.7		5.8	26.2
9:30							.1		.5		.8	.6	2.0
Other	3.7		1.6		.2		.7	.1	1.4	.1	2.1	30.6	40.4
Total	4.3		1.7		3.3	1.0	8.6	1.3	14.9	12.8	11.6	40.5	100.0

484

THE FINANCE, INSURANCE, AND
REAL ESTATE DIVISION

TABLE 50

The Finance, Insurance, and Real Estate
Industries and Employment in Manhattan's
CBD, September, 1958

SIC	Industry	Employment
60	Banking	92,359
61	Credit agencies other than banks	9,814
62	Security and commodity brokers, dealers, exchanges, and services	41,092
63	Insurance carriers	126,984
64	Insurance agents, brokers, and service	17,534
65	Real estate	84,212
66	Combinations of real estate, insurance, loans, law offices	890
67	Holding and other investment companies	5,405
	Total	378,290

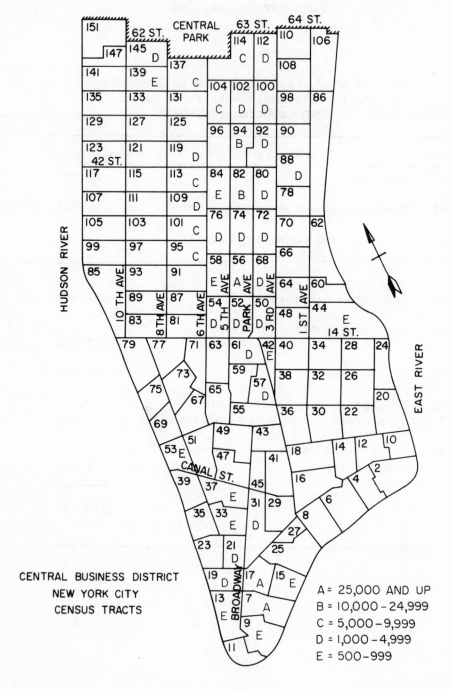

FIGURE 26
LOCATION OF EMPLOYMENT IN THE FINANCE,
INSURANCE, AND REAL ESTATE DIVISION

CENTRAL BUSINESS DISTRICT
NEW YORK CITY
CENSUS TRACTS

A = 25,000 AND UP
B = 10,000 - 24,999
C = 5,000 - 9,999
D = 1,000 - 4,999
E = 500 - 999

486

TABLE 51

Selected Scheduled Starting-Stopping Times of Work, Regular Weekdays:
Estimated Numbers of Employees of the Finance and Insurance Industries

Stop / Start	3:30	3:45	4:00	4:15	4:30	4:45	5:00	5:15	5:30	5:45	6:00	Other	Total
7:30	25											6	44
7:45		7										13	20
8:00		39	2,337			38						56	2,470
8:15			78	38	33							14	163
8:30			130	2	34,208	1,926	74	3	27			777	37,147
8:45				99	10,838	42,387	12,807	20	29			247	66,427
9:00					7,106	12,679	126,086	72	861		5	4,425	151,234
9:15						247	39	533	27			2,982	3,828
9:30							3		2,237			597	2,837
Other	177	966	3,109	221	871	60	3,265	627	76	19	530	14,319	23,613
Total	202	1,012	5,654	360	53,069	57,337	142,274	627	3,257	19	535	23,437	287,783

TABLE 52

Selected Scheduled Starting-Stopping Times of Work, Regular Weekdays: Estimated
Per Cents of Employees of the Finance and Insurance Industries

Stop / Start	3:30	3:45	4:00	4:15	4:30	4:45	5:00	5:15	5:30	5:45	6:00	Other	Total
7:30													
7:45													
8:00			.8									.1	.9
8:15												.1	.1
8:30					11.9	.7						.3	12.9
8:45					3.8	14.7	4.5					.1	23.1
9:00					2.5	4.4	39.2		.3			6.2	52.6
9:15						.1		.2				1.0	1.3
9:30									.8			.2	1.0
Other	.1	.4	1.2	.1	.2		5.7				.2	.2	8.1
Total	.1	.4	2.0	.1	18.4	19.9	49.4	.2	1.1		.2	8.3	100.0

488

TABLE 53

Selected Scheduled Starting-Stopping Times of Work, Regular Weekdays:
Estimated Numbers of Employees of the Real Estate Industry

Start \ Stop	3:30	3:45	4:00	4:15	4:30	4:45	5:00	5:15	5:30	5:45	6:00	Other	Total
7:30	159		254	46	256							163	878
7:45						83						9	92
8:00	9		1,374		1,098	18	3,318					229	6,046
8:15				9								522	531
8:30					306	1,946	245	28	2,496			424	5,445
8:45						1,130			37	203		37	1,407
9:00						9	19,013		4,341	46	1,300	2,127	26,836
9:15								2,385			565	80	3,030
9:30							188		502		513	1,236	2,439
Other	453	9	2,058		1,024	18	99	540	64	74	561	32,608	37,508
Total	621	9	3,686	55	2,684	3,204	22,863	2,953	7,440	323	2,939	37,435	84,212

TABLE 54

Selected Scheduled Starting-Stopping Times of Work, Regular Weekdays:
Estimated Per Cents of Employees of the Real Estate Industry

Start \ Stop	3:30	3:45	4:00	4:15	4:30	4:45	5:00	5:15	5:30	5:45	6:00	Other	Total
7:30	.2		.3	.1	.3							.1	1.0
7:45						.1							.1
8:00			1.6		1.3		3.9					.4	7.2
8:15												.6	.6
8:30					.4	2.3	.3		3.0			.5	6.5
8:45						1.3				.2		.2	1.7
9:00							22.6		5.2	.1	1.5	2.5	31.9
9:15								2.8			.7	.1	3.6
9:30							.2		.6		.6	1.5	2.9
Other	.5		2.5		1.2	.1	.2	.7		.1	.7	38.7	44.6
Total	.7		4.4	.1	3.2	3.8	27.2	3.5	8.8	.4	3.5	44.5	100.0

490

TABLE 55

The Service Industries and Employment in
Manhattan's CBD, September, 1958

SIC	Industry	Employment
70	Hotels, rooming houses, camps, and other lodging places	34,535
72	Personal services	15,472
73	Miscellaneous business services	104,103
75	Automobile repair, automobile services, and garages	4,954
76	Miscellaneous repair services	2,451
78	Motion pictures	18,051
79	Amusements and recreation services, except motion pictures	13,590
80	Medical and other health services	5,226
81	Legal services	16,375
82	Educational services	2,557
84	Museums, art galleries, botanical and zoological gardens	65
86	Nonprofit membership organizations	20,308
88	Private households	4,539
89	Miscellaneous services	33,003
	Total	275,229
Less:	Central administrative offices	5,083
	Total	270,146

FIGURE 27
LOCATION OF EMPLOYMENT IN THE SERVICES DIVISION

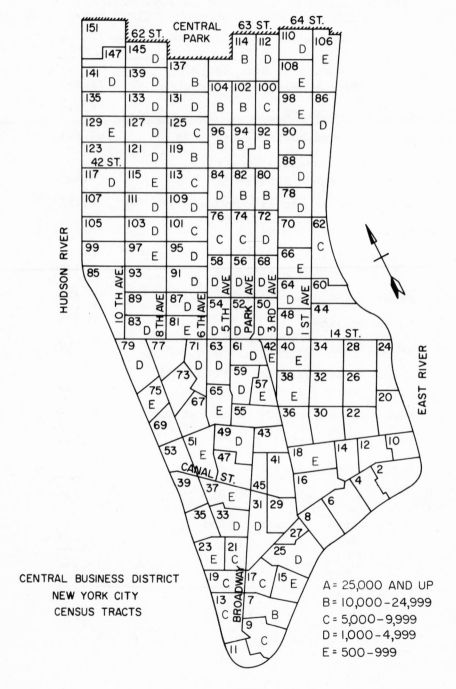

CENTRAL BUSINESS DISTRICT
NEW YORK CITY
CENSUS TRACTS

A = 25,000 AND UP
B = 10,000 - 24,999
C = 5,000 - 9,999
D = 1,000 - 4,999
E = 500 - 999

TABLE 56

Selected Scheduled Starting-Stopping Times of Work, Regular Weekdays:
Estimated Numbers of Employees of the Services Division

Stop / Start	3:30	3:45	4:00	4:15	4:30	4:45	5:00	5:15	5:30	5:45	6:00	Other	Total
7:30	231		43		163							119	556
7:45			24									42	66
8:00	570	8	7,473		3,734	95	2,146					1,957	15,983
8:15				94	29		777					14	914
8:30			53		676	1,473	7,086	807	4,506			1,619	16,220
8:45						26,301	2,195	2,282	5,359	46		292	36,475
9:00					110	2,317	65,916	5,812	21,958	110	3,419	660	100,302
9:15						438	29	4,317	8,652			138	13,574
9:30							386		13,062	35	1,540	1,424	16,447
Other	2,811	6	1,827	235	846		1,256	60	1,396	10	4,019	49,097	61,563
Total	3,612	14	9,420	329	5,558	30,624	79,791	13,278	54,933	201	8,978	55,362	262,100

493

TABLE 57

Selected Scheduled Starting-Stopping Times of Work, Regular Weekdays:
Estimated Per Cents of Employees of the Services Division

Stop \ Start	3:30	3:45	4:00	4:15	4:30	4:45	5:00	5:15	5:30	5:45	6:00	Other	Total
7:30	.1				.1								.2
7:45													
8:00	.2		2.9		1.4		.8					.8	6.1
8:15							.3						.3
8:30					.3	.6	2.7	.3	1.7			.6	6.2
8:45						10.0	.8	.9	2.0			.2	13.9
9:00						.9	25.2	2.2	8.4		1.3	.3	38.3
9:15						.2		1.7	3.3				5.2
9:30							.2		5.0		.6	.5	6.3
Other	1.1		.7	.1	.3		.4		.5	.1	1.5	18.7	23.5
Total	1.4		3.6	.1	2.1	11.7	30.4	5.1	20.9	.1	3.4	21.2	100.0

494

THE CENTRAL ADMINISTRATIVE OFFICES

TABLE 58

Total and Central Administrative Office
Employment in Selected Major Industry
Divisions in Manhattan's CBD

Industry Division	Total Employment	Central Administrative Employment
Mining	1,184	1,927
Manufacturing	462,282	97,282
Wholesale trades	226,731	13,755
Retail trades	193,186	22,152
Services (selected)	275,229	5,083
Total		140,199

TABLE 59

Selected Scheduled Starting-Stopping Times of Work, Regular Weekdays:
Estimated Numbers of Employees of the Central Administrative Offices

Stop / Start	3:30	3:45	4:00	4:15	4:30	4:45	5:00	5:15	5:30	5:45	6:00	Other	Total
7:30	60	11	3	9	40							17	140
7:45	23					6						25	54
8:00			1,166	37	698	57	23					51	2,032
8:15				6	14	570	9					34	633
8:30			17		1,955	829	1,855	197	48			7	4,908
8:45					3,563	7,285	9,551	1,753		6			22,158
9:00					2,557	18,090	68,314	7,000	3,950		14	1	99,926
9:15								3,340	51	3	60	6	3,460
9:30									2,719			23	2,742
Other	5		42		3	23	25	6	95		764	3,183	4,146
Total	88	11	1,228	52	8,830	26,860	79,777	12,296	6,863	9	838	3,347	140,199

496

TABLE 60

Selected Scheduled Starting-Stopping Times of Work, Regular Weekdays:
Estimated Per Cents of Employees of the Central Administrative Offices

Stop / Start	3:30	3:45	4:00	4:15	4:30	4:45	5:00	5:15	5:30	5:45	6:00	Other	Total
7:30												.1	.1
7:45													
8:00			.8		.5							.2	1.5
8:15						.4						.1	.5
8:30					1.4	.6	1.3	.1				.1	3.5
8:45					2.5	5.2	6.8	1.3					15.8
9:00					1.8	12.9	48.7	5.0	2.8			.1	71.3
9:15								2.4				.1	2.5
9:30									1.9			.1	2.0
Other					.1	.1	.1		.2		.6	1.9	3.0
Total			.8		6.3	19.2	56.9	8.8	4.9		.6	2.5	100.0

497

GOVERNMENTS

TABLE 61

Government Employment in Manhattan's CBD,
September, 1958

SIC	Government	Employment
91	Federal	51,948
92	State	12,009
93	Local	54,984[a]
94	International	3,300
95	New York County	722
96	Interstate authorities and commissions and other	6,161
97	Other U.S. governments	96
	Total	130,994

[a] Before transfer of 5,118 New York City Transit Authority employees.

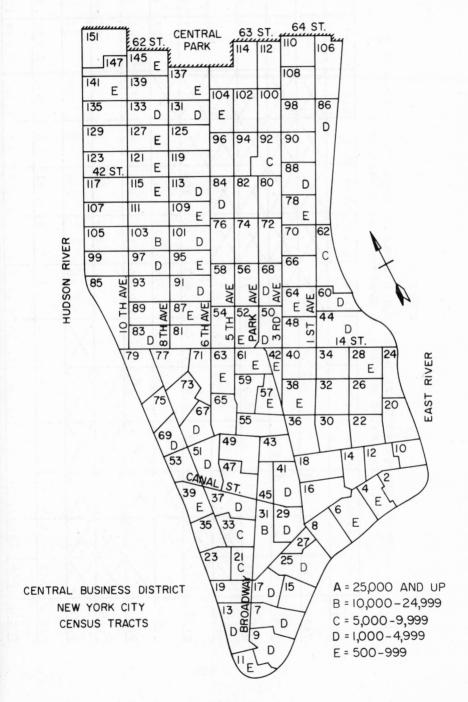

FIGURE 28
LOCATION OF EMPLOYMENT IN GOVERNMENTS

CENTRAL BUSINESS DISTRICT
NEW YORK CITY
CENSUS TRACTS

A = 25,000 AND UP
B = 10,000 - 24,999
C = 5,000 - 9,999
D = 1,000 - 4,999
E = 500 - 999

499

TABLE 62

Selected Scheduled Starting-Stopping Times of Work, Regular Weekdays: Estimated Numbers of Employees of Governments

Stop / Start	3:30	3:45	4:00	4:15	4:30	4:45	5:00	5:15	5:30	5:45	6:00	Other	Total
7:30	53	10	458		22							56	599
7:45		24	4	676		3						161	868
8:00	141		3,540	12	8,885	7	315					351	13,251
8:15				7	51	1,562						435	2,055
8:30			39	2	1,940	4,044	16,943	22	104			717	23,811
8:45				4	999	3,655	4,319	1,279	17	45		327	10,645
9:00					612	433	26,200	1,135	935	7	579	2,688	32,589
9:15								399	96	9	17	247	768
9:30							48		204	2	236	34	524
Other	352	111	1,755	2	394	2	89	35	21	1	536	28,658	31,956
Total	546	145	5,796	703	12,903	9,706	47,914	2,870	1,377	64	1,368	33,674	117,066

TABLE 63

Selected Scheduled Starting-Stopping Times of Work, Regular Weekdays: Estimated Per Cents of Employees of Governments

Start \ Stop	3:30	3:45	4:00	4:15	4:30	4:45	5:00	5:15	5:30	5:45	6:00	Other	Total
7:30			.4									.1	.5
7:45				.6								.1	.7
8:00	.1		3.0		7.6		.3					.3	11.3
8:15						1.3						.5	1.8
8:30					1.7	3.5	14.5		.1			.5	20.3
8:45					.9	3.1	3.7	1.1				.3	9.1
9:00					.5	.4	22.4	1.0	.8		.5	2.2	27.8
9:15								.3	.1			.3	.7
9:30									.2		.2	.1	.5
Other	.4	.1	1.6		.3					.1	.5	24.4	27.3
Total	.5	.1	5.0	.6	11.0	8.3	40.9	2.4	1.2	.1	1.2	28.8	100.0

501

TABLE 64

Functionally Feasible Alternative Starting Times for Industries
in Manhattan's Central Business District

SIC	Industry	Study Number	Number of Employees	Alternative Start Times 7:30	8:00	8:30	9:30
Div. A	Agriculture, forestry, and fisheries		318				
Div. B	Mining	(a)	1,884		yes	yes	yes
Div. C	Contract construction, offices Sites	(b) (b)	14,993 20,336		yes	yes	yes
	Central administrative offices	(a)			yes	yes	yes
231	Men's, youths', and boys' suits, coats, and overcoats	(c)	12,570	yes	yes		
232	Men's, youths', and boys' furnishings, work clothing, and allied garments	(c)	11,326	yes	yes	yes	
233	Women's, misses', and juniors' outerwear	(c)	84,950		yes	yes	
234	Women's, misses', children's, and infants' undergarments	(c)	20,761		yes	yes	
235	Hats, caps, and millinery	(c)	13,129		yes	yes	
236	Girls', children's, and infants' outerwear	(c)	12,976		yes	yes	
237	Fur goods	(c)	9,524	yes	yes		

238	Miscellaneous apparel and accessories	(c)	12,436		yes	yes	yes
239	Miscellaneous fabricated textile products	(c)	23,911		yes	yes	yes
271	Newspapers: publishing, publishing and printing		22,982		yes	yes	yes
272	Periodicals: publishing, publishing and printing	(d)	20,737		yes	yes	yes
2731	Books: publishing, publishing and printing		9,935		yes	yes	yes
2732	Books: printing	(e)	1,778	yes	yes	yes	
274	Miscellaneous publishing		3,231		yes	yes	yes
275	Commercial printing	(e)	25,720	yes	yes	yes	
276	Manifold business forms manufacturing		604	yes	yes	yes	
277	Greeting card manufacturing		2,706	yes	yes	yes	
2782	Blankbooks, looseleaf binders and devices		1,549	yes	yes	yes	
2789	Bookbinding, and miscellaneous work	(e)	7,599	yes	yes	yes	
2791	Typesetting	(e)	4,260	yes	yes	yes	
2793	Photo-engraving	(e)	4,203	yes	yes	yes	
2794	Electrotyping and stereotyping	(e)	1,307	yes	yes	yes	
2799	Service industries for the printing trades, n.e.c.	(e)	56	yes	yes	yes	

(Notes and explanations at end of table.)

(continued)

TABLE 64 (continued)

SIC	Industry	Study Number	Number of Employees	7:30	8:00	8:30	9:30
	"Other" manufacturing industries	(f)	112,512	yes	yes	yes	
40	Railroad transportation	(g)	9*		yes	yes	yes
41	Local and suburban transit and interurban passenger transportation	(g)	20,957**				
421	Local and long distance trucking	(g)	18,355	yes	yes		
422	Public warehousing	(g)	2,322	yes	yes		
441-4	Deep sea foreign, deep sea domestic, Great Lakes-St. Lawrence Seaway and rivers and canals transportation	(g)	20,550		yes	yes	yes
445	Local water transportation	(g)	2,590				
4463	Stevedoring: offices	(g)	3,000		yes	yes	yes
	other	(g)	6,523				
446	Services incidental to water transportation, except stevedoring	(g)	1,237				
451	Air transportation, certified carriers	(g)	8,363		yes	yes	yes
452	Air transportation, non-certified carriers	(g)	112				

458	Airports and flying fields	(g)	709	yes	yes	
4712	Freight forwarding	(g)	6,771		yes	
4721	Arrangement of transportation	(g)	8,101		yes	
47	Transportation services, except freight forwarding and arrangement of transportation	(g)	935			
481	Telephone communication		30,560			
482	Telegraph communication		8,575			
483	Radio and television broadcasting		8,870	yes	yes	yes
489	Communication services, n.e.c.		95			
49	Electric, gas, and sanitary services		11,499			
501	Wholesale trade--motor vehicles and automotive equipment	(h)	4,117	yes	yes	yes
502	--drugs, chemicals and allied products	(h)	14,458	yes	yes	yes
503	--dry goods and apparel	(h)	54,311	yes	yes	yes
504	--groceries and related products	(h)	17,722	yes	yes	yes
505	--farm products--raw materials	(h)	2,854	yes	yes	yes
506	--electrical goods	(h)	12,200	yes	yes	yes
507	--hardware, and plumbing and heating and supplies	(h)	6,855	yes	yes	yes

(continued)

TABLE 64 (continued)

SIC	Industry	Study Number	Number of Employees	Alternative Start Times			
				7:30	8:00	8:30	9:30
508	--machinery, equipment, and supplies	(h)	31,636		yes	yes	yes
509	--miscellaneous wholesalers	(h)	82,578		yes	yes	yes
52-59	Retail trades (except 5323)		191,285				
5323	Mail order houses, except general merchandise		1,901		yes	yes	yes
6021	Commercial and stock savings banks: Branches, loan and credit, commercial letters of credit, trust	(i)	26,928			yes	
	Operations and services, mail tellers--international department, administration	(i)	38,152	yes	yes	yes	
	Investment, trading in foreign currency, collection of drafts, and bankers' acceptances	(i)	4,185				
	Agency	(i)	12,223		yes	yes	yes
6031	Mutual savings banks	(i)	3,362				yes
6041	Trust companies not engaged in deposit banking	(i)	1,058			yes	

506

Code	Description	Ref	Number			
6051	Establishments performing functions closely related to banking	(i)	6,452			
6111	Rediscount and financing institutions for credit agencies other than banks	(i)	45			
6121	Savings and loan associations	(i)	735			
6131	Agricultural credit institutions	(i)	3			
6141	Personal credit institutions	(i)	3,793	yes		
6151	Business credit institutions	(i)	5,037			
6153	Short-term business credit institutions	(i)	32	yes		
6161	Loan correspondents and brokers	(i)	169			
6211	Security brokers, dealers, and flotation companies	(j)	35,701		yes	
6221	Commodity contracts brokers and dealers	(j)	295		yes	
6231	Security and commodity exchanges	(j)	3,650			
6281	Services allied with the exchange of securities or commodities	(j)	2,446	yes	yes	
63	Insurance carriers	(k)	126,979	yes	yes	yes

(continued)

TABLE 64 (continued)

SIC	Industry	Study Number	Number of Employees	Alternative Start Times 7:30	8:00	8:30	9:30
64	Insurance agents, brokers and service	(k)	17,534				yes
65	Real estate--company offices	(l)	47,321		yes	yes	yes
66	Building operation	(l)	36,892			yes	yes
	Combinations of real estate, insurance, loans and law offices		890				
67	Holding and other investment companies		5,405				
70	Hotels, rooming houses, camps, and other lodging places		34,535				
72	Personal services, except 721		11,436				
721	Laundries, laundry services, and cleaning and dyeing plants		4,036	yes	yes	yes	
7311	Advertising agencies	(m)	22,945				
7312,9	Outdoor advertising services, miscellaneous advertising		3,235				yes
7321	Consumer credit reporting agencies, etc.		3,696		yes	yes	yes

508

733	Duplicating, addressing, blue-printing, photocopying, mailing, mailing list, and stenographic services	9,791	yes	yes	yes
734	Services to dwellings and other buildings	13,090	yes	yes	yes
7361	Private employment agencies	1,308		yes	yes
7391	Research, development, and testing laboratories (n)	4,886		yes	yes
7392	Business and management consulting services (o)	15,948		yes	yes
7399	Business services, n.e.c.	26,852		yes	yes
75	Automobile repair, automobile services, and garages	4,954			
76	Miscellaneous repair services	2,451			
781	Motion picture production and distribution	10,818		yes	yes
782	Motion picture service industries	2,069			
783	Motion picture theaters	5,164		yes	yes
79	Amusement and recreation services, except motion picture	13,590			
80	Medical and other health services	5,226			
81	Legal services	16,375		yes	yes

(continued)

TABLE 64 (continued)

SIC	Industry	Study Number	Number of Employees	Alternative Start Times			
				7:30	8:00	8:30	9:30
82	Educational services		2,557				
84	Museums, art galleries, botanical and zoological gardens		65				
86	Nonprofit membership organizations	(p)	20,308			yes	yes
88	Private households		4,539				
8911	Engineering and architectural services	(q)	15,529		yes	yes	yes
8921	Nonprofit educational and scientific research agencies		631				
8931	Accounting, auditing, and bookkeeping services	(r)	13,323				
8999	Services, n.e.c.		3,520				
91	Federal government: other than post office		22,821		yes	yes	yes
	Post office		29,127				
92	New York State government		12,009		yes	yes	yes
93	New York City government, as follows:						
931	Judicial and legal		1,876				
932	Public safety		11,503				

Code		Amount			
933	Housing, planning and building	2,474	yes	yes	yes
934	Transportation, communication, and public utilities	7,162	yes	yes	yes
935	Fiscal, economic, labor, agricultural, and marketing services	2,714	yes	yes	yes
9361	Medical and health	9,756	yes	yes	yes
9362	Sanitation	2,865	yes	yes	yes
9363	Air pollution	97			
937	Welfare	3,952	yes	yes	yes
938	Education	5,721			
939	Recreation and culture	2,025			
93X	Other	3,020	yes	yes	yes
93Y	Public works	1,619	yes	yes	yes
94	United Nations	3,300			
95	New York County government	722			
96	Interstate Authorities and Commissions, as follows:				
964	Transportation, communications and public utilities	2,530	yes	yes	yes
97	All other	3,631			
98	Foreign governments	96			
		1,774			

NOTES AND EXPLANATIONS

Alternative Start Times

"<u>Yes</u>" means that the industry is considered capable, on functional grounds, of starting at the indicated time.

<u>No entry</u> means that no assessment as to the industry's capability of starting at the particular time is being offered. It may or may not be capable of adopting the time. If there are no entries at all for an industry, any of the following reasons may be responsible. (1) There may have been no investigation made of the industry's capability of changing its schedule, usually because it is small or because it is too heterogeneous. (2) Investigation may have revealed that a common starting time or a general schedule change cannot be proposed. (3) The industry consists of one or a few large firms whose capability of schedule change must be assessed in consultation after a general CBD pattern has been established.

Study Numbers

The study numbers, given by letters in parentheses ( ), refer to the studies of work scheduling in which the findings as to functional capability of changing schedules are reported. The studies are as follows:

(a) Central Administrative Offices
(b) Contract Construction Industries
(c) Apparel Industries
(d) Periodical Publishing Industries
(e) Commercial Printing and Bookbinding Industries
(f) "Other" Manufacturing Industries
(g) Transportation Industries
(h) Wholesale Trades
(i) Banking and Credit Agencies Other Than Banks
(j) The Securities Industry

(k) The Insurance Industry
(l) Real Estate
(m) Advertising Agencies
(n) Research and Development Laboratories
(o) Management Consulting Firms
(p) Nonprofit Membership Organizations
(q) Engineering and Architectural Firms
(r) Accounting and Auditing Firms

Other

*This is the number of employees reported in the Tabulation of Covered Employment. It was not possible to revise this obviously incorrect number.

**This includes the New York City Transit Authority's employees in the CBD.

M

INDUSTRY GROUPS
AND THEIR SCHEDULE
ALTERNATIVES

This appendix presents the large industry groups of the CBD. Each group is defined by its component industries; and, where possible, its total and modifiable employment is presented in table form. Then the character of the group is discussed, and each section ends with an evaluation of the schedule alternatives for the group.

THE PRODUCTION INDUSTRIES

Three sets of industries are put together to form the production industries group. They are: manufacturing (factories, not central administrative offices), trucking and warehousing, and three service industries--laundries and cleaning and dyeing plants; duplicating, addressing, blueprinting, photocopying, mailing, mailing lists, and stenographic services; and services to dwellings and other buildings. Appendix Table 65 presents the total CBD employment for each of the groups and the employment of their modifiable portions. Altogether they have 469,399 people, or 22 per cent of the CBD, of which 416,557, or 20 per cent, are in industries which are functionally capable of modifying their work schedules.

The production industries form a group which is readily distinguishable from other CBD industries. They are engaged in performing "productive" functions, or directly related services. They produce a physical product to which they have contributed

514

some aspect of physical modification, including transport. Most are employed in factories or in factory-type establishments and their work has the form and organization of the typical factory (hence the service industries are included). The occupations are predominantly physical, or blue collar, although substantial numbers of white-collar people are also employed in them. The distinguishing characteristic of these industries is given by their production rather than by their administrative and clerical labor force. This differentiates them from other CBD industries and allows them to be combined into a single group.

TABLE 65

Total and Modifiable Employment in the
Production Industries Group

	Total	Modifiable
Manufacturing	421,805	368,963
Trucking and warehousing	20,677	20,677
Three service industries	26,917	26,917
Total	469,399	416,557

But most importantly, the production industries are combined into a group because they can serve as a single scheduling unit. The productive part of these industries--manufacturing, transport, storage, laundering, cleaning, duplicating, etc.--are substantially independent of most of the administrative, clerical, professional, commercial, and financial functions of the rest of the CBD, at least for a moderately short period of the day. Their relations with other industries have much in common. Their critical contacts are with suppliers of materials and services, transportation, and others who contribute directly to productive activity. This

similarity of interindustry relations gives the
group certain common determinants of schedule. It
should also be noted that a great deal of relationship occurs among the industries of the group itself. This includes processing as well as transport
and storage. These many common characteristics make
it possible to combine the production industries into a group and to treat them as a scheduling unit
for purposes of this study.

The name assigned to this group--the production
industries--is more useful to this study than it may
be to the community at large. The term itself is
rarely if ever used in public or in academic discussion. The term "productive" is sometimes used within a firm to designate the functions which produce
the output, and the services directly related to
them. The common feature of these three sets of industries is akin to the productive functions within
a firm. It will prove helpful, if this group is
ever addressed, to supplement its title by the names
of its principal subgroups: manufacturing, trucking
and warehousing, laundries, and others. The people
in the industries will readily recognize themselves
when these titles are used.

Alternative Schedules

The individual industries of the production
group have various possible alternative starting
times. Some are able to shift to 7:30 or 8:00, others to 7:30, 8:00, or 8:30, and still others to 8:00
or 8:30. The 9:30 starting time is not attributed
to any of the industries.

There are three possible general schedule patterns for the production industries. The first is
an earliest possible pattern. This would assign
each industry to the earliest starting time which it
is capable of adopting. By this pattern, some industries would start at 7:30 and others at 8:00.
The second pattern is the uniform one in which all
the industries would start at 8:00. The third pattern is the latest possible one. This would schedule

all the industries at either 8:00 or 8:30 a.m., depending on their individual capability.

Of the three possible patterns, only one is
feasible from the viewpoint of the total work staggering program. In order to relieve congestion it
is necessary to shift as many people as possible to
the 7:30 a.m. starting time. The only industries
which were found capable of starting at 7:30 are in
the production group. For this group, therefore,
there is no choice of schedules. In the interests
of staggering they have to be shifted to 7:30.

There remain the other employees of the production group whose earliest starting time is 8:00
a.m. These employees belong to several branches of
the apparel industry. They have various alternative
times and they could conceivably be shifted to 8:00
or 8:30 or not changed at all. This group of industries has to be assigned to the 8:00 start rather
than to any of the other alternatives open to it,
for several reasons. First, these industries now
have schedules which contribute significantly to the
present congestion: 33.6 per cent of their employment starts at 8:30, 9.7 at 8:45, and 41.9 at 9:00.
These starting times have the greatest congestion
and as many people as possible have to be shifted
out of them. The apparel branches constitute significant blocks of people scheduled at the congested
times and, because of their strong internal organization, are more readily available for a general
schedule change. Hence the alternative of no change
at all for this group is not actually a good one.

Second, the only possible time to which this
group could be shifted--in view of the relationship
between work schedules and congestion--is to the
8:00 starting time. A shift to any other time could
not produce any relief of congestion.

Third, it is desirable to achieve as much uniformity as possible in industry scheduling. If the
other industries are asked to shift to 7:30, the apparel branches ought to be scheduled as closely as

possible to them. Partly, this is a matter of
equalizing the burden among the industries. Partly,
it is determined by interindustry relations which
will be best served by placing these production industries as close as possible to the same schedule.
Partly, it establishes an important scheduling pattern for the CBD which ought to facilitate the work
staggering program. It fixes 7:30 and 8:00 as the
starting times for these production industries.

Of the three possible schedule patterns, the
only feasible one for the production industries is
thus the earliest possible. While brought about by
the exigencies of the scheduling problem, it nevertheless has certain decided advantages. Historically, the production industries have tended to be
scheduled earlier than the office and other groups
in the CBD. This relationship will be retained.
The difference in starting times within the group is
also an historic one. Under present schedules 34.7
per cent of the earlier group now starts between
7:30 and 8:00 a.m., as contrasted with 4.4 per cent
for the later group. On the other hand, only 18.7
per cent of the earlier groups start at 8:45 and
9:00, while 51.6 per cent of the later group starts
at those times. There is thus ample precedent in
scheduling relationships for this difference in
starting times.

THE ADMINISTRATIVE OFFICES

Offices are the most prevalent form of employment establishment in the CBD. Almost every enterprise employs some clerical or office personnel,
even if only part time. But there are some industries in which the principal occupations are clerical and in which the product is produced by the office occupations. These are treated in this study
as the office industries. The office industries
have been subdivided into five main divisions. They
are: the administrative offices, the business professions and services, the financial industries, the
insurance carriers, and the government agencies.

This subdivision was made partly to get smaller
scheduling units and partly to obtain units with
common scheduling interests.

The administrative offices group consists of
nongovernmental establishments and industries whose
principal function is administration. They differ
in this respect from other nongovernmental office
industries which have specialized functions, such as
professional service to other companies, banking or
insurance. Some of the establishments and industries included in this group also have other functions, but they are classified here because they are
office establishments which do not fall into any
other office industries.

The administrative offices group consists of
thirteen industries employing 316,246 people. Because of its size, it is further subdivided into
four groups. They are: the central administrative
offices, with 140,199 employees; the transportation
company offices, with 46,788 employees; the radio,
television, motion picture companies and organizations, with 42,065 employees; and other administrative offices, with 87,197 employees. The titles of
these subgroups are, if anything, less descriptive
than the group as a whole. It is therefore necessary to identify the administrative offices group
and its subdivisions by specifying the individual
industries.

The composition and scheduling capabilities of
these subgroups will now be explained.

THE CENTRAL ADMINISTRATIVE OFFICES

The central administrative offices group consists of office establishments which, according to
the Standard Industrial Classification, are "primarily engaged in general administrative, supervisory,
purchasing, accounting and other management functions performed centrally for other establishments
of the same company." The CBD is an important

national center for the head offices and district
offices of United States and international companies.

The central administrative offices are not usually called by this name. They are classified on
the basis of the principal function of the company
to which they belong. This is by no means an improvement over classifying them functionally, as in
this study, because the companies of which they are
part are usually large multiproduct enterprises
which cannot be fitted accurately into the industrial classification scheme. While the title assigned here is not a common one, the establishments
will have little difficulty in recognizing themselves if the title is supplemented by such phrases
as company headquarters, or district or regional
offices.

These central administrative offices form an
appropriate scheduling unit. They employ a clerical labor force drawn from the local market. Their
internal functions have many common characteristics.
The enterprises differ from each other primarily in
the range of activities which they carry out. Some
companies assign more, others fewer functions to
their New York offices. Their interfirm and interindustry relations accordingly are also very similar. They maintain contact with other establishments of the same company, for the most part located
outside of New York City. Within the city they deal
with the financial community, with business professions and services such as advertising, law, accounting, and engineering, and with other supplier
and customer industry offices. There is sufficient
uniformity among these establishments to justify
treating them as a unit for purposes of scheduling.

Alternative Schedules

The central administrative offices were judged
capable of starting at 8:00, 8:30, or 9:30 a.m., at
least on functional grounds. Since grouping has not
changed this aggregate, the original alternatives
assigned to it remain the same.

Of the three alternative times, however, only
one proves feasible in rescheduling the CBD. The
combination of industry schedules which will be described later in this chapter allows the central
administrative offices only a 9:30 starting time.
Whenever this large group was shifted experimentally
to its other two times--8:00 or 8:30 a.m.--the result was a work schedule for the CBD which failed to
relieve traffic congestion.

In addition, since the bulk of the central administrative offices represent United States companies, a later schedule can only be helpful to them
in dealing with their various out-of-town branches
due to the difference in time zones.

TRANSPORTATION COMPANY OFFICES

The CBD is an important center for all forms of
transportation: rail, truck, water, and air. Many
companies have headquarter offices in the CBD.
There are also important terminal and handling facilities here. The industrial group now under consideration consists only of company offices and not
the other establishments.

Of the many parts of the transportation industries, five subdivisions were shown on Appendix
Table 64 to be capable of modifying their schedules.
They are: the offices of the shipping companies,
stevedores, airlines, freight forwarders, and arrangers of transportation. Some of these are company administrative offices. Others are operating
facilities engaged in the sale of transportation and
related services. All are offices and carry out
principally office, clerical, and administrative activities. Their employment, as shown on Appendix
Table 66, totals 46,785.

The group was put together primarily on the basis of its transportation function, but it also has
useful scheduling properties. The relationships of
this group to other industries in the CBD, precisely

because they are transportation companies, have many
similarities. They are primarily service functions
to other industries requiring transportation of personnel or freight. Since many common schedule determinants are thus shared by the transportation industry offices, they can be combined into a scheduling unit for present purposes.

TABLE 66

Employment in the Transportation Company Offices

Transportation Company Offices	Number
Deep sea foreign, deep sea domestic, Great Lakes-St. Lawrence Seaway, and rivers and canals transportation	20,550
Stevedoring	3,000
Air transportation, certified carriers	8,363
Freight forwarding	6,771
Arrangement of transportation	8,101
Total	46,785

Alternative Schedules

Three different alternative schedules were formulated for this group. Of its five industries,
only three are shown by Appendix Table 64 to be capable of starting at 8:00, 8:30, and 9:30. They are
the shipping companies, the stevedoring offices, and
the airlines offices. The freight forwarders are
considered able to start at 8:00 and 8:30 and the
arrangers of transportation only at 8:30. These
mixed capabilities were combined to form the total
group's alternative schedules. Three alternatives
were set up, the 8:00, 8:30, and 9:30 starting times.

Each industry capable of starting at these times is included in the alternative; those not, are excluded. For this group, therefore, the alternative schedules have a unique characteristic. There are uniform starting times for the entire group, but only for those capable of starting at each time. Those not capable of starting at a particular time are considered as not changing their schedules at all.

While the three alternatives exclude the industries which cannot adopt them, the other industries have some preference among the schedules. The 8:00 starting time, while functionally possible, is undoubtedly the least satisfactory of the three. As between the other two, however, there appears to be no basis for favoring one or the other. They will be treated, therefore, as equally satisfactory in this study.

RADIO, TELEVISION, AND MOTION PICTURE COMPANIES AND ORGANIZATIONS

The third group of administrative offices is made up of four industries which constitute the smallest segment of the administrative office group, having 42,065 employees in the CBD. The industries and their employment are given on Appendix Table 67.

TABLE 67

Employment in Radio, Television, and Motion Picture Companies and Organizations

Industry	Number
Radio and television broadcasting	8,870
Motion picture production and distribution	10,818
Motion picture service industries	2,069
Nonprofit membership organizations	20,308
Total	42,065

This group was formed primarily for scheduling reasons. It represents the office industries which, according to Appendix Table 64, are capable of starting at 8:30 or 9:30, but whose preference by a very large margin is for a 9:30 starting time. The radio and television industries have important relationships with advertising and other professional occupations and industries in the CBD which also prefer--and practice--later hours. Similarly, the motion picture industries are allied with professions and industries in the entertainment field which tend to operate later in the work day. The organizations, partly on account of their work force and partly because of their relationships to industries and professions, are habitually a later industry. Thus, while there is very little uniformity in their interindustry relations, they are joined together primarily because of this scheduling characteristic.

Alternative Schedules

This group as a whole has two alternative possible starting times, 8:30 and 9:30. However, because its tendency is so clearly toward a later starting time, the 8:30 alternative may, for practical purposes, be disregarded. While it is used in the computations, it is not considered a realistic alternative for these industries.

OTHER ADMINISTRATIVE OFFICES

There still remain four important industries belonging to the general category of administrative offices. The industries and their employment are given in Appendix Table 68.

Although dissimilar from the viewpoint of their products and services, this group was formed for scheduling reasons. Its member industries are considered capable, according to Appendix Table 64, of starting at 8:00, 8:30, or 9:30. They are also clearly distinguishable from the other three

administrative office groups. The group's title is
wholly unilluminating, and the members will have to
be specified by their individual industry titles, if
they are to be recognized in the CBD.

TABLE 68

Employment in Other Administrative Offices

Other Administrative Offices	Number
Contract construction offices	14,993
Newspapers: publishing, publishing and printing	22,982
Mail order houses, except general merchandise	1,901
Real estate company offices	47,321
Total	87,197

Alternative Schedules

     The alternative schedules of this group are the
same as those of its individual members: 8:00, 8:30,
and 9:30. These alternatives are handled as uniform
times for the entire group in all the subsequent
computations. This is a convenience for the feasibility calculations. In the event of any subsequent
implementation of work staggering, however, it ought
to be possible to treat each of these individually
if desired.

     The order of preference among the alternative
schedules is: no change, 8:30, 9:30, and 8:00. It
is assumed that no change is the preferred option of
the group. Although 8:30 precedes 9:30, they are regarded here as approximately equal. The least desirable of the alternative times is 8:00.

CONCLUSIONS

The administrative offices, with their 316,246
employees, are a massive bloc of people working in
the CBD. To achieve greater scheduling flexibility
this total group is subdivided into four groups.
The definitions of each--and more important, the
specific industries included in each--are described
in detail in the preceding sections. More than
their titles, the naming of the individual industries must be relied upon to identify each of the
groups.

The whole aggregate was subdivided in order to
achieve greater maneuverability in rescheduling
these industries. As a single group they make up
15 per cent of the total CBD. A group of this size,
largely concentrated at a 9:00 starting time, has to
be shifted in any work staggering program. The only
alternative starting time to which it could be
shifted would be 9:30. By breaking the group into
smaller scheduling units, it might be possible to
schedule some of them to other than 9:30.

The alternative schedules for each of the
groups were set forth in detail. It was also shown
that the real range of choice was somewhat smaller
than the actual number of alternatives. Effectively, the central administrative offices will have to
be scheduled at 9:30. The radio, television, motion
picture production and organizations will also have
to be scheduled at 9:30, if their schedules are
changed at all. This leaves the transportation industries and the other administrative industries
with choices of no change, 8:30, or 9:30 starting
times. These are the two practical consequences of
subdividing the total group.

A problem now arises as to the best pattern of
scheduling for these administrative offices. Should
they be scheduled uniformly, or should there be some
variation in their schedule? If uniformly, the entire group would have to start at 9:30. If varied,
the central administrative offices and the radio,

television, motion picture industries, and organizations would start at 9:30. The transportation offices and the other administrative offices would
start at their present schedule (principally 9:00),
or 8:30 or 9:30. These alternatives allow for nine
possible different combinations. (Two groups with
three alternatives each, and two groups with one
alternative each.)

The choice between uniform or varied schedules
cannot be made decisively. There are persuasive arguments in favor of each. A uniform schedule has
the advantage of establishing a common community
time for opening the administrative offices. This
would establish a clear and simple pattern for these
industries and for their employees. On the other
hand, a varied schedule, with some starting at 8:30,
some at 9:00, and some at 9:30, has the advantage of
offering the clerical employees of the CBD a choice
of starting times. It should be noted, however,
that even if a uniform time were established, the
choices of the office employees would by no means be
wholly restricted to 9:30. There are many other office industries in the CBD which will have to be
scheduled at other times even if the administrative
offices are all set at 9:30. As between the two
patterns there are no salient functional or industrial considerations which weigh in favor or against
either one.

Accordingly, no preferences arise at this point
as to the various alternative patterns for the administrative offices. There are, however, other
criteria which will be encountered later, when all
CBD schedules are combined for an over-all CBD pattern.

                BUSINESS PROFESSIONS AND SERVICES

The second major division of offices in the CBD
consists of establishments performing professional
and other services, principally to businesses. They
differ from the administrative offices described
above in several important particulars. Their

principal functions are not administrative. Rather,
they are professional in character and the chief occupations of these establishments--those performing
the output functions--usually employ professionally
trained people. They include editors, writers, art-
ists, engineers, accountants, architects, lawyers,
and the like. Some establishments are subprofessional, but with clients rather than customers. For the
group as a whole, the important interbusiness relationships are concerned with advice and professional
service rather than with transactions. This group
is an important one in the CBD, both functionally
and numerically. It has an estimated 151,000 employees.

There are twelve industries in this group. The
groups and their present employment are given in
Appendix Table 69.

TABLE 69

Employment in Business Professions and Services

Industry	Number
Periodicals: publishing, publishing and printing	20,737
Books: publishing, publishing and printing	9,935
Miscellaneous publishing	3,231
Insurance agents, brokers, and services	17,534
Advertising agencies	22,945
Consumer credit reporting agencies, etc.	3,696
Private employment agencies	1,308
Research, development, and testing laboratories	4,886
Business and management consulting services	15,948
Business services, n.e.c.	26,852
Legal services	16,375
Engineering and architectural services	15,529
Total	151,005

The formation of this group is based on three considerations. First, the principal occupations in these groups are professional and quasi-professional. Second, their interindustry relationships have the common quality of service to other firms and industries. Third, there is a decided preference on the part of most--but not all--of the group for a later starting time rather than an earlier one. These considerations provide a functional and scheduling basis for treating the component industries, however different their specific functions, as a scheduling unit.

Alternative Schedules

The component industries of this group have somewhat differing scheduling alternatives, as shown on Appendix Table 64. Six are considered capable of starting at 8:00, 8:30, and 9:30; two at 8:30 and 9:30; one at 8:30 only; and two at 9:30 only. There is no one starting time shared by all. Accordingly, there is no possibility of a uniform starting time.

Two alternative schedules were formulated for this group. The first one assigns a starting time of 8:30 to all industries except two. These--the insurance agents and brokers and the advertising agencies--are scheduled at 9:30. In the second schedule, all industries are assigned to 9:30 except the consumer credit reporting agencies, the private employment agencies, and the other business services. Their schedules remain unchanged in the group's second alternative schedule.

In subsequent computations, when industries are combined for the tests of feasibility, both the 8:30 and 9:30 schedules are used. However, only the 9:30 alternative is retained as a practical one because of the decided preferences of this group for the later starting time.

THE WHOLESALE TRADES

One of the largest and most variegated industrial aggregates in the CBD is the wholesale trades.
As a function, it consists in selling at any stage
of distribution short of retailing. The function as
such is found in a very large number of establishments. Some are classified as manufacturing, others
as central, regional, or district offices. The
group now under consideration comprises only the
establishments whose primary function is wholesaling.
They employ 226,731 people, or 11.1 per cent of the
CBD's total.

The wholesale trades in the CBD exhibit exceedingly great diversity. They sell a vast range of
products. They sell to customers over the entire
world. Their establishments vary in size from one-
man jobbers to large selling establishments employing hundreds, even thousands, of people. As a whole,
it is one of the most diverse industrial aggregates
to carry a single rubric.

The wholesale trades as a group are usually
classified by their products. The Standard Industrial Classification has nine large subdivisions
(one of which is miscellaneous). Within each there
are numerous further subdivisions. This study follows the Standard Industrial Classification and subdivides the industry into its nine component groups.

There is merit to this grouping from the viewpoint of scheduling. To these trades, the most significant aspect of their operation is the relationship with customers. The trades, classified by
product, bring together enterprises which, depending
on the scope of the product class, operate within
the same or reasonably related markets. In a general way, therefore, the product classification
tends to group together industries which share very
important schedule determinants.

Because the wholesale trades are large, they
are a cumbersome scheduling unit when treated as a

single group. It proved desirable after some experimentation, to break the aggregate into smaller
units. An obvious subdivision of the group is suggested by the nine product subgroups. This, however, would fragment the total into too many individual units. Moreover, since not all are equally
distinct and identifiable, some may be difficult to
recognize. An an alternative, the wholesale trades
are subdivided into two groups for purposes of rescheduling. This does not exclude further subdivisions should they be desirable. But for the present
the two subgroups are considered adequate.

The component industries and their numbers of
employees are given in Appendix Table 70.

TABLE 70

Employment in the Wholesale Trades

	Number
Earlier Trades:	
Groceries and related products	17,722
Electrical goods	12,200
Hardware, and plumbing and heating and supplies	6,855
Machinery, equipment, and supplies	31,636
Miscellaneous wholesalers	82,578
Total	150,991
Later Trades:	
Motor vehicles and automotive equipment	4,117
Drugs, chemicals, and allied products	14,458
Dry goods and apparel	54,311
Total	72,886

The basis for the division into two is given by
the present schedules of the wholesale trades. An
analysis of their schedules reveals that some of the

trades are characteristically scheduled to start
somewhat earlier than others. This provides a basis
for dividing the entire aggregate into the two
groups, one called the earlier wholesale trades, the
other the later trades. These descriptions apply to
their present scheduling practices, not necessarily
to any future modifications.

The earlier group now has 60.6 per cent of its
people starting at 8:45 and 9:00 a.m. and 22.8 per
cent starting at 8:00 to 8:30 a.m. This contrasts
with the later group which has 89 per cent starting
at 8:45 and 9:00 a.m. and 6.9 per cent starting between 8:00 and 8:30 a.m. The difference is by no
means drastic. But it is perceptible and it reflects differences in scheduling requirements arising from the differences in their markets.

Alternative Schedules

Each of the eight component trades for which
alternative schedules are shown on Appendix Table 64
has three possible starting times: 8:00, 8:30, and
9:30. These are assigned to the two larger subgroups on uniform bases. Each of the subgroups has
the same three alternatives, and their respective
member trades are modified uniformly. Thus, in the
later computations there are two groups of wholesale
trades, the earlier and the later, which are modified independently of each other. But within each,
schedules are uniform. As noted above, this uniformity is not necessary for any functional reason.
It is a convenience for computational purposes and
it may be an advantage if modified schedules are to
be implemented in these trades.

While each of these two subgroups has three
alternative possible starting times, the alternatives are by no means equally desirable. From the
viewpoint of a successful work staggering program,
it would probably be best not to modify the schedules of the wholesale trades at all. No change is
the preferred alternative for both groups. The
reason for this stems from the variegated character
of the industry. Because of their heterogeneity in

product, and especially in size, it is possible that
a large proportion of firms might not even learn
about a proposed change in hours, much less comply
with it. The few large wholesale units are very attractive candidates for schedule change, but the
vast majority are exceedingly small and have other
characteristics which would make it difficult to
communicate with them. This does not exclude the
possibility that individual trades which have only
a few firms or which are well organized might be
asked to modify their schedules, if work staggering
is introduced. But in the aggregate, from the perspective of this study and the feasibility computations, it is considered preferable to proceed as far
as possible without reliance on the wholesale trades.

If their schedules are to be modified, then a
fairly clear order of preference is discernible. A
uniform starting time of 8:30 for both groups would
be the preferred change. This would have the advantage of uniformity, clarity, and simplicity and
stands a reasonable chance of becoming known in
time. The next preferred change would be for the
later trades to shift to 8:30 and the earlier trades
remaining unchanged. This preference is based on
two considerations. The later trades consist of
three quite well-defined groups with a considerable
number of large firms. Since they are later than
the others, their shift would tend to reduce the
disparity which now exists in their scheduling. The
third choice would be to shift the earlier trades to
8:30, leaving the later trades unchanged. This
would have the desirable feature of fixing a time
uniformly for these trades close to the one toward
which they now tend.

The less desirable alternatives still remain.
In the first the earlier trades would be unchanged
and the later trades shifted to 9:30 starting time.
This represents a shift toward the present scheduling tendency of the later trades and involves the
next lesser amount of dislocation. The final alternative would be an 8:30 starting time for the earlier trades and 9:30 for the later trades. This, in

effect, would carry out both the scheduling tendencies of the two groups.

Conspicuously absent from this set of alternatives are any which contain an 8:00 starting time. While this is regarded by Appendix Table 64 as functionally feasible for the wholesale trades, it is by no means a desirable schedule--except possibly in individual cases, such as some of the food trades.

THE FINANCIAL INDUSTRIES

The financial industries consist of three principal branches employing 143,265 people in the CBD. Of this total, 122,260 employees are in industries which are capable of modifying their work schedules. Appendix Table 71 gives, for each of the finance industries, its total employment and the employment in its modifiable subdivisions. In the section to follow, each of these three branches will be taken up individually.

TABLE 71

Total and Modifiable Employment
in the Financial Industries

Financial Industries	Total Number	Modifiable Number
Banking	92,359	81,490
Credit agencies other than banks	9,814	5,069
Security and commodity brokers, dealers, exchanges, and services	41,092	35,701
Total	143,265	122,260

Banking

The banking group contains one industry--the commercial banks. This one industry is internally subdivided into four parts on Appendix Table 64 which correspond to one or more departments of the commercial banks. Each of these parts has a different capability of modifying its schedule.

The commercial banks are kept as a separate scheduling group partly because of their size and partly because they make up a single industry. Their operation and scheduling capabilities are sufficiently unique to warrant separating this industry from others in the financial group.

Alternative Schedules

To construct alternative schedules for the commercial banks the various departments were combined into three scheduling units, depending upon their individual capabilities. The public departments form a separate group with a single alternative starting time, 8:30 a.m. The second group consists of a series of departments with alternative starting times of 8:00 and 8:30. They are: operations and services, mail tellers--international department, administration, and agency. The third group contains the investment, trading in foreign currency, collection of drafts and bankers' acceptances departments which, according to Appendix Table 64, have a 9:30 alternative time.

Not all of the possible alternative schedules for the commercial banks are equally desirable. From certain viewpoints, no change at all is preferred to any of the modifications. This, however, is not a practical preference from the viewpoint of work staggering, at least not for the entire commercial banking industry. The 8:00 starting time is the least attractive alternative, and if possible ought to be avoided in the feasibility computations. The 8:30 and 9:30 starting times, where they apply, are the preferred ones if a change is made.

Given the three units and their alternative
starting times--including no change as one option--
there are twelve possible schedule combinations for
the banks. The ones involving no change and the
8:30 and 9:30 starting times are regarded as the
preferred ones. Those which combine with the 8:00
a.m. starting time of the earlier unit must be
ranked as the least preferable. The four preferred
alternatives have the earlier group of departments
starting at 8:30, and the public and later departments at 8:30 or 9:30, respectively, or at no change.

Credit Agencies Other Than Banks

Within this industry there are two subgroups
capable of modifying their schedules. They are
shown on Appendix Table 64 as business credit institutions and short-term business credit institutions.
Together they employ 5,069 people and may for present purposes be treated as a single group.

The business credit institutions are separated
from the commercial banks for scheduling purposes
primarily because the former constitute a single
industry.

Alternative Schedules

The alternative starting times for this group
are the same as the ones shown on Appendix Table 64,
namely, 8:00 and 8:30 a.m. Of the two, 8:30 is
clearly the preferred one. Because of the similarity of this group to the public departments of the
commercial banks, their schedules ought to be the
same in any CBD modifications.

Security and Commodity Brokers, Dealers, Exchanges, and Services

The third of the financial industries consists
of the security and commodity brokers, dealers, exchanges, and services. Of the 41,092 employees in
this industry, 35,702 are included among those whose
schedules are considered modifiable. These are
employees of the security brokers, dealers, and

flotation companies. Two other smaller groups may
also be associated with their schedule changes.
They are the commodity contracts brokers and dealers
and the firms engaged in services allied with the
exchange of securities and commodities. The schedules of the security and commodity exchanges, as
discussed in Chapter 4, are not considered modifiable.

Alternative Schedules

This group, according to Appendix Table 64, is
capable of adopting a 9:30 starting time. No change
is involved on account of industry grouping, since
this industry has not been combined with any other.

Alternative Schedules in the
Financial Industries

For purposes of modifying schedules, the financial industries were subdivided, in the preceding
sections, into five scheduling units. The commercial banks have three--the earlier group (8:00 and
8:30), the public departments (8:30), and the later
group (9:30). The business credit institutions form
a single group with 8:00 and 8:30 starting times.
The security companies are the third group and they
have a 9:30 alternative time. The alternative schedules of these five groups can be combined in seventy-
two different ways. They are not all equally desirable. Certain constraints eliminate some of the
possible combinations, and others may be placed very
low in order of preference.

It is assumed that the financial industries
prefer no change to any of the alternatives, simply
on grounds of minimizing inconveniences. This applies to each of the five subgroups.

The earlier departments' preference for schedule change is considered to be the 8:30 start time.
An 8:00 start is to be avoided in the computations,
if possible.

The 8:30 starting time for the public departments is suitable, and probably as acceptable as the
no change. Similarly, the 9:30 and no change alternatives are probably equally preferred for the later
departments of the banks.

The business credit institutions ought to be
scheduled at the same time as the public departments
of the commercial banks. This then eliminates the
8:00 alternative from this group.

Finally, the securities group and the later departments of the commercial banks are functionally
linked, and hence ought to be scheduled at the same
time.

These preferences and combinations reduce the
number of alternative schedules for the financial
industries. There are twelve possible schedules if
the 8:00 alternative for the earlier departments of
the commercial banks is used; otherwise there are
eight.

INSURANCE CARRIERS

The insurance carriers located in the CBD employ 126,979 people. Of these, 119,095 are in subdivisions which are capable of modifying their
schedules. Appendix Table 72 presents the total and
modifiable employment of the several categories of
insurance carriers.

Two of the subdivisions of the industry are
able to modify their work schedules. They are the
life insurance carriers and fire, marine, and casualty insurance carriers. Together they represent 94
per cent of the industry. For purposes of reschon-
uling these two subdivisions are treated separately.
This is partly in order to enlarge the flexibility
of rescheduling--the life insurance group is a large
one--and partly because the two groups have somewhat
different schedules at the present time.

TABLE 72

Total and Modifiable Employment
of Insurance Carriers

Insurance Carriers	Total Number	Modifiable Number
Life insurance	80,000	80,000
Accident and health insurance	4,284	-
Fire, marine, and casualty insurance	39,442	39,095
Surety insurance	1,569	-
Title insurance	409	-
Insurance carriers, not elsewhere classified	1,275	-
Total	126,979	119,095

Alternative Schedules

Each of the subdivisions has three alternative
starting times: 8:00, 8:30, and 9:30. Since they
are treated as separate units, it is possible to retain these three times as their subgroup alternatives.

Of the three times, 8:30 is considered the preferred one. However, as it turns out, there is very
little possibility of shifting these groups to the
8:30 starting time. As between the other two, 8:00
and 9:30, there is no basis for a choice, at least
on available evidence. Since both branches of the
industry tend to be scheduled between 8:30 and 9:00,
there may be less dislocation in shifting to an 8:00
starting time. However, because of the size of
these groups, there is very little choice in the final industry combinations.

GOVERNMENT

The CBD contains a large number of government establishments. They belong to a wide range of governments: local, county, state, interstate, and federal, as well as international and foreign governments. In total they employ 130,994 people. Appendix Table 73 presents the number of employees in each of the seven categories of governmental agencies. It also shows that 71,122 people are employed in governmental establishments whose schedules are considered capable of being changed.

TABLE 73

Total and Modifiable Employment in Government

Government	Total Number	Modifiable Number
Federal government	51,948	22,821
New York State government	12,009	12,009
New York City government	54,984	33,762
United Nations	3,300	–
New York County government	722	–
Interstate Authorities and Commissions	6,161	2,530
Foreign governments	1,774	–
N.E.C.	96	–
Total	130,994	71,122

The modifiable agencies are confined to establishments of the United States government, New York State, New York City, and the interstate agencies.

The international governments, New York County, and
other United States governments are not included
among the modifiable ones.

The government agencies are separated from the
other private employment groups primarily because
they are governmental. As such, they may be particularly accessible to a schedule change which comes
about as public policy, provided the specific
changes are otherwise acceptable. The four modifiable groups represent three distinct governmental
jurisdictions and an intergovernmental one. Combining them here into a single group does not imply
that any one government will have the authority to
modify the schedules of the others.

Alternative Schedules

The agencies which are considered capable of
modifying their schedules have three alternative
starting times: 8:00, 8:30, and 9:30. There is no
need for the individual subgroups--federal, state,
local, and intergovernmental--to have the same
starting times. However, the alternatives formulated for the governmental group are based on uniform times. This is partly a matter of convenience
and partly a result of scheduling considerations.

The government agencies, no less than private
enterprise, have scheduling determinants. While
their relationships with other establishments are
primarily not commercial, they nevertheless impose
many constraints upon their schedules. Both the
8:00 and 9:30 starting times are functionally possible for many of the agencies. At either schedule
they would be capable of carrying out their functions. Both, however, might tend to inconvenience
the publics which these agencies serve. An 8:00
starting time would require an early closing time.
The 9:30 starting time would make governments available later than much private employment. Hence as
a matter of public policy, the preferred alternative
starting time for the governmental agencies is 8:30.

The real alternatives for these four government
groups is either no change or an 8:30 starting time.
With these two alternatives there might be some variability among the four agencies. However, precisely
because they are an accessible group for rescheduling, it turns out that a uniform 8:30 starting time
is the best alternative for these groups.

APPENDIX N THE LATENESS
ADJUSTMENT

This appendix will describe the method by which
a lateness adjustment table was constructed. The
purpose of the table is to change the numbers of
people by authorized starting times into the numbers
by actual starting times. The work schedules, when
multiplied by the lateness adjustment matrix, are
thus converted into actual starting numbers. A description of the data, the analysis, and the method
will now be given.

THE DATA

Two sources of data are employed in this derivation. From the work schedule survey, estimates are
available on the per cents of people in the CBD
scheduled to start work at various times. The per
cents are given in Appendix Table 74. These estimates are considered an accurate representation of
the prevailing official starting times of people who
work in the CBD. (They will be treated as the universe in a statistical sense.) The sociological survey produced percentages of people (in the sample)
by their actual starting times.* These data are considered to be reliable sample statistics drawn from
the universe of people who work in the CBD.

Both these sets of data are given in Appendix
Table 74. In this table the first column of numbers
gives the per cents scheduled for each of the starting times. The starting times include the regular

---

*See Appendix P for a description of the survey
data used here.

15-minute intervals from 7:30 to 9:30 plus two additional ones. The first is before 7:30, which contains the per cents who start between 4:00 and 7:15
a.m. The other is after 9:30, which includes the
per cents starting between 9:45 a.m. and 12:30 p.m.
The total of this range of starting times is 89.2
per cent of the entire 24-hour day.

TABLE 74

Per Cents of People Scheduled to Start
and Actually Starting Work

Start Time ($\pm$ 7 1/2 Minutes)	Scheduled Start		Actual Start
	24-Hour Basis	4-12:30 Basis	(Soc. Study)
Before 7:30	3.3	3.7	3.8
7:30	.4	.4	1.0
45	.1	.1	.8
8:00	10.1	11.3	7.9
15	1.5	1.7	3.3
30	14.0	15.7	13.6
45	11.0	12.3	11.5
9:00	39.5	44.3	37.0
15	4.1	4.6	10.4
9:30	2.2	2.5	5.2
After 9:30	3.0	3.4	5.6

The second column of Table 74 converts these
per cents to a base of 89.2 per cent. This conver-
sion was performed in order to make the schedule conform to the time range of the next column.

The sociological study asked the respondents a
series of questions concerning the times they usually do certain things on weekdays. One of the questions in the series asked the respondents when they
actually start work. (This question immediately followed one which asked when they arrive at work.)
The last column of Table 74 gives the per cents of
the total sample reporting that they actually started
work at each of the indicated times.

A comparison of the two tables is given in Appendix Table 75. The comparison is made in two ways.
The first two columns contain the per cents of each
interval as given in the preceding table. Columns
four and five cumulate the percentages of each set
of data. Columns three and six show the differences
between the two sets by interval and cumulatively.
From these comparisons certain observations may be
made.

The first two columns show a considerable
amount of similarity in their contours. The main
peaks occur together and are of very similar magnitudes. There is some variation in the troughs of
the tables, but these in general are all proportional.
The differences which arise in the cumulative columns
are substantially more systematic. The per cent of
actual starts exceed the scheduled starts at an increasing rate during the first three time periods,
through 7:45. By 8:00 there is a large re-
versal, and at 8:15 the difference falls to a low of
.4 of a per cent. Beginning with 8:30 the scheduled
percentages begin to mount steadily over the actual
percentages until 9:00, and then the excess of scheduled over actual gradually reduces to zero at the
end of the table.

A substantive distinction is now drawn between
the definitions of the two sets of statistics.

TABLE 75

Comparison: Scheduled and Actual Starting Per Cents, by Interval and Cumulatively

Start Time (± 7 1/2 Minutes)	Per Cents per Interval			Cumulative Per Cents		
	Scheduled	Actual	Actual Minus Scheduled	Scheduled	Actual	Actual Minus Scheduled
Before 7:30	3.7	3.8	+ .1	3.7	3.8	+ .1
7:30	.4	1.0	+ .6	4.1	4.8	+ .7
7:45	.1	.8	+ .7	4.2	5.6	+ 1.4
8:00	11.3	7.9	-3.4	15.5	13.5	- 2.0
8:15	1.7	3.3	+1.6	17.2	16.8	- .4
8:30	15.7	13.6	-2.1	32.9	30.4	- 2.5
8:45	12.3	11.5	- .8	45.2	41.9	- 3.3
9:00	44.3	37.0	-7.3	89.5	78.9	-10.6
9:15	4.6	10.4	+5.8	94.1	89.3	- 4.8
9:30	2.5	5.2	+2.7	96.6	94.5	- 2.1
After 9:30	3.4	5.6	+2.2	100.0	100.1	0

546

Scheduled starting times are defined as the times
people are authorized to start work. Actual start
times are defined as the times at which people report that they actually begin their work. The difference in the two sets of statistics will be interpreted as a reflection of lateness (and early arrivals)
in starting work.

The justification for this interpretation lies
in the original questions eliciting the data, and in
the resulting statistics. There is no doubt about
the specific meaning of the scheduled starting times.
The statistics were defined and collected as the official and authorized starting times of employees.
The per cents given are of people who are supposed
to start work at these scheduled starting times.

The interpretation of the <u>actual</u> start is based
on the original question and its immediate environ-
ment.* The question asked the respondent when he
<u>actually</u> started work, after his arrival at work.
It is being interpreted as the moment the respondent
actually began fulfilling his employment obligations,
as defined by his employer. This moment is considered as different from arrival time and possibly
from scheduled starting time.

Standing in the way of this interpretation are
two possible obstacles. The first one is whether or
not the respondent understood the question this way.
This cannot be known conclusively, but it is clear
that different time answers were given to arrival
and actual start, and the actuals clearly differ
from the scheduled per cents. The second obstacle
is whether, having made such an interpretation, the
respondents would provide valid answers to the question. The questionnaires were administered on a confidential basis, and the respondents were assured

---

*See Appendix P for a full statement of the
question and for an explanation of <u>actually start to
work</u>.

their employers had no access to the information
which the employees might furnish. Moreover, the respondents' names were not attached to their replies.
To the extent that such assurance is effective, the
conditions were presumably set for answers which
would allow differences between actual and authorized
starting times to be accurately reflected.

The differences between the two sets of data
arise then from two principal sources. One source
is sampling differences. In any sample drawn from a
universe some variation from the universe values
must be expected, entirely as a matter of chance.
The other source of variation between the two is interpreted as substantive differences between scheduled starting time and actual starting time. The
substantive differences are interpreted--where the
numbers are positive--as lateness.

Allowing for sampling variation, latenesses begin showing up in a pronounced way at the 8:00 starting time.*

In developing the lateness adjustment, the data
prior to 8:00 a.m. will be disregarded. The grounds
upon which they are eliminated are: the proportion
of lateness in those periods is assumed to be negligible; the statistics do not make a lateness analysis
possible; and finally, the data may be reasonably
treated as arising from small sample representation
in these early periods. Accordingly, the analysis
of lateness and the derivation of the matrix will be
confined to the period starting 8:00 a.m.

Two lateness adjustment tables were constructed
from these data. One begins at 8:00 a.m., the other
at 8:30 a.m. The 8:00 a.m. table is justified

---

*The negative percentages signifying earlier
than scheduled starting times are by no means incon-
ceivable for the period prior to 7:45. As may be
seen in Appendix P, a substantial portion of people
arrive at work considerably before their scheduled
or actual starting times.

primarily on the grounds that lateness per cents first begin to appear at that time on Appendix Table 75. The 8:30 a.m. table is justified on the grounds that industries starting before this time in general place greater emphasis upon punctuality. Both tables will be given in this Appendix.

THE CONSTRUCTION OF THE LATENESS MATRICES

The method by which the lateness matrices were constructed will be illustrated by the 8:30 table.

An adjustment has to be made in the actual start percentages in order to make them serviceable in the subsequent derivation. Between 8:30 a.m. and the after 9:30 group, 82.8 per cent of the employees are scheduled to start work. Within this same range 83.3 per cent of the sample actually start work. The percentages in the actual column are therefore adjusted by a factor of 82.8 over 83.3 in order to bring the two totals to a similar amount. This adjustment is made necessary by reason of the matrix properties.

The construction begins by forming a matrix. This first step is illustrated in the table below.

Scheduled Start Time	Actual Start Time 8:30	8:45	9:00	9:15	9:30	After 9:30	Total
8:30							15.7
8:45							12.3
9:00							44.3
9:15							4.6
9:30							2.5
After 9:30							3.4
Total	13.5	11.4	36.8	10.3	5.2	5.6	82.8

The rows of the table give the scheduled starting
times, ranging from 8:30 to after 9:30. The columns
of this matrix give actual starting times ranging
from 8:30 to after 9:30. The final column of the
table gives the total per cents of people scheduled
to start work at the various times, as obtained from
the work schedule survey. The bottom row of the
table gives the total per cents of people actually
starting work as adjusted by 82.8/83.3.

        The table shows that 15.7 per cent of the people
are scheduled to start at 8:30, while 13.5 per cent
actually start then. The per cent who actually
start, 13.5 per cent, is inserted in the cell whose
scheduled and actual starting times are 8:30. This
leaves a difference of 2.2 per cent of the people
who were scheduled to start at 8:30 but actually did
not. The assumption is thereupon made that this 2.2
per cent actually started in the next time period,
8:45. The results of this first operation are given
on the next table.

Scheduled Start Time	Actual Start Time					After 9:30	Total
	8:30	8:45	9:00	9:15	9:30		
8:30	13.5	2.2					15.7
8:45							12.3
9:00							44.3
9:15							4.6
9:30							2.5
After 9:30							3.4
Total	13.5	11.4	36.8	10.3	5.2	5.6	82.8

        At 8:45 11.4 per cent of the people actually
start work; 2.2 per cent have already been carried
over from 8:30, which leaves a net balance of 9.2
per cent to start at this time. This 9.2 per cent

is inserted in the cell denoted by the 8:45 scheduled
and actual starting time. Since 12.3 per cent of the
people who are scheduled to start work at 8:45, and
9.2 of them actually started at this time, there is
again a carry-over of 3.1 per cent to the next time
period, 9:00 a.m. The results of this calculation
are shown below.

Scheduled Start Time	Actual Start Time					After 9:30	Total
	8:30	8:45	9:00	9:15	9:30		
8:30	13.5	2.2					15.7
8:45		9.2	3.1				12.3
9:00			33.7	10.3	.3		44.3
9:15				0	4.6		4.6
9:30					.3	2.2	2.5
After 9:30						3.4	3.4
Total	13.5	11.4	36.8	10.3	5.2	5.6	82.8

    The main assumptions in constructing this table
may be made explicit. First, 8:30 a.m. is taken as
the origin time and it is assumed that there are no
late employees starting at 8:30 who were scheduled
to start earlier. Next, the per cent actually starting at any given time constitutes the maximum allowed in any actual start column. There can therefore be no more assigned to the column than are recorded as actually starting. Third, wherever this
rule is enforced, and there are still excess employees
who are scheduled at the time interval, they are
placed in the next actual starting interval. In
one instance, at 9:00, it was necessary by this
procedure to carry employees over to a second interval, representing an estimated one-half hour of lateness. By using these assumptions according to the
procedure described, a first distribution was made
of the percentages, as shown on the above table.

The first results of this procedure, however, are not entirely satisfactory. According to this first calculation, none of the 4.6 per cent scheduled to start at 9:15 are able to start at that time. The carry-over from 9:00 a.m. absorbs the entire 10.3 per cent who actually start at 9:15. Accordingly, the total 4.6 per cent scheduled to start at 9:15 are assigned to actually start at 9:30. This produces the next unsatisfactory consequence of only .3 per cent of the 2.5 per cent scheduled to start at 9:30 actually starting at that time. The bulk of those scheduled at 9:30 are thus assigned actually to start after 9:30. These are considered to be somewhat distorted results which follow from the arithmetic logic of the procedures invoked at the outset.

Some fairly arbitrary adjustments were thereupon made in the matrix. These adjustments began with a recomputation of the percentages of the table above into percentages of the total scheduled to start at each time. The results of this computation are given on the table below.

Scheduled Start Time	Actual Start Time						
	8:30	8:45	9:00	9:15	9:30	After 9:30	Total
8:30	86.0	14.0					100.0
8:45		74.8	25.2				100.0
9:00			76.1	23.3	.6		100.0
9:15					100.0		100.0
9:30					12.0	88.0	100.0
After 9:30						100.0	100.0

The bases for the adjustments are taken directly from this table. It is observed first that 86 per cent of the people scheduled to start at 8:30 are presumed to start work on time and 14 per cent to start fifteen minutes late. The percentages of

people scheduled to start work at 8:45 and 9:00 a.m.
who actually start on time are 75 and 76, respectively. At fifteen minutes late, 25 and 23 per cent respectively start work. Disregarding minor differences, it appears from the data that about three
quarters of the work force start on time and about
one quarter starts late. These two percentages were
thereupon assigned to the 9:15 and 9:30 starting
times. As a consequence, however, it became necessary again to modify the 9:00 group.   The 24
per cent starting late were retained, but the percentages were distributed over three later starting
times. The final results of this adjustment are
given on the table below. Here again, the results
of the computations seem to accord with the reported experience in the central business district.

Scheduled Start Time	Actual Start Time					After 9:30	Total
	8:30	8:45	9:00	9:15	9:30		
8:30	86.0	14.0					100.0
8:45		74.8	25.2				100.0
9:00			76.1	15.3	5.0	3.6	100.0
9:15				75.0	25.0		100.0
9:30					75.0	25.0	100.0
After 9:30						100.0	100.0

     A second lateness adjustment matrix, with origin
at 8:00 a.m., was also constructed by using the same
procedure as the one just described. The results
show some differences in the 8:30 and later times.
These differences arise because, as shown earlier,
the original sets of data have different relationships over the range of starting times. The final
results of this second matrix will be given below.

THE ADJUSTMENT MATRICES

The final adjustment tables, in the form of matrices are given in Appendix Tables 76 and 77. There are some similarities between these tables and some very significant differences. The percentages for 9:15 and 9:30 are the same in both tables simply because they were arbitrarily made that way. The 9:00 percentages are very similar without having been given special adjustments. The 8:30 and 8:45 percentages are significantly different. In Appendix Table 77, the three-quarters:one-quarter distribution is preserved at 8:30, while in Appendix Table 76 it is replaced by approximately seven-eighths:one-eighth, the 86 and 14 per cents. Similarly, in Table 77 the 8:45 per cent is approximately two-thirds:one-third, while in Table 76 the 8:45 per cent is again three-quarters:one-quarter.

EVALUATION

There are no obvious bases for determining which of the two tables corresponds the more closely to actual conditions in the CBD. In the absence of actual lateness statistics a judgment cannot be made as to which is the more accurate. From the viewpoint of the procedures by which they were constructed, both tables employ the same operations, the same assumptions, and the same type of arbitrary adjustments. Hence neither is preferable on the grounds of method. Finally, if the tables are contrasted on the basis of their inherent reasonableness--a purely qualitative and subjective judgment in the absence of factual data--a case can be made for each of the tables. However, at their principal points of contact and difference, at 8:30 and 8:45, it is difficult to determine which corresponds the more closely to actual conditions. Arguments may be advanced for either side, but no conclusive judgment is available.

The determination as to which of these two

TABLE 76

Lateness Adjustment Matrix, 8:30 A.M. Origin:
From Scheduled to Actual Start

Scheduled Start Time	Actual Start Time										
	Before 7:30	7:30	7:45	8:00	8:15	8:30	8:45	9:00	9:15	9:30	After 9:30
Before 7:30	100										
7:30		100									
7:45			100								
8:00				100							
8:15					100						
8:30						86	14				
8:45							75	25			
9:00								76	15	5	4
9:15									75	25	
9:30										75	25

555

TABLE 77

Lateness Adjustment Matrix, 8:00 A.M. Origin:
From Scheduled to Actual Start

Scheduled Start Time	Actual Start Time										
	Before 7:30	7:30	7:45	8:00	8:15	8:30	8:45	9:00	9:15	9:30	After 9:30
Before 7:30	100										
7:30		100									
7:45			100								
8:00				71	18	11					
8:15					75	25					
8:30						77	23				
8:45							66	34			
9:00								75	16	5	4
9:15									75	25	
9:30										75	25
After 9:30											100

tables is preferable has to be made with reference
to some external criterion. For purposes of the
present study, such a criterion is available: the
closeness of fit to the actual cordon counts.   Its
application is described in the text of Chapter 6.

APPENDIX   O   SUBWAY
RIDERS

Estimates and computation tables will be derived in this appendix for the proportion of people
working in the CBD who use the subway in traveling
to work. The results will be given both on an over-
all basis and by actual starting times.

The sociological study provides information on
the respondents' modes of travel to and from work.
For present purposes, information is available for
each respondent on the mode of transportation he
uses to enter the CBD and, if different, the mode of
transportation he uses within the CBD. From these
data it has been possible to identify the respondents
who cross the subway cordons to work. It is also
possible to identify the employees who enter the CBD
by means other than the subway, but who, within the
CBD, use the subway to work. These include, for example, the people who arrive at Grand Central Station, Pennsylvania Station, or the bus terminal and
who then take subways. Both of these subgroups--
the subway riders who cross cordons and those who
originate within the CBD--have been further identified with respect to their actual start times. (For
the definition of actual start time see Appendix P.)

Appendix Table 78 gives the percentages of the
sample, by actual start times, who cross the cordon
in the subway, or who enter the CBD by other means
but take the subway afterward, and the total of all
subway riders.

Appendix Table 79 is the adjustment for reducing
the total number of employees in the CBD, by actual
starting times, to the numbers who cross subway cordons

558

TABLE 78

Subway Riders as Per Cents of Total CBD
Employees, by Actual Start Work Time

Actual Start Time	Cross Cordons	CBD Origin	Total
Before 7:30	74.5	7.3	81.8
7:30	73.7	5.3	79.0
7:45	*72.2	*4.5	*76.7
8:00	70.7	3.8	74.4
8:15	70.0	6.0	76.0
8:30	75.0	7.2	82.2
8:45	60.8	17.6	78.4
9:00	69.0	9.9	78.8
9:15	61.0	6.9	67.9
9:30	69.6	12.7	82.3
After 9:30	55.3	8.2	63.5
Sample Mean	67.1	9.6	76.7

*Interpolated between 7:30 and 8:00.

TABLE 79

Adjustment Matrix: Per Cents of CBD Employees Who Cross Subway Cordons

Scheduled Start Time	Actual Start Time										
	Before 7:30	7:30	7:45	8:00	8:15	8:30	8:45	9:00	9:15	9:30	After 9:30
Before 7:30	74.5										
7:30		73.7									
7:45			72.2								
8:00				70.7							
8:15					70.0						
8:30						75.0					
8:45							60.8				
9:00								69.0			
9:15									61.0		
9:30										69.6	
After 9:30											55.3

560

APPENDIX P THE ARRIVAL
ADJUSTMENT

The arrival adjustment consists of a table and
a method by which to convert statistics of actual
starting times into statistics of times of arrival
at work.* The arrival table to be derived in this
appendix applies only to people who work in the CBD
and cross subway cordons on their journey to work,
not to all who work in the CBD, nor to all who use
the subway. The data employed in constructing the
table will be described in the section immediately
following. Thereafter, the method will be explained.
Finally, the tables will be presented and evaluated.

THE START-ARRIVAL STATISTICS

The data employed in constructing the arrival
adjustment tables were obtained from the sociological survey. The questionnaire asked about the respondents' daily schedules. Question 13 was as
follows:

---

*The data utilized in constructing the arrival
adjustment connect actual start times to arrival
times. The adjustment table can also be used to
connect scheduled start to arrival--if the assumption is made that people actually start work at
their scheduled start times ($\pm$ 7 1/2 minutes).

561

At what time do you <u>usually</u> do the following
things on weekdays?

Get up at........................ ____o'clock
Eat breakfast.................... ____o'clock
Leave home for work............. ____o'clock
Arrive at work.................. ____o'clock
Actually start to work......... ____o'clock
Actually leave work for
     the day...................... ____o'clock
Actually start home............ ____o'clock
Arrive home.................... ____o'clock
Begin eating dinner............ ____o'clock
Go to bed...................... ____o'clock

The replies to four of these questions are now
of particular interest. They are the questions eliciting the times at which the respondents eat breakfast, leave home for work, arrive at work, and actually start to work. Before presenting the statistical results, the meanings of these questions and
their answers will be briefly examined.

Actually Start to Work

The question "Actually start to work" is interpreted here--as in the lateness adjustment--to mean
the time that the employee reports to work. It is
the act by which the employee satisfies the start of
his working day. This act has, within the particular enterprise, an official definition. It may mean
the punching of the time clock, entering the employer's premises, entering the employee's department
or immediate work area. Consistent with the previous interpretation, it is the act which defines the
employee's official presence, availability, and in-
auguration of the performance of his work. It is
the act which is supposed to occur at the moment of
the official and authorized starting time, wherever
and however this is identified within the individual
establishment.

Arrive at Work

The specification, "Arrive at work," is interpreted in this study to mean arrival at the employer's premises. In fixing this interpretation, it is
explicitly noted that it is by no means the only one
which might be made, nor is it necessarily the one
which the respondents might make of it. As a matter
of fact, as will be shown, even the term "premises"
lacks precision. Nevertheless, this interpretation
will be followed because it is easily the most likely to have been made and because its imprecision
will not adversely affect the use of the statistic.

The location, at work, can readily be applied
over a range of places. It might be the exact work
place of the respondent--desk, work bench, sales
counter, and the like. It might be the room or department in which the work is performed, the entrance to the employer's premises, the floor on
which the employer's premises are located, the ele-
vator of the building, or the entrance to the building. It might even be interpreted as arrival at the
destination subway station. "At work" allows this
range of possible meanings.

Nor is the term "arrive" a precise one. It can
mean the first crossing of the line of demarcation
of the place "at work." It might also cover a range
of further possibilities up to and including a state
of complete readiness to start work.

For this study, "arrival at work" is defined as
crossing the demarcation line of the employer's premises. This interpretation conforms to the common
sense meaning of arrival at work, and it is reenforced
by the position of the question within the series
about the respondent's schedule. In addition, this
interpretation is supported by two other considerations. First, the statistics which will be presented
later in this appendix suggest that the respondents
made, on the whole, a significant separation in time
between arrival and actual start. The events denoted as arrival: crossing the line of the premises,
and as actual start: the act of complying with the

rules of employment, are, in fact, separated by a
considerable amount of time. Secondly, the replies
to this question were coded by 15-minute time intervals, each time representing a quarter hour ± 7 1/2
minutes. The half range of 7 1/2 minutes will cover
most of the possible ambiguities in interpreting the
meaning of arrival time.

Eat Breakfast, Leave Home

The two remaining questions elicited the times
of eating breakfast and leaving home for work.
These questions raise no issues as to meaning. Moreover, the replies were utilized in such a way that
precise definitions were not actually essential.

The Reply Data

To each of the questions the respondents were
asked to record the usual times at which they performed each of the acts on weekdays. The replies,
accordingly, depend entirely upon the cooperation of
the respondents. This involves the willingness of
the respondent to give such personal information,
the accuracy of his judgments with respect to time,
as well as his judgment as to usual weekday practice.
In general, it can be reported that employees answered these questions using 5-, 10-, and 15-minute
intervals. Even their estimated accuracy falls within the range of ± 2 1/2 minutes.

The validity of replies to the study as a whole
is considered extensively in the reports of the
sociological study. Despite the fact that the answers to these questions rely upon the voluntary cooperation of the respondent, even with respect to
information which might be considered confidential,
there is no evident reason for impeaching the results. An evaluation of the findings will be given
at the end of this appendix.

THE ACTUAL START-ARRIVAL TABLES

From the data as described above three actual
start-arrival tables were constructed. The method
of construction and the results will now be presented.

The first table utilized the responses to two
of the questions: actual start time, and arrive at
work. The sample was first divided into two parts.
One part contained the respondents who crossed subway cordons to work; the second part consisted of
all the other respondents. In this analysis only
those crossing the cordons were used. A tabulation
of their replies was then made, relating actual
start times to arrival times, and the numbers of replies having each possible pair of start-arrival
times were counted. This procedure took the form of
a correlation or scatter diagram table. The sample
numbers in each start-arrival time were converted
to per cents of the total number actually starting
at each of the times. The results of this procedure are given in Appendix Table 80.

Each row of the table is an actual start work
time (± 7 1/2 minutes) beginning with before 7:30
and concluding with after 9:30. Each column of the
table is an arrival time at work (± 7 1/2 minutes)
using the same time periods as in the rows. The
body of the table gives the per cents of persons who
start work at each of the times and who arrive at
the times indicated in the columns. Thus, using
the 8:00 start time as an illustration, of the
100 per cent of persons who actually start work
at 8:00 (± 7 1/2 minutes), 28.8 per cent replied
that they arrive at work in the same interval,
47.5 per cent in the 15-minute interval preceding,
11.3 per cent in the 30-minute interval preceding,
and 12.5 per cent earlier.

Appendix Table 81 has a similar structure to
the preceding one, but it measures a slightly different variable. The preceding question relates
the time at which people arrive at work (however

TABLE 80

Estimated Per Cents of People: Who Work in the CBD and Who Travel Through Subway Cordons to Work--Who Actually Start Work at Selected Times, by the Times They Arrive at Work

Actual Start Time (± 7 1/2 Minutes)	Time Arrive at Work (± 7 1/2 Minutes)										
	Before 7:30	7:30	7:45	8:00	8:15	8:30	8:45	9:00	9:15	9:30	After 9:30
Before 7:30	100.0										
7:30	54.5	45.5									
7:45		75.0	25.0								
8:00	12.5	11.3	47.5	28.8							
8:15	6.1	3.0	9.1	42.4	39.4						
8:30		1.3	3.2	15.8	48.1	31.7					
8:45			.9	1.9	13.1	45.8	37.4				
9:00	.3		.3	1.1	3.7	8.8	35.0	50.3			
9:15					1.0	1.0	2.0	49.0	47.0		
9:30					1.9			7.5	37.7	52.8	
After 9:30						4.3		2.2	19.6		73.9

TABLE 81

Estimated Per Cents of People: Who Work in the CBD and Who Travel Through Subway Cordons to Work--Who Actually Start Work at Selected Times, by the Times They Arrive at Work or Eat Breakfast in the CBD, Whichever Occurs Earlier

Actual Start Time (± 7 1/2 Minutes)	The Earlier of: Time Arrive at Work or Eat Breakfast in CBD (± 7 1/2 Minutes)										
	6:30-7:15	7:30	7:45	8:00	8:15	8:30	8:45	9:00	9:15	9:30	9:45-10:30
6:30 - 7:15	89.0										
7:30	63.6	36.4									
7:45		75.0	25.0								
8:00	13.8	12.5	46.3	27.5							
8:15	9.1	3.0	9.1	39.4	39.4						
8:30	.6	2.5	3.8	18.4	46.2	28.5					
8:45		.9	.9	5.6	14.0	43.0	35.5				
9:00			.3	1.3	4.0	9.4	36.0	48.7			
9:15					1.0	1.0	3.0	50.0	45.0		
9:30					1.9		1.9	5.7	39.6	50.9	
9:45 - 10:30						.5	1.7	2.3	6.3	22.8	54.1

interpreted) with the time they start work. The observation was made that a certain proportion of the
people who work in the CBD have their breakfast, or
at least a supplement to it, immediately before
starting work. The information from the sociological study allowed the possibility of investigating
this practice among the CBD people.

An analysis was made of the respondents to identify those who eat breakfast later than the time
they leave home for work. Of this group, those who
eat breakfast a considerable time after leaving home
or shortly before arriving at work were separated
out. Since the questionnaire also contains information on residence and on subway origin and destination stations, it was possible to isolate those who
have breakfast after arrival at their destination
stations in the CBD. Of this group, still another
subdivision was made to identify those who eat breakfast before actually starting work. (Some reported
having breakfast after they started work.) This
final group of respondents represented people whose
place of breakfast in the CBD was reached earlier
than their place of employment. Hence they could be
expected to travel on the subway system even earlier
than those going directly to work.

Appendix Table 81 was constructed by modifying
Appendix Table 80 to reflect these early arrivals.
It will be noted that the effect of this additional
modification is not very large, but it is systematically in the direction of moving the percentages
somewhat to the left. The earlier percentages are
increased and the later ones reduced, both slightly.
Thus, for example, instead of 28.8 per cent arriving and starting at the 8:00 interval, it is
now reduced to 27.5 per cent; or instead of 50.3
per cent arriving and starting at the 9:00 interval, it now becomes 48.4 per cent. The construction
of the first and last rows is described in Appendix S.

A third actual start-arrival table was constructed, using the original data of Appendix Table
81--the sample numbers of arrival and eat breakfast

in the CBD by times. Both Tables 80 and 81 distributed the original sample replies according to the
various starting times and arrival times. In the
third table the sample data were distributed according to the number of minutes of early arrival irre-
spective of the specific times. This made it possible to construct a table showing the proportions of
people who arrive on time ($\pm$ 7 1/2 minutes), 15 minutes early ($\pm$ 7 1/2 minutes), 30 minutes early
($\pm$ 7 1/2 minutes), and so forth. The results of
this analysis are given in Appendix Table 82.

TABLE 82

Per Cent of Respondents Reporting
Early Arrival by Varying Intervals

Early Arrivals (Minutes)	Per Cent of Respondents
0	41
15	41
30	11
45	3
60	3
75	1
Total	100 per cent

The material of Appendix Table 82 is given in
Appendix Table 83, but arranged in a form similar to
Tables 80 and 81. This last table corresponds to
Table 81 in its caption, but instead of using the
particular percentages associated with each starting
time, it uses the uniform per cent for the sample as
a whole. Appendix S explains the construction of
the first and last rows of the table.

TABLE 83

Adjustment Matrix: From Actual Start to Arrival Time in Per Cents

Actual Start Time	Arrival Time										
	6:30–7:15	7:30	7:45	8:00	8:15	8:30	8:45	9:00	9:15	9:30	9:45–10:30
6:30 – 7:15	89										
7:30	59	41									
7:45	18	41	41								
8:00	7	11	41	41							
8:15	4	3	11	41	41						
8:30	1	3	3	11	41	41					
8:45		1	3	3	11	41	41				
9:00			1	3	3	11	41	41			
9:15				1	3	3	11	41	41		
9:30					1	3	3	11	41	41	
9:45 – 10:30						1	2	2	6	23	54

EVALUATION

An assessment of these tables now has to be made.

First, for reasons already stated, the original data are accepted as useful representations of the behaviors they purport to measure. In the main this means that errors in judgment of time do not exceed the ± 7 1/2 minute interval employed in the interval. Moreover, this same interval can be counted on to cover variations in the respondents' interpretations of the question.

Second, the final results are reasonable and commend themselves as a useful instrument for the purpose at hand. The reasonableness of the results is perhaps easiest to see in Appendix Table 82. According to this table, 41 per cent of the employees (who cross subway cordons) arrive at work within 7 1/2 minutes of the time they actually start work. It must be remembered that arrival is being related to the actual start time, not the scheduled start time, and that actual start time may already be later than the scheduled time. Simply on the basis of logic, since people have to arrive before they start, 41 per cent declared that they arrived within the 7 1/2 minute interval.

Forty-one per cent also reported that they arrived at work (or at breakfast in the CBD, whichever occurs first) between 7 1/2 and 22 1/2 minutes before actually starting to work. As noted earlier, the respondents answered this question generally by 5-minute intervals, so that, in effect, the overwhelming majority of this 41 per cent is made of people whose replies showed a 10-, 15-, or 20-minute early arrival. Of these, it is safe to assert that most reported arriving 10 minutes before actually starting, and would therefore be coded in the 15-minute interval.

The 18 per cent who arrive 30, 45, 60, and 75 minutes early seem to belong to very special parts of the CBD working population. People are known to

arrive early on account of special transportation
arrangements or, in the case of executive and managerial personnel, to get an early start on the day's
work. These four categories of answers appear acceptable simply because they fall clearly outside
the expected range of exaggerated or even self-
serving answers to the question.

The crucial issue raised by the table is whether
the first two intervals are properly divided. The
proportion arriving within the 7 1/2 minute interval
may actually be larger than the 41 per cent. The
proportion in the 7 1/2 to 22 1/2 interval would
then be correspondingly smaller than the 41 per cent.
Within these two intervals, the effects of the imprecision and the self-serving potentialities of the respondents are undoubtedly felt most keenly. Despite
the question which this issue raises, the reported
distribution remains acceptable. It does so because
there is a prior adjustment to cover lateness and because there is no rational way in which to redistribute those first two percentages.

A still further support to the acceptability of
these tables may be gleaned from the internal patterns which are disclosed in Appendix Table 81. For
this purpose, attention is directed to the 8:00,
8:30, 8:45, and 9:00 a.m. distributions, which are
by far the principal ones in the CBD. Within these
groups the per cents arriving in the same interval
as the actual starts rise systematically from 27.5
through 28.5 to 35.5, up to 48.4. Similarly, the
per cents arriving in the preceding 15-minute interval diminish with the approach to 9:00. The
other actual start times do not show the same pattern,
but their statistics are based on much smaller proportions of the sample and greater sampling distortion may therefore have occurred. Furthermore,
these are small and special segments of CBD employment. The observations of the principal times lead
to a statable generalization: The people who start
work earlier tend to arrive somewhat earlier, and
those who start work later in the morning tend to
arrive much more closely to their actual starting
times. It is this generalized pattern which lends
additional credibility to the findings of these tables.

APPENDIX

Q

THE TRAVEL TIME-
CORDON INTERVAL
ASSIGNMENT TABLES

There are twenty-one travel time-cordon interval assignment tables, one for the total CBD and one
for each of the twenty cordon stations. This appendix will describe the method by which these tables
were constructed.

The travel time-cordon interval tables perform
two operations. First, they provide for the travel
time from each cordon station to place of employment
(or first CBD destination). Second, they convert
the statistics from the 15-minute work schedule intervals to the 20-minute cordon count intervals.
The tables are applied to the arrivals at work: the
numbers of people arriving at work, by 15-minute intervals. They convert these statistics to the numbers passing through each cordon station by 20-minute
intervals. The results assign the total CBD passengers to each station. These totals are reduced by
the next computation to the estimates of each station's passengers.

PROCEDURE

A fairly complicated procedure was employed to
construct these twenty-one tables. In this section
a brief description of the procedure will be given.
The supporting data, however, will be omitted, since
it involves a large number of tables and computations. Enough, however, will be shown to disclose
the method as well as its assumptions and limitations.

The procedure involved three steps. These will
be identified here and described more fully later.

573

In the first step a table of travel time ranges was
calculated. This spelled out ranges of travel time
which linked the 20-minute intervals and the 15-
minute arrival intervals. Next, the distribution of
passengers conforming to these travel time ranges
was computed. A separate distribution was made for
each cordon station. Third, an arrival-cordon interval table was computed for each cordon station.
These steps will now be explained somewhat more fully.

Travel Time Ranges

The travel time ranges take the form of a hypothetical table. This table expresses the relationship between the time a person passes through a cordon station and his arrival time by ranges of travel
time. The theory behind this table will help explain
its substance.

If a person arrives at work at a given time,
when did he pass through his cordon station? The
answer to this question is: It depends upon his
travel time. His arrival time minus the travel time
ought to be the time at which he passes through the
cordon station.

For example, if a person passes through a cordon station during the 7:40-8:00 a.m. cordon count
interval, and if his travel time is fifteen minutes,
he will arrive at his destination between 7:55 and
8:15. Conversely, if a person arrives at his destination at 8:15 and his travel time is twenty minutes, he will have passed through the cordon station
at 7:55, and be counted in the 7:40-8:00 a.m. cordon
interval.

The available data make it necessary to consider
a somewhat more complicated situation. The cordon
count intervals are twenty minutes in length, while
the arrival time intervals are fifteen minutes in
length. They are expressed as a single time $\pm$ 7 1/2
minutes. Accordingly, people who are said to arrive
at 8:00 a.m., actually arrive during the interval

$7:52\frac{1}{2}$ to $8:07\frac{1}{2}$ a.m.   If a person has a 20-minute
travel time and he arrives--according to the time
intervals of the data--between $7:52\frac{1}{2}$ and $8:07\frac{1}{2}$ a.m.,
in which cordon interval will he be counted?   Clear-
ly, if he arrived at $7:52\frac{1}{2}$ a.m., he will have passed
through the cordon station twenty minutes earlier,
or $7:32\frac{1}{2}$ a.m., which will put him into the 7:20-7:40
cordon interval.   On the other hand, if he arrives
at his destination at $8:07\frac{1}{2}$ a.m., he will have passed
through the cordon station twenty minutes earlier, at
$7:47\frac{1}{2}$ a.m., or during the 7:40-8:00 a.m. interval.

The data thus create an overlap in cordon intervals.   Persons coming at any arrival time, given
their travel time, might actually come through two
cordon count intervals.

To overcome this indefiniteness, a simplifying
assumption is made.   It is assumed that the density
of arrival remains uniform within the component
times of each 15-minute interval.   This is further
simplified by dividing the interval into three parts,
each five minutes in length, and assuming that one
third of the employees arrive during each 5-minute
interval.   The midpoint of each interval then covers
a range of $\pm$ 2 1/2 minutes.*

The computation of travel time ranges is given
on Appendix Table 84.   This table is constructed for
a one-hour arrival cycle; repetitions of the cycle
will follow the identical pattern.   The first column
gives the arrival times: --:00, --:15, --:30, --:45.
Each of these 15-minute intervals has three subdivisions, and the midpoints of these one-third intervals are given in the second column.   The third
column involves a new datum and will be explained
later.   The remaining columns of the table are
headed by cordon count interval.   They start at
--:40 and contain the intervals --:40 to --:00, and
so forth, at 20-minute intervals corresponding to
cordon count time intervals.

_____

*Experimental computations were also made using
one-minute time intervals with a range of $\pm$ 1/2 minute.   The results were not sufficiently different
from the 5-minute intervals to warrant the substantially extra computational work.

TABLE 84

Travel Time Ranges Between Arrival and Cordon Count Time Intervals

Arrival Time	1/3 Interval Midpoint	Midpoint Less Walk Time	Cordon Count Interval											
			40-00	00-20	20-40	40-00	00-20	20-40	40-00	00-20	20-40	40-00	00-20	20-40
00	55	48½	49-68½	29-48½	9-28½	0-8½								
	00	53½		34-53½	14-33½	0-13½								
	05	58½		39-58½	19-38½	0-18½								
15	10	03½					24-43½	4-23½	0-3½					
	15	08½					29-48½	9-28½	0-8½					
	20	13½					34-53½	14-33½	0-13½					
30	25	18½					39-58½	19-38½	0-18½					
	30	23½								24-43½	4-23½	0-3½		
	35	28½								29-48½	9-28½	0-8½		
45	40	33½								34-53½	14-33½	0-13½		
	45	38½								39-58½	19-38½	0-18½		
	50	43½											24-43½	4-23½	0-3½

576

The third column of the table gives the midpoint of the one-third intervals less 6 1/2 minutes.
Thus, the first one-third interval midpoint is 55.
Subtracting 6 1/2 minutes from 55 gives a time of
48 1/2 minutes. The 6 1/2 minutes is a roughly calculated average walking time from the subway train
to the employee's destination. This time was obtained by time studies of walking time during rush
hour between arrival at the Union Square station and
an address specified by floor at 12th Street and University Place. It is assumed to be approximately
representative of the required walking time for this
part of the journey to work.

Appendix Table 84 was constructed by calculating
the ranges of time between the numbers of Column 3
and each of the cordon count intervals. For example,
a person arriving at the station platform at 48 1/2
minutes, would have passed through the cordon at
48 1/2 minutes if he had 0 travel time. If his travel
time were 8 1/2 minutes, he would have passed through
the cordon station at 40 minutes to the hour. Anyone
passing through the cordon interval of 40 to 00, having between 0 and 8 1/2 minutes of travel time,
would arrive at the destination platform at 48 1/2
minutes of the hour.

The body of Appendix Table 84 gives the ranges
of travel time between each cordon count interval
and the number in Column 3 (the midpoint of the arrival time less the constant 6 1/2 minute walking
time). The constant 6 1/2 minutes is also part of
the travel time. It is convenient, however, to sub-
tract this time from the one-third interval midpoint,
so that the ranges in the table refer strictly to
train travel time.

Travel Times

The next data required for this computation consist of the travel time from cordon station to destination station. These data, once obtained, have
to be arranged in a form suitable for inclusion in
this sequence of computations.

There are two sources of data for the computation of the travel time. The New York City Transit Authority provided train running times between each cordon station and each station on the various lines. In addition, they furnished an estimated five minutes as the average time for transferring from train to train including waiting times. Thus, on the basis of these data it is possible to determine the train travel time from each cordon station to each destination platform, including the necessary transfers. The question which remains is: What proportion of the passengers traveling through a given cordon station go to each of the destination stations in the CBD?

The journey to work questions of the sociological study provided the information on the respondents' routes of travel to work. From this information, it was possible to determine for each respondent the cordon station through which he passed and his subway destination station, and thus to distribute the sample by cordon and exit stations. From this, twenty-one tables were constructed, one for each cordon station and one for the total CBD. These tables give the number of people (in the sample) traveling to each CBD station through each cordon station.

By combining the two sets of data--the travel time to each station and the sample numbers--a third distribution was made. Each destination station was replaced by its travel time, including transfer time. The third distribution thus gives, for each cordon station, the proportion of the sample by travel time to the destination station.

For the purpose at hand, however, all possible travel times are not needed. Those which are, are given on Appendix Table 85. The ranges which are utilized on this table are, for example, 0 to 3 1/2 minutes, 0 to 8 1/2 minutes, 0 to 13 1/2 minutes, etc. These required travel time ranges constitute the column headings of Appendix Table 85.

TABLE 85

Per Cent of Sample, by Cordon Station, Having Specified Travel Time Ranges

Cordon Station	Travel Time Ranges											
	$0-3\frac{1}{2}$	$0-8\frac{1}{2}$	$0-13\frac{1}{2}$	$0-18\frac{1}{2}$	$4-23\frac{1}{2}$	$9-28\frac{1}{2}$	$14-33\frac{1}{2}$	$19-38\frac{1}{2}$	$24-43\frac{1}{2}$	$29-48\frac{1}{2}$	$34-53\frac{1}{2}$	$39-58\frac{1}{2}$
A	—	22	44	82	99	78	56	18	1	—	—	—
B	23	58	73	92	75	42	27	8	3	—	—	—
C	—	47	71	91	100	53	29	9	—	—	—	—
D	40	54	79	84	58	46	21	16	2	—	—	—
E	—	9	21	56	90	88	78	43	10	3	1	1
F	18	82	85	91	82	18	15	9	—	—	—	—
G	—	55	63	72	96	45	37	28	4	—	—	—
H	—	18	23	80	96	82	77	20	4	—	—	—
I	13	30	55	85	87	70	45	15	—	—	—	—
J	12	27	67	85	88	73	33	15	—	—	—	—
K	—	53	69	76	87	43	31	24	13	4	—	—
L	50	100	100	100	50	—	—	—	—	—	—	—
M	6	22	39	78	94	78	61	22	—	—	—	—
N	16	32	80	89	84	68	20	11	—	—	—	—
O	—	—	72	72	86	86	21	28	14	14	7	—
P	—	5	64	93	98	95	36	7	2	—	—	—
Q	11	51	74	86	82	48	26	14	7	1	—	—
R	—	61	83	88	96	39	17	12	4	—	—	—
S	—	23	63	80	90	72	37	20	10	5	—	—
T	—	35	65	88	94	59	35	12	6	6	—	—
CBD	8	38	62	82	87	61	37	18	4	1	—	—

579

Appendix Table 85 gives the per cent of the
sample, by cordon station, having each of the travel
time ranges required by Table 84.

To use the data of Appendix Table 85, still another computation had to be made. The data of Table
85 were multiplied by one third, so that the resulting percentages would correspond to the one-third
intervals already set up for the final calculation.

The results of these computations may be illustrated by the final table for the CBD as a whole.
These results are shown on Appendix Table 86. The
travel time ranges are given in four groups.

TABLE 86

Travel Time Ranges and Per Cent of
Passengers, CBD

| Travel Time | Per Cent of Sample | |
Ranges	Total	1/3
0- $3\frac{1}{2}$	8.3	2.8
4-$23\frac{1}{2}$	87.4	29.1
24-$43\frac{1}{2}$	4.4	1.5
Total	100.0	33.3
0-$13\frac{1}{2}$	62.4	20.8
14-$33\frac{1}{2}$	37.6	12.5
Total	100.0	33.3
0- $8\frac{1}{2}$	38.4	12.8
9-$28\frac{1}{2}$	60.6	20.2
29-$48\frac{1}{2}$	1.0	.4
Total	100.0	33.3
0-$18\frac{1}{2}$	81.9	27.3
19-$38\frac{1}{2}$	18.1	6.1
Total	100.0	33.3

These are the groups which will be used in later con-
structions. It will be noted that each group consists of a sequential set of ranges from 0 to the
maximum. This is reflected in the per cents totaling 100 and 33 1/3.

Cordon Station Percentages

The final twenty-one travel-cordon station assignment tables can now be computed. They will require two operations. These operations will be described, using the total CBD tables as illustrations.

In the first operation the 15- to 20-minute assignment table (Appendix Table 84) and the 1/3
travel time percentages (as derived from Appendix
Table 85) are combined. This produces twenty-one
tables, giving for each cordon station and the CBD
the hypothetical per cent of people arriving at each
5-minute interval by the interval they pass through
the cordon station. Appendix Table 87 shows the results for the total CBD.

The table has four sections, each corresponding
to one 15-minute interval of the hour. The numbers
on the table are taken from Appendix Table 86, each
line consisting of one of the groups of that table.
It will also be observed that Table 87 is constructed
by repeated cycles of these four groups. Thus, the
first line of the table appears also as the fifth
and the ninth lines; the second as the sixth and the
tenth lines.

Appendix Table 87 may be interpreted as follows.
In the first row, of the people arriving at their
destination in the 55-minute interval (1/3 of the 15-
minute interval centering on the hour), .4 per cent
pass through the cordon stations between the hour and
twenty past the hour; 20.2 per cent pass through the
cordon stations between twenty and forty minutes past
the hour; 12.8 per cent pass through the cordon stations in the interval between forty past the hour and
the next hour. Line four gives the totals for the
first 15-minute interval.

TABLE 87

Per Cent of Passengers, by Arrival Time and Cordon Interval Time, on 5-Minute (1/3) Intervals, for the Total CBD

Arrival Time Intervals		Cordon Interval					
15-Minute	5-Minute	--:00 / --:20	--:20 / --:40	--:40 / --:00	--:00 / --:20	--:20 / --:40	--:40 / --:00
--:00	--:55	.4	20.2	12.8			
	--:00		12.5	20.8			
	--:05		6.1	27.3			
	Total	.4	38.8	60.9			
--:15	--:10		1.5	29.1	2.8		
	--:15		.4	20.2	12.8		
	--:20			12.5	20.8		
	Total		1.8	61.9	36.3		
--:30	--:25			6.1	27.3		
	--:30			1.5	29.1	2.8	
	--:35			.4	20.2	12.8	
	Total			7.9	76.6	15.5	
--:45	--:40				12.5	20.8	
	--:45				6.1	27.3	2.8
	--:50				1.5	29.1	
	Total				20.1	77.2	2.8

   The four total lines on Appendix Table 87 are
the estimated per cents of people arriving during
each 15-minute interval, by their cordon interval.
The totals of each 15-minute interval on Table 87
equal 100 per cent (with some minor deviations on
account of rounding).

   The second operation consists in forming the
arrival-cordon interval assignment tables. In this
operation, the results of the preceding one, as prepared for twenty-one tables, are transferred to an
actual time range table. The preceding results are
given for a one-hour arrival cycle (divided into
5-minute intervals) and whatever cordon cycle is required by each cordon station. In the second operation the generalized one-hour cycles are applied to
the actual arrival time intervals, ranging from before 7:30 to 9:30.

   Again, by way of illustration, the results of
this second operation for the total CBD are shown on
Appendix Table 88. This table merely transfers the
four subtotals of Appendix Table 87 to their appropriate rows and columns. (The construction of the
first and last rows is described in Appendix S.)
This yields a 100 per cent table, because each row
totals to 100 per cent. It means, for example, that
of all people arriving in the CBD at 7:30 a.m., 7.9
per cent pass through cordon stations between 6:40
and 7:00 a.m.; 76.6 per cent between 7:00 and 7:20;
and 15.5 per cent between 7:20 and 7:40.

   These two operations produce twenty-one tables,
each representing a cordon station and the total CBD.
Any one of these final tables, used as a multiplier
of the schedule of CBD arrivals, assigns the total
number of CBD passengers to each cordon station at
each of the intervals from 6:20 to 10:00 a.m. These
tables must be used after the work schedule of the
total CBD has been reduced to those crossing subway
cordons on their journey to work.

TABLE 88

Arrival-Cordon Interval Assignment Table, CBD

	6:20 / 6:40	6:40 / 7:00	7:00 / 7:20	7:20 / 7:40	7:40 / 8:00	8:00 / 8:20	8:20 / 8:40	8:40 / 9:00	9:00 / 9:20	9:20 / 9:40	9:40 / 10:00
6:30 – 7:15	51.2	27.2	.3								
7:30		7.9	76.6	15.5							
7:45			20.1	77.2	2.8						
8:00				38.8	60.9						
8:15					1.8	61.9	36.3				
8:30						7.9	76.6	15.5			
8:45							20.1	77.2	2.8		
9:00								38.8	60.9		
9:15									1.8	61.9	36.3
9:30									7.9	76.6	15.5
9:45 – 10:30									11.6	54.9	24.7

584

EVALUATION

The travel time-cordon interval assignment
tables can only be evaluated here by reference to
their underlying data and the methods employed in
constructing them. On these bases, several comments
may be made.

An assumption was made concerning the uniform
density of passengers within the 15-minute arrival
times. This assumption was not a valid one, but the
amount of error involved in making it is of minor
significance. Actually, during the period prior to
the morning peak, the first third of each interval
is probably smaller than the second third, which is
probably smaller than the third third. The middle
interval probably comes fairly close to the average,
while the first interval is probably an overestimate
and the third interval is somewhat underestimated.
After the peak period the situation is reversed.
The amount of distortion involved in this assumption
is not large and is offset in part by changing the
totals at each 15-minute interval. Moreover, the implied distortion could be removed only by introducing
a procedure which is probably more precise than the
data and the other procedures would warrant.

The second assumption involved in the construction of the tables is that the destinations from
each cordon station are constant over this morning
time period. This assumption is introduced by using
Appendix Table 85 with its travel time ranges for
each of the arrival times. There is unquestionably
some degree of distortion as a consequence of this
assumption, but its extent cannot be measured. Nor,
in fact, can anything be done about it with the
available limitations on data. There are some area
differences in work schedules. Given these differences, it would be expected that subway destination
stations would be used in differing percentages over
the various time intervals of the morning. The
sample, however, was not large enough to determine
the destinations by arrival time. As a consequence,
it was necessary to use a single distribution of

travel time ranges for each arrival time interval.*

The walking time statistic of 6 1/2 minutes is by no means beyond question. It has, however, certain strengths. It represents a distance which may really be close to the average distance between subway platforms and destination in the CBD.

The final assumption to be noted is that the time between passing the cordon station and arrival at the first destination is assumed to be spent entirely in traveling on the train. This assumption admittedly is not based on evidence other than reported experiences of individuals. It is probable, however, that this coincides with the practices of the vast majority of people who work in the CBD.

The directions of the biases implied in these assumptions are by no means clear, nor is their overall effect discernible. Hopefully, they offset each other, thus minimizing the amount of distortion in the final results. On purely pragmatic grounds--the final test computations--the resulting tables are considered satisfactory from the point of view of the use to which they are to be put.

---

*The sample may also have been too small to obtain suitable estimates of the proportions of passengers traveling through each cordon station in the CBD. There are twenty cordon stations and seventy-six destination stations in the CBD, giving 1,520 possible combinations of cordon stations and destination stations. Of this 1,520, a very large number must be ruled out on the grounds that they would make senseless travel routes. The realistic number is much smaller than this, although it was never actually computed. But even of this smaller number, the 1,060 respondents who crossed cordons may also prove insufficient to reach suitable estimates for some of the smaller stations. For the purpose at hand, however, the grouping of destinations into travel time ranges significantly reduces the sample size requirement. The resulting data are considered to have a high degree of reliability.

APPENDIX

R

COMPARISON OF
ALTERNATIVE
ADJUSTMENT FACTORS

Alternative tables were developed for three of
the adjustment factors. The lateness adjustment, described in Appendix N, provides a table for lateness
starting at 8:30 and another for lateness starting
at 8:00 a.m. Appendix O gives two factors for estimating the number of people working in the CBD who
cross subway cordons to work. One is a single percentage (67.1 per cent) and the other multiple percentages, one for each starting time. The arrival
adjustments derived in Appendix P provide for a uniform set of percentages to be applied to each starting time and for a variable set of percentages, one
for each starting time. This appendix will present
an evaluation of these alternative tables.

Computations were made for each possible combination of these alternatives. In all, there were
eight computations. The results are given in Appendix Table 89.

The combination of adjustment factors used in
the last column gives the preferred result. The
preference is based upon two criteria: the lowest
peak and closeness to the cordon count during the intervals before and after the peak. All the combinations give contours similar to the preferred one,
and hence are fairly similar to the cordon count.
The sixth and eighth columns have the lowest peaks,
differing from each other almost insignificantly.
The eighth is preferred because it involves less
deviation from the actual count than the sixth. It
is of interest to note that the very slight difference between the two originates with the cordon

TABLE 89

Computed Cordon Counts, Based upon Various Adjustment Factors

Lateness Cordon crossing Arrival	8:00 Single Single	8:00 Single Multiple	8:00 Multiple Single	8:00 Multiple Multiple	8:30 Single Single	8:30 Single Multiple	8:30 Multiple Single	8:30 Multiple Multiple
6:20-6:40	18,463	23,142	20,236	25,117	19,449	24,975	21,277	27,056
6:40-7:00	11,462	14,006	12,510	15,161	12,268	15,309	13,360	16,539
7:00-7:20	27,959	28,370	29,528	30,058	33,447	34,812	35,318	36,850
7:20-7:40	85,339	82,647	89,532	87,398	99,043	96,433	104,027	101,960
7:40-8:00	143,414	146,114	151,089	154,347	141,901	141,670	149,618	149,776
8:00-8:20	231,580	206,566	236,543	210,003	224,065	199,682	228,881	202,994
8:20-8:40	320,909	301,489	320,181	301,023	314,097	295,120	313,492	294,759
8:40-9:00	207,260	234,930	204,575	231,063	202,490	229,399	199,995	226,548
9:00-9:20	63,142	69,323	59,702	65,880	62,357	68,462	58,989	65,098
9:20-9:40	24,290	25,237	20,849	21,832	24,290	25,237	20,849	21,832
9:40-10:00	8,175	8,175	6,735	6,735	8,175	8,175	6,735	6,735

crossing adjustment. The lateness and arrival adjustments make for the greatest differences among
the combinations; the cordon crossing adjustment accounting for very little. This is also evident from
the comparisons of the other columns.

These computed distributions were compared with
the cordon counts by a goodness-of-fit test consisting of the sum of squared deviations. The results
again indicated the final column as the best fit--
that is, its squared deviations were the lowest.
However, this test offers little by way of decision
criteria because the cordon count is not a useful
standard, especially during the three peak intervals.

S

THE RELATIONSHIP AND
FORECASTING EQUATIONS
DERIVATION, DIMENSION,
DATA TABLES

This appendix presents the relationship and
forecasting equations in rigorous form, suitable for
use in programming and computation. It also deter-
mines the dimensions of the vectors and matrices in
the equations. Finally, it adjusts the data tables
to conform to the dimensional requirements of the
equation.

EQUATIONS

Let i be the index of scheduled start times:
$i = 1,\ldots,11$; 1 is the interval 6:30-7:15, 2 is
7:30,...., 10 is 9:30, 11 is the interval 9:45-11:30.

$A = [a_i]$ is a 1 x 11 row vector. The element
a_i is the number of persons in the CBD who are now
scheduled to start work at time i.

$B = [b_i]$ is a 1 x 11 row vector. The element
b_i is the number of persons who are scheduled to
start work at time i under an alternative CBD work
schedule.

Let j be the index of actual start time inter-
vals: $j = 1,\ldots,11$; $1 = 6:30$ to $7:15 \pm 7.5$ minutes,
$2 = 7:30 \pm 7.5$ minutes, $10 = 9:30 \pm 7.5$ minutes,
$11 = 9:45$ to $11:30 \pm 7.5$ minutes.

Let w be the index of adjustment tables for D,
K, and E: $w = (1)$ or (2) and is the superscript of
D, K, and E.

590

$D^{(w)} = [d_{ij}^{(w)}]$ is an 11 x 11 matrix. The element $d_{ij}^{(w)}$ is the per cent (%) of people who are
scheduled to start at time i and actually start in
interval j, according to adjustment table w = (1)
or (2).

Let m be another index for actual start times
similar to j.

$K^{(w)} = [k_{jm}^{(w)}]$ is an 11 x 11 matrix. The element $k_{jm}^{(w)}$ is the per cent (%) of people who actually start work in interval j (=m) and cross subway
cordon stations on their way to work, according to
adjustment tables w = (1) or (2).

Let n be the index of intervals during which
people arrive at work or eat breakfast in the CBD,
whichever is earlier: n = 1,......,11; 1 = 6:30 to
7:15 $\pm$ 7.5 minutes, 2 = 7:30 $\pm$ 7.5 minutes, 10 =
9:30 $\pm$ 7.5 minutes, 11 = 9:45 to 10:30 $\pm$ 7.5 minutes.

$E^{(w)} = [e_{mn}^{(w)}]$ is an 11 x 11 matrix. The element
$e_{mn}^{(w)}$ is the per cent (%) of people who cross subway
cordons who actually start work in interval m and
who arrive at work or eat breakfast in interval n,
according to adjustment table w = (1) or (2).

Let z be the index of subway cordon stations:
z = 1,......,20.

Let u and v be indexes of 20-minute intervals
during which people pass through subway cordon stations: p = 1,....,11; q = 1,....,11; 1 = 6:20 to
6:40,.....,11 = 9:40 to 10:00.

$F^{(z)} = [f_{nv}^{(z)}]$ are 20 11 x 11 matrices, each
matrix referring to a cordon station z. The element
$f_{nv}^{(z)}$ is the per cent of people arriving during interval n who pass through cordon station z during interval q.

$$F = \sum_{t=1}^{20} F^{(t)}$$

$$F^{(z)} = T^{(z)} \, S^{(z)}$$

$T^{(z)} = [t^{(z)}_{nu}]$ are 20 11 x 11 matrices, each matrix referring to a cordon station z. The element $t^{(z)}_{nu}$ is the per cent of people arriving during interval n who, assuming all arrivals came through station z, crossed the subway cordon during interval u (at cordon station z, and then traveled from z to their arrival destination).

$S^{(z)} = [s^{(z)}_{uv}]$ are 20 11 x 11 (diagonal) matrices, each matrix referring to a cordon station z. The element $s^{(z)}_{uv}$ is the per cent of passengers going through cordon station z during intervals uv, out of all people passing through all cordon stations during interval uv.

$G^{(z)} = [g^{(z)}_{v}]$ are 20 1 x 11 row vectors, each vector referring to a cordon station z. The element $g^{(z)}_{v}$ is the computed number of persons entering the CBD through cordon station z during interval v.

$$G = \sum_{t=1}^{20} G^{(z)} = [g_v]$$

C = $[c_v]$ is a 1 x 11 row vector whose element c_v is the total number of persons estimated to enter the CBD through all cordon stations during interval v.

$H = [h_v]$ is a 1 x 11 row vector whose element h_v is the forecast of the number of persons entering the CBD through all cordon stations during interval v, given an alternative CBD work schedule.

Equations

(1) Equation of relationship

By station:

$$p[a_i] [d^{(2)}_{ij}] [k^{(2)}_{jm}] [e^{(2)}_{mn}] [t^{(z)}_{nu}] [s^{(z)}_{uv}] =$$

$$[g^{(z)}_v]$$

Total CBD:

$$p[a_i] [d^{(2)}_{ij}] [k^{(2)}_{jm}] [e^{(2)}_{mn}] [f_{nv}] = [g_v]$$

(2) Forecasting equation

$$p[b_i] [d^{(2)}_{ij}] [k^{(1)}_{jm}] [e^{(1)}_{mn}] [f_{nv}]$$

$$- p[a_i] [d^{(2)}_{ij}] [k^{(2)}_{jm}] [e^{(2)}_{mn}] [f_{nv}]$$

$$+ [c_v] = [h_v]$$

DIMENSION

The terms of the forecasting equation are vectors, matrices, and a scalar. The scalar is $p = .97$, the proportion present at work. A and B, the work schedule data, and C and H, the cordon count data, appear in the equation as row vectors. D, K, E, T, S, and F are matrices. The dimensions of these terms refer to the number of columns in the row vectors and the numbers of rows and columns in the matrices. Their dimensions must be fixed in order to prepare the data and proceed with the computations.

There are two requirements which have to be

satisfied in fixing the dimensions of the vectors
and matrices. The first is that the forecasting
equation must compute its results accurately. This
means that none of the required numbers must be lost
during any intermediate operation, and that the entire computation must deliver arithmetically correct
results. Second, the dimension must satisfy the
mathematical requirements of matrix addition, subtraction, multiplication, and division, all of which
occur in actual computation.

The result produced by the equation is vector H,
the forecasted cordon counts. The number of elements in H is governed both by the desired final information and by computational convenience. The desired information leads to ten intervals, 6:20 to
9:40 a.m., since shifts in the flow of traffic as a
result of work staggering will occur principally during this period. An additional period, 9:40 to
10:00, results from computational considerations,
thus yielding an H vector with eleven elements.

At the input end of the equation, work schedule
data are given in 15-minute intervals ranging from
7:30 to 9:30. This produces A and B vectors with
nine elements. Available data, however, make it possible to extend this range if necessary.

The D, K, E, and F matrices consist of nine individual time intervals ranging from 7:30 to 9:30
and two grouped intervals, before 7:30 and after 9:30.
They can serve as 11 x 11 matrices.

The problem of dimension arises primarily from
the need to produce complete computations in each
operation, to preserve all the needed numbers, and
to achieve arithmetically correct final results.
The nature of this problem will become clear in describing its solution. The solution consists in
tracing the inputs required at each operation in
order to produce the necessary outputs. This procedure starts with the final output, the vector H
with its eleven elements.

The vector H, the forecasted cordon count, is the result of multiplying the numbers of persons arriving at work at various times by the matrix F. It will be recalled that F = TS. For convenience, the dimension problem can be handled through F rather than its factors. Appendix Table 90 presents the matrix F which would be required in order to provide complete computations of the cordon intervals between 6:20 and 10:00 a.m. The eleven columns of the table correspond to each of the cordon interval times. The rows of the table are the arrival times. The numbers in the body of the table are the percentages of the people arriving at each arrival time who pass through the cordon station at the time stated at the head of each column. In order to obtain complete forecasted cordon counts, it is necessary that each column contain all the percentages of arrivals passing through the cordon during the indicated interval. The range of the arrival times has been extended, both earlier and later, in order to calculate all people in each cordon interval. Thus it turns out that arrival times and arrival numbers must be specified for the period 6:30 to 10:30 a.m. in order to compute complete cordon counts between 6:20 and 10:00 a.m. (In this range of arrival times, partial computation of cordon counts from 5:40 to 6:20 will also be possible. Since they are not needed for the final results, they can be neglected in the computation without adversely affecting the outcome.)

The significance of Appendix Table 90 may be illustrated further. If the arrival times were cut off at 9:30 (as in the text of the chapter), then the final three cordon intervals from 9:00 onward would be incomplete because they would not receive the passengers arriving at work between 9:45 and 10:30. Similarly, if the arrival times were to begin at 7:30, the first three cordon intervals on the table would be incomplete because they would not contain the people who arrive between 6:30 and 7:15. Accordingly, it is necessary to provide arrival intervals ranging from 6:30 to 10:30 in order to satisfy the eleven cordon count intervals between 6:20 and 10:00 a.m.

TABLE 90

Arrival-Cordon Interval Assignment Table, Extended to 6:30–10:30 A.M.

Per Cents

Arrival Time	Cordon Intervals										
	6:20 6:40	6:40 7:00	7:00 7:20	7:20 7:40	7:40 8:00	8:00 8:20	8:20 8:40	8:40 9:00	9:00 9:20	9:20 9:40	9:40 10:00
6:30	16										
6:45	77	3									
7:00	39	61									
7:15	2	62	36								
7:30		8	77	16							
7:45			20	77	3						
8:00			–	39	61						
8:15				2	62	36					
8:30					8	77	16				
8:45						20	77	3			
9:00						–	39	61			
9:15							2	62	36		
9:30								8	77	16	
9:45									20	77	3
10:00									–	39	61
10:15										2	62
10:30											8

596

The cordon crossing matrix K is a diagonal and
its dimensions are determined by the preceding and
succeeding ones, D and E. Accordingly, Appendix
Table 91 applies to both matrices, D and K. The
columns of Table 91 are the arrival times taken from
the preceding table, ranging from 6:30 to 10:30 a.m.
The rows are designated by the actual starting times
which are required in order to compute all the arrivals at each time. The body of the table consists
of the L matrix given in Appendix Table 83, extended
to satisfy the larger range of actual starting times.
To produce complete numbers of arrivals within the
range of 6:30 to 10:30, it is necessary to fix a
range of 6:30 to 11:45 for actual starting.

   The range of actual starting times begins at
6:30, the same as the arrival range. The 6:30 actual start time also contributes people to arrival
times earlier than 6:30, but these are not needed
for subsequent computation and no loss is incurred
by dropping them. It is necessary to extend the actual starting times beyond the 10:30 arrival time.
Of the people who arrive at 10:30, according to
Appendix Table 83, 1 per cent actually start at
11:45. Thus in order to provide a complete computation of 10:30 arrivals, it is necessary to give the
number actually starting as late as 11:45.

   If the actual starting range were confined to
7:30 to 9:30, as in Appendix Table 83, then the numbers arriving between 6:30 and 7:15 and between 8:30
and 9:30 would be incomplete. There would be no numbers available for 9:45 to 10:30. Thus, to furnish
complete computations of arrivals between 6:30 and
10:30, the actual starting range must be between
6:30 and 11:45. Similarly, the range for matrix K,
the cordon crossing table, must also be from 6:30
to 11:45.

   The final step consists of determining the
range of scheduled starting times necessary to produce the actual starting range of 6:30 to 11:45.
The basis for this determination is given on Appendix Table 92. The required actual starting times

TABLE 91

Arrival Adjustment Table, Extended to 6:30–11:45 A.M.

	Arrival Times																
Actual Start Time	6:30	6:45	7:00	7:15	7:30	7:45	8:00	8:15	8:30	8:45	9:00	9:15	9:30	9:45	10:00	10:15	10:30
							Per Cents										
6:30	41																
6:45	41	41															
7:00	11	41	41														
7:15	3	11	41	41													
7:30	3	3	11	41	41												
7:45	1	3	3	11	41	41											
8:00		1	3	3	11	41	41										
8:15			1	3	3	11	41	41									
8:30				1	3	3	11	41	41								
8:45					1	3	3	11	41	41							
9:00						1	3	3	11	41	41						
9:15							1	3	3	11	41	41					
9:30								1	3	3	11	41	41				
9:45									1	3	3	11	41	41			
10:00										1	3	3	11	41	41		
10:15											1	3	3	11	41	41	
10:30												1	3	3	11	41	41
10:45													1	3	3	11	41
11:00														1	3	3	11
11:15															1	3	3
11:30																1	3
11:45																	1

TABLE 92

Lateness Adjustment Table, Extended to 6:30-11:45 A.M.

Scheduled Start	Actual Start Time																
	6:30	6:45	7:00	8:30	8:45	9:00	9:15	9:30	9:45	10:00	10:15	10:30	10:45	11:00	11:15	11:30	11:45
	Per Cents																
6:30	100																
6:45		100															
7:00			100														
8:30				86	14												
8:45					75	25											
9:00						76	15	5	4								
9:15							75	25									
9:30								75	25								
9:45									75	25							
10:00										75	25						
10:15											75	25					
10:30												75	25				
10:45													75	25			
11:00														75	25		
11:15															75	25	
11:30																75	25
11:45																	75

599

are extended from 6:30 to 11:45 shown at the heads
of the columns. To conserve space, the five intervals each of actual and scheduled starting time from
7:15 to 8:15 are excluded. These will behave exactly as the 6:30 to 7:00 intervals.

To produce the actual starting times from 6:30
to 11:45 Appendix Table 92 discloses that the scheduled starting range must also be from 6:30 to 11:45.
Between 6:30 and 8:15 the D matrix is simply a diagonal and hence the same time intervals are required
on both the scheduled and actual starting table. Beginning with 8:30, however, the main diagonals are
less than 100 per cent and the remainders are shown
in later columns. A small residue scheduled at
11:45 actually starts at 12, but it is not needed
for the computation of the numbers actually starting
at 11:45.

The required range of scheduled start times, as
derived from Appendix Table 92, is from 6:30 to 11:45.
The information given by the scheduled starts corresponds to the work schedule data of vectors A and B.
Their range, however, is only from 7:30 to 9:30. It
is possible to show that scheduled starting times of
7:30 to 9:30 produce complete cordon count forecasts
only in the two intervals from 7:20 to 8:00 a.m.
Thus, the scheduled range of 7:30 to 9:30 yields a
complete actual range from 7:30 to 9:45. Actual
starts for 7:30 to 9:45 complete arrival figures
only for the interval 7:30 to 8:30. These in turn
would give complete cordon count intervals only from
7:20 to 8:00 a.m. The schedule range of 7:30 to
9:30 contributes numbers to cordon intervals ranging
from 5:20 to 10:00 a.m. However, the cordon intervals from 5:20 to 6:20 are not of particular interest, because the numbers which may be shifted to
them will not affect the problem under examination.

The results of the foregoing analysis may therefore be summarized on the tabulation which follows.

Term of Equation	Title of Column Row	Title of Column Column	Required Range Row	Required Range Column	Dimension Term	Dimension Output	Computation Employ in	Computation Result
A, B	Work Schedule	Scheduled Start Time	–	6:30–11:45	1 X 22	1 X 22	Given	Scheduled Starts
D	Scheduled Start Time	Actual Start Time	6:30–11:45	6:30–11:45	22 X 22	1 X 22	pAD	Actual Starts
K	Actual Start Time	Actual Start Time	6:30–11:45	6:30–11:45	22 X 22	1 X 22	pADK	Cross Cordons
E	Actual Start Time	Arrival Time	6:30–11:45	6:30–10:30	22 X 17	1 X 17	pADKE	Arrivals
F	Arrival Time	Cordon Interval	6:30–10:30	6:20–10:00	17 X 11	1 X 11	pADKEF	Computed Cordon Count
C	Cordon Count	Cordon Interval	–	6:20–10:00	1 X 11	1 X 11	p(BDKE– ADKE)F + C	Forecasted Cordon Count

THE DATA TABLES

The forecasting equation requires data tables which conform to its dimensional characteristics. The row vectors must be 1 x 11 and the matrices 11 x 11. In addition, the tables must be so constructed that they produce logical and arithmetically accurate results. Tables corresponding to the terms of the equation are presented in Chapters 2, 3, and 6. This appendix will explain how the tables were adapted for use in the forecasting equation.

Adjustments had to be made wherever the data apply to more than a single time interval. The multiple intervals in the tables are: 6:30 to 7:15, 9:45 to 10:30, and 9:45 to 11:45. The 6:30 to 7:15 interval occurs in A, B, D, K, E, and F. The interval 9:45 to 11:45 occurs in A, B, D, and K. 9:45 to 10:30 is found in E and F. These intervals are the first and last elements of the vectors A and B and rows and columns 1 and 11 of the matrices D, K, E, and F.

Multiple intervals do not occur in the cordon count data, the vectors C and H. Hence, no adjustments are required for the tables of vectors C and H. The cordon counts can be taken directly from the original source data.

Work Schedules

The forecasting equation contains two work schedule terms, A and B. A is the present work schedule of the CBD. B is a variable, corresponding to any projected alternative schedule. Both are 1 x 11 row vectors.

Work schedule data presented in Chapter 3 and Appendix K contained nine numbers, corresponding to the numbers of people scheduled to start work at each 15-minute time from 7:30 through 9:30. Alternative work schedules have the identical form. For both, two additional numbers are required. One is the numbers of people scheduled to start from 6:30 to 7:15, and the other, from 9:45 to 11:45.

The A matrix--the present work schedule--can be
extended to the required intervals from the data now
available, but which are not included in Chapter 3.
The estimates of numbers starting work between 6:30
and 7:15 and 9:45 and 11:45 are:
>   Before 7:30 (6:30 to 7:15), 38,937
>   After 9:30 (9:45 to 11:45), 50,755

These two numbers will serve as elements 1 and 11,
respectively, in vector A.

The same numbers may be used in all alternative
work schedules B. This is possible because the alternatives are constructed over the range, 7:30 to
9:30. No changes are made in any schedules prior to
7:30 or after 9:30. Thus, for computation purposes
(though not necessarily in reality) the same numbers
can be used in A and B.

The Lateness Matrices

Two lateness tables are presented in Appendix N.
Appendix Table 76 is the lateness adjustment matrix
with the 8:30 a.m. origin. Appendix Table 77 has
the 8:00 a.m. origin. In Appendix T additional lateness tables are shown. They reflect various degrees
of reduced lateness. All these tables can be adapted
to the needs of the forecasting equation by the same
procedure.

The two Appendix Tables 76 and 77 both have before 7:30 and after 9:30 rows and columns. In each,
the entry is 100 per cent. The construction of
these tables, as described in Appendix N, allows the
use of these 100 per cents in the intervals now under
consideration, 6:30 to 7:15 and 9:45 to 11:45.   In
the later interval, the use of 100 per cent creates
a very slight inflation of the computed number.   Actually, 25 per cent of those scheduled to start at
11:45 should be placed in the 12 o'clock interval
and left there. By using 100 per cent they are retained in the 9:45 to 11:45 data. Their number is
estimated at forty people and the error may therefore be neglected as inconsequential.

These same Rows 1 and 11 may be incorporated
into the tables of D^1, the reduced degrees of lateness tables.

Cordon Crossing

Appendix O gives data for constructing the cordon crossing adjustment tables. One datum consists
of the sample mean 67.1 per cent. This is the per
cent of the total sample who cross subway cordons on
the way to work. From this per cent a diagonal matrix may be constructed, including the required
first and eleventh rows and columns.

Appendix Table 79 is the cordon crossing adjustment matrix with percentages varying by start time.
This table already shows 74.5 per cent before 7:30
and 55.3 per cent after 9:30. These two percentages
may be used for Rows 1 and 11 of the adapted matrix K.
In each case, there may be a slight overestimate because a part of the sample from which they are drawn
have actual starting times earlier than 6:30 and
later than 11:45. The difference between the required ranges and those from which the data are
taken have not been computed, but they are negligible.

The Arrival Matrices

The arrival matrices in the forecasting equation
are designated by $E^{(w)}$. Two arrival tables corresponding to E are described in Chapter 6 and are presented in Appendix P. Appendix Table 81 gives percentages which vary by actual start time. In Appendix Table 83 the percentages are uniform for all actual start times. Degrees of adjustments in early
arrivals give rise to additional tables of E, which
are based on the uniform arrival table. The data
for constructing these tables are given in Appendix
Table 101. Any adaptation made for the uniform percentage arrival table will be automatically applicable with the different degrees of adjustment.

It has been necessary to compute Rows 1 and 11

for both arrival tables, Appendix Tables 81 and 83.
The procedure consisted of computing the number of
arrivals at each time 6:30, 6:45, 7:00, 7:15, and
9:45, 10:00, 10:15, 10:30, based upon the equation:
arrivals = pADKE, and using the work schedule data
for A, the adjusted matrices for L and K, and the
uniform arrival percentages for E. The next step
was to calculate the numbers in each interval as per
cents of those actually starting. These percentages
are the Rows 1 and 11 of both arrival matrices. The
procedure and the computations will be briefly explained.

Appendix Tables 93 and 94 show the computation
of arrivals between 6:30 and 7:15. In the first
table the numbers of people starting at each scheduled start time are given in the second column.
This number is reduced to 97 per cent in the third
column. The numbers actually starting are given in
the diagonal line of the table. These are 100 per
cent of the number present at work. These same numbers turn up in the total row. The totals are next
multiplied by the cordon crossing adjustment of 74.5
per cent. This produces the final row of Appendix
Table 93.

In Appendix Table 94 the numbers actually starting, recorded in the second column, are taken from
the final row of the preceding table. The body of
the arrival table gives the numbers as distributed
by the percentages of the uniform arrival matrix.
The numbers in the final row are the totals arriving
at each arrival time.

The first rows of the two tables, E, are computed from the results of Appendix Table 94. This
table shows that 28,152 people are estimated to
start work between 6:30 and 7:15. Of this total
25,040 people are estimated to arrive at work between 6:30 and 7:15. The arrivals constitute 89.0
per cent of those actually starting. This then is
the per cent which may be used in the first rows of
the arrival matrices of the forecasting equation.

TABLE 93

Computation: Numbers Actually Starting Work
and Crossing Cordons, 6:30-7:15 A.M.

Scheduled Start Time	Number	X.97	Actual Start Time			
			6:30	6:45	7:00	7:15
6:30	2,986	2,896	2,896			
6:45	398	386		386		
7:00	34,967	33,918			33,918	
7:15	586	568				568
Total	38,937	37,768	2,896	386	33,918	568
xK =	74.54	28,152	2,159	288	25,282	423

TABLE 94

Computation: Numbers Arriving at Work,
6:30-7:15 A.M.

Actual Start Time	Number	Arrival Time			
		6:30	6:45	7:00	7:15
6:30	2,159	885			
6:45	288	118	118		
7:00	25,282	2,781	10,366	10,366	
7:15	423	13	47	173	173
Total	28,152	3,797	10,531	10,539	173

A similar computation is given for the 9:15 to
10:30 arrivals in Appendix Tables 95 and 96. In order to determine the number who actually start work
at 9:45 and thereafter, it is necessary to begin
with a scheduled start of 9:00. Four per cent of
the people scheduled to start at 9:00 actually start
at 9:45, and 25 per cent of the people scheduled to
start at 9:30 actually start at 9:45. Accordingly,
these earlier schedules have to be included. The
total row of the table gives the numbers who actually start work at each time from 9:45 through 11:45.
The cordon crossing adjustment 55.3 per cent is then
applied to these totals. The final row of the tables
gives the estimate of the numbers of people crossing
cordons by the time they actually start work.

This final row is transferred to the second
column of Appendix Table 96 on which the number of
arrivals is computed. The distribution of the actual
start numbers to arrival times is based on the uniform arrival table. The total row shows the results
of the computation. These totals, however, are not
complete. They include only the numbers of people
arriving between 8:30 and 10:30 who actually start
work between 9:45 and 11:45. There are others who
also arrive at these times but who actually start
earlier than 9:45. They are not included on this
table. There are also people who start between 9:45
and 11:45 and who arrive after 10:30. They are also
excluded from the arrival totals because they are
not of interest to this problem.

The final rows of the two arrival matrices are
taken from Appendix Table 97. This table shows the
arrivals as percentages of those actually starting
work between 9:45 and 11:45. The percentages for
each arrival time, from 8:30 to 9:30, are used as
given in Appendix Table 97. The percentages between
9:45 and 10:30 are totaled and used as a single entry
for the eleventh column of the eleventh row. The
total arrivals between 8:30 and 10:30 amount to 87.6
per cent of the total actually starting between 9:45
and 11:45.

TABLE 95

Computation: Numbers Actually Starting Work and Crossing Cordons, 9:45—11:45 A.M.

Scheduled Start Time	Number	X.97	Actual Start Time								
			9:45	10:00	10:15	10:30	10:45	11:00	11:15	11:30	11:45
9:00	808,579	784,321	31,373								
9:15	84,739	82,196									
9:30	43,928	42,610	10,653								
9:45	2,196	2,130	1,598	533							
10:00	30,752	29,829		22,372	7,457						
10:15	605	587			440	147					
10:30	4,337	4,207				3,155	1,052				
10:45	197	191					143	48			
11:00	9,572	9,285						6,964	2,321		
11:15	66	64							48	16	
11:30	2,867	2,781								2,086	695
11:45	162	157									118
Total			43,624	22,905	7,897	3,302	1,195	7,012	2,369	2,102	813
xK = 55.29			24,120	12,664	4,366	1,826	661	3,877	1,310	1,162	450

TABLE 96

Computation: Numbers Arriving at Work, 8:30–10:30 A.M.

Actual Start Time	Number	Arrival Time								
		8:30	8:45	9:00	9:15	9:30	9:45	10:00	10:15	10:30
9:45	24,120	241	724	724	2,653	9,889	9,889			
10:00	12,664		127	380	380	1,393	5,192	5,192		
10:15	4,366			44	131	131	480	1,790	1,790	
10:30	1,826				18	55	55	201	749	749
10:45	661					7	20	20	73	271
11:00	3,877						39	116	116	426
11:15	1,310							13	39	39
11:30	1,162								12	35
11:45	450									5
Total	50,445	241	851	1,148	3,182	11,475	15,675	7,332	2,779	1,525

609

TABLE 97

Computation: Arrivals During 8:30-10:30 A.M. as
Per Cents of Actual Starts During 9:45-11:45 A.M.

	Arrival Time							
	8:30	8:45	9:00	9:15	9:30	9:45	10:00	10:15	10:30
Per Cents of Actual Starts	.48	1.69	2.28	6.31	22.75	31.07	14.53	5.51	3.02
						54.13			

Both sets of percentages, for 6:30 to 7:15 and
for 9:15 to 10:30 can be used in constructing the reduced degree E matrices.   The method is described in
Appendix T.

The Travel Time-Cordon Interval
Assignment Matrices

The travel time-cordon interval assignment matrices are designated in the forecasting equation as
$F_1^{(z)}$.   In all, twenty-one matrices are needed, one
for the total CBD, and the remaining twenty for the
individual cordon stations.

Appendix Q describes the method by which the
travel time-cordon interval assignment tables were
constructed.   The procedure is illustrated for the
case of the total CBD, and the result is given in Appendix Table 88.   The data of this table (and also of
the other twenty) consist of repeated patterns of
four lines each.   It is thus possible to extend the
table to earlier and later times by repeating this
internal pattern.   (The repetition cannot proceed beyond the period in which subway riders are substantially made up of people who work in the CBD.   One
of the components of the tables is the travel time
from cordon station to destination station.   It is
based upon the sample of people who work in the CBD,
not upon the total sample of subway riders.)   However, the required Rows 1 and 11 cannot be obtained
by simply extending the table one line above 7:30

and one line below 9:30. The percentages in the pattern apply to individual times and not to grouped intervals. Accordingly, the required percentages for
the first and eleventh rows have to be computed by
an appropriate procedure. This will again be illustrated by the total CBD table.

The first row of the F matrix must contain percentages which distribute the numbers of people arriving at work between 6:30 and 7:15 to the 20-minute
intervals during which they pass through the cordon
stations. These three intervals are 6:20-6:40, 6:40-
7:00, and 7:00-7:20. Similarly, the eleventh row of
the F matrix must distribute the people who arrive
at work between 9:45 and 10:30 to the cordon intervals during which they pass through the cordon stations. Here too there are three intervals: 9:00-
9:20, 9:20-9:40, and 9:40-10:00.

On Appendix Table 90, the percentages of the
CBD F table are extended to each arrival time from
6:30 to 10:30. The first four rows, consisting of
the arrival interval of 6:30 to 7:15, have to be compressed into three percentages which will distribute
all arrivals in this interval to the three cordon intervals between 6:20 and 7:20. Similarly, the four
arrival times of 9:45 to 10:30 must be compressed
into a single interval and the required percentages
must distribute this total of arrivals to the three
cordon intervals from 9:00 to 10:00 a.m.

There is no simple way of compressing these
four lines of percentages into single lines. Each
line has to be weighted by the number of persons
arriving at its time. The weighting procedure will
make it possible to add the numbers in each column,
and thereby arrive at a single set of percentages
for the two arrival intervals.

To compute these weighted percentages, the procedure described in connection with the arrival
matrices must now be extended to the computed cordon
counts. The method and computations will be briefly
explained.

Appendix Table 98 shows the computation of the
cordon counts. The second column of this table contains the numbers of calculated arrivals at each
time from 6:30 to 7:15. These numbers are taken
from Appendix Table 94. The remaining columns contain the estimated numbers of people arriving at
each of the arrival times who cross cordons during
each of the three intervals. These are computed by
the percentages of the extended F table. The total
row gives the number of persons who arrive between
6:30 and 7:15 who pass through the cordons during
each of these three intervals. The final line of
the table shows each column total as a per cent of
the total number arriving between 6:30 and 7:15. Of
the people who arrive between 6:30 and 7:15, 78.6
per cent cross cordons between 6:20 and 7:20. The
remaining 21 per cent cross the cordons earlier and
are of no interest here. The three percentages at
the bottom of the cordon interval columns become the
first row of the travel time-cordon interval assignment matrix.

TABLE 98

Computation: Numbers of People in Cordon
Intervals, 6:20-7:20 A.M.

Arrival		Cordon Interval		
Time	Number	6:20 6:40	6:40 7:00	7:00 7:20
6:30	3,797	590		
6:45	10,531	8,131	290	
7:00	10,539	4,088	6,416	
7:15	173	3	107	63
Total	25,040	12,812	6,813	63
Per cent (of 25,040)		51.2	27.2	.3

Appendix Table 99 duplicates this procedure for arrivals between 9:45 and 10:30. It produces the result given in the final row of the table. These are the percentages of the people arriving between 9:45 and 10:30 who pass through the cordon stations respectively between 9:00-9:20, 9:20-9:40, and 9:40-10:00. These three percentages become the eleventh row of the travel time-cordon interval matrix for the total CBD.

TABLE 99

Computation: Numbers of People in Cordon
Intervals, 9:00-10:00 A.M.

Arrival Time	Number	Cordon Intervals		
		9:00 9:20	9:20 9:40	9:40 10:00
9:45	15,675	3,143	12,103	431
10:00	7,332	26	2,844	4,464
10:15	2,779		50	1,719
10:30	1,525			120
Total	27,311	3,169	14,997	6,734
Per cent (of 27,311)		11.6	54.9	24.7

The first and eleventh rows of the other twenty F matrices are computed by the following procedure. The second column of Appendix Table 98 gives the numbers of people estimated to arrive at each time between 6:30 and 7:15. Similarly, the second column of Appendix Table 99 gives the numbers of people estimated to arrive at each time between 9:45 and 10:30. Each of these arrival numbers is calculated as a per cent of the total number arriving in the interval. The percentages are as follows:

Arrival Time	Percentage
6:30	15.2
6:45	42.1
7:00	42.1
7:15	.7
Total	100.0
9:45	57.4
10:00	26.9
10:15	10.2
10:30	5.6
Total	100.0

These percentages serve as the weights by which to multiply the percentages in the individual F tables and thereby compress each set of four arrival percentages to single rows.

APPENDIX

T

THE DEGREES OF
THE ARRIVAL
ADJUSTMENTS

The forecasting equation requires several degrees of lateness and early arrival adjustments corresponding to the amounts of early and late arrival
which may be expected to occur under specified conditions. The need for these additional adjustments
is established in Chapter 6, and its final section
shows how they are to be used and how their results
are to be interpreted. This appendix will present
the required additional tables.

The analysis presented in Chapter 6 establishes
a framework for the development of the tables. It
defines the original Appendix Tables 76 and 83 as
the maximum degrees, respectively, of lateness and
early arrival. This means that under any conditions
contemplated by the alternative work schedules projected in this study, it is not anticipated that
people will arrive earlier or later than by the percentages shown on these tables. They therefore
serve as one boundary of the range of tables.

The chapter also expresses the concept of a
minimum degree of early and late arrival. This is
the amount which would remain after subway congestion has been minimized--or eliminated--and after
some of the slack in interoccupational relations
time has been taken up by the projected alternative
work schedules. The amount of early and late arrival
attributable to residual causes, such as special occupational practices, personal and social considerations, or transportation arrangements, is considered
to be the irreducible minimum. No quantification is
offered in the chapter for this minimal concept.

615

The development of the tables, including the number of degrees, their definitions and their quantities, must be based entirely upon qualitative and heuristic considerations. There are no available quantitative data which can produce the tables. Hence the method will consist of reasonable and consistent arithmetic procedures applied to the existing tables on the basis of logical notions about the adjustments and their intended end uses.

Two notions, in fact, provide the foundation for developing the tables. The first is that the tables have to satisfy primarily a computational requirement, and only slightly a substantive one. The procedure for using the tables states that the minimum degree should be used first. If the minimum degree does not produce a suitable result, the procedure requires the use of the remaining degrees, but only for the purpose of finding the one which satisfies the operative criterion. Thus, only the minimum has some quasi-qualitative significance (the lowest, for some reason, the adjustment can be), while the rest are simply convenient intervals on the road to the maximum. For this reason, a low number of degrees can be formulated to satisfy the requirements of the forecasting equation, at least at the outset.

The second notion is that the degrees can be quantified by shifting the existing tables systematically by fixed amounts of average reduction in lateness and early arrival. For example, a fixed average reduction of fifteen minutes can be introduced by moving each percentage one cell closer to the main diagonal of the table. This will increase the main diagonal by the amount of its adjacent cell; and the adjacent one will then receive the amount previously in the one next to it, and so forth. This same procedure can be used to provide any other average amount of shift, such as one minute (= 1/15 of each cell), or 5 minutes (= 1/3 of each cell), or 7 1/2 minutes (= 1/2 of each cell). These notions, applied to the maximum tables, produce usable results.

LATENESS

Appendix Table 100 presents the lateness table modified by the arithmetic procedure just described. It shows a reduction by 0 minutes (the present maximum table), 5 minutes, 10 minutes, and 15 minutes.

TABLE 100

Degrees of Adjustment: Lateness

		8:30	8:45	9:00	9:15	9:30	After 9:30
0	8:30	86.0	14.0				
	8:45		75.0	25.0			
	9:00			76.0	15.0	5.0	4.0
	9:15				75.0	25.0	
	9:30					75.0	25.0
	After 9:30						100.0
5	8:30	90.7	9.3				
	8:45		83.3	16.7			
	9:00			81.0	11.7	4.6	2.7
	9:15				83.3	16.7	
	9:30					83.3	16.7
	After 9:30						100.0
10	8:30	95.3	4.7				
	8:45		91.7	8.3			
	9:00			86.0	8.3	4.3	1.3
	9:15				91.7	8.3	
	9:30					91.7	8.3
	After 9:30						100.0
15	8:30	100.0					
	8:45		100.0				
	9:00			91.0	5.0	4.0	
	9:15				100.0		
	9:30					100.0	
	After 9:30						100.0

The 15-minute reduction table produces a table
which is logically the minimum. All percentages except those at 9:00 a.m. are transferred to the main
diagonal. This means that all lateness falls within
the limit of 7 1/2 minutes. The irreducible minimum
of lateness may perhaps be somewhat greater than
this amount, but there is no systematic way of prov-
ing it. The 9:00 a.m. percentages also seem quite
reasonable. This is the scheduled start time which
now has the greatest amount of lateness, and which
will probably continue to show a noticeable amount.
Many people now scheduled at 9:00 will have their
start times changed; and even under an alternative
schedule, present habits may be expected to persist,
at least in part. On these grounds, the 15-minute
reduction is accepted as the basis for the minimum
degree of lateness.

EARLY ARRIVAL

The uniform arrival adjustment is used in the
forecasting equation, not the multiple (by start
time) adjustments. (Appendix Table 83 is used instead of Appendix Table 81). Appendix Table 101
shows the modifications in the uniform adjustment
which would arise from 0-, 5-, 10-, and 15-minute reductions in early arrival.

TABLE 101

Degrees of Adjustment: Early Arrival

Minutes of Reduction in Early Arrival	Minutes of Early Arrival					
	75	60	45	30	15	0
0	1.0	3.0	3.0	11.0	41.0	41.0
5	.7	2.3	3.0	8.3	31.0	54.7
10	.3	1.7	3.0	5.7	21.0	68.3
15	—	1.0	3.0	3.0	11.0	82.0

The reason for accepting the 15-minute reduction as the basis for the minimum arrival adjustment
is the belief that it makes an important differentia-
tion in the population and in the causes of early
arrival. The 15-minute reduction table combines the
percentages of the first two intervals, totaling 82
per cent, and maintains the remaining four intervals
exactly as they were in the original table (0 reduction). The boundary between the second and third intervals amounts to 22 1/2 minutes, and the 82 per
cent arrive early by not more than this amount. The
thesis is urged that the range 0 - 22 1/2 minutes
contains mostly those who arrive early on account of
congestion, while the higher range consists primarily of people who arrive early for other reasons--an
early start on their work (executives, managers,
etc.), special transportation arrangements, and the
like. The decision to treat the 15-minute reduction
as the minimum table is supported principally by the
belief that it eliminates from early arrival primarily those who are affected by congestion, and that
it retains as early arrivals most of those who do so
for other reasons. This is at best a judgment, without support of actual evidence.

APPENDIX   U   CBD CORDON
COUNTS AT
COMFORT LEVEL

This appendix will derive and present the
cordon count standards which are employed in testing
the feasibility of work staggering. The criterion
of feasibility consists of cordon counts which do
not exceed the comfort level of travel (see Chapter
2 and Appendix H). The tests are applied on a total
CBD basis (not by individual cordon stations) and to
the traffic entering the CBD during the morning peak
periods. The standards which will be developed here
refer only to the traffic which will be tested, and
to no other times, places, or conditions of subway
transit.

METHOD

A crucial problem of approach and method has to
be solved before the appropriate standards can be
developed. The most straightforward approach and
method cannot be used to determine the desired standards for reasons which will be set forth. It has
therefore to be replaced by a more roundabout procedure which will supply suitable standards of comfort level traffic, but only for the test of this
inquiry and not for general use.

Comfort level standards are based on the capacity of the individual subway cars employed by the system. Each type of car, as explained in Appendix H,
has an evaluated maximum comfort level. This car
capacity multiplied by the capacity of cars per
train yields the maximum comfort level capacity per
train. For any station, the maximum number of

trains during a 20-minute interval multiplied by the comfort level per train will produce the station's maximum 20-minute comfort level capacity. If this procedure is extended to the twenty stations of the system, the result will be the maximum comfort level capacity of the system entering the CBD.

This logical procedure is not applicable to the case at hand. The result would essentially overstate the comfort level capacity of the system, insofar as the actual traffic problem is concerned. A certain number of stations have a traffic volume below their capacity. To include these uncongested stations at their maximum capacity would unnecessarily inflate the total CBD capacity. Similarly, the congested stations require more than their available capacity. If a total CBD capacity were calculated in the manner described, the requirements of the congested stations would be met by available capacity from uncongested stations. The maximum comfort level computed in this way would distort the capacity conditions by suggesting that the system can provide comfort level when in reality it cannot meet the conditions of some of the congested stations.

The irregular way in which congestion occurs among the stations also prevents the use of the partial comfort level capacity presented in Appendix H. According to Appendix Table 22, the comfort level capacity (entering the CBD during the a.m.) is 233,734 passengers in 20 minutes. If this capacity were instituted during all 20-minute intervals of the peak period, there would still be congestion in parts of the system because capacity at individual stations is insufficient for the present passenger load. Hence, to use the number 233,734 as a standard will produce erroneous results: If all traffic is brought to at least this level, there will still be congestion in amounts which will be specified below. It should also be noted that this same capacity is greater than the Transit Authority's present maximum cordon count during the morning.

Neither of these direct methods of determining comfort level capacity is suitable for the problem at hand. A different approach is required—one which meets directly the phenomenon of the uneven distribution of subway congestion among the stations. This approach can set suitable standards, but its implications for the rest of the system must also be pointed out.

If the entire system is to provide acceptable riding conditions—assuming present facilities and capacities—then no station may have, under normal conditions, more traffic than its comfort level. To produce such a condition without increasing the physical capacity of the stations having a net excess of passengers (see Chapter 2), the total CBD cordon counts must be reduced during the intervals in which congestion occurs. The required reduction in the CBD cordon count is determined by computing the total equivalent net excess passengers of each congested interval. This computation and its results are given (on a preliminary, uncorrected basis) in Chapter 2, Table 12. To produce comfort level conditions in all stations, the total CBD count must be reduced by the maximum equivalent amount in each 20-minute interval. Only by such a reduction will all stations be cleared of excess passengers. Any lesser amount of reduction will leave excess in one or more stations.

This implies that only one station will have comfort level traffic during each interval—the one with the maximum equivalent excess of passengers. All other stations will have less than comfort level traffic unless schedules or train sizes are modified to conform to the reduced passenger loads. This can prove costly for the system. It is however an inescapable implication of reducing congestion by work staggering.

The method by which the comfort level standards will be derived is as follows: (1) for each interval, the maximum net excess of passengers will be determined; and (2) these maximums will be subtracted from

the reconstructed cordon counts. The remainders
will be the maximum cordon counts capable of providing comfort level traffic throughout the system.

EQUIVALENT NET EXCESS OF PASSENGERS (CORRECTED)

Appendix Table 102 presents the corrected--and
final--estimates of the equivalent net excess of
passengers, by station and cordon interval. The
data of Appendix Table 102 are based upon Table 12,
but corrected for underestimate by a procedure which
will now be described.

TABLE 102

Equivalent Net Excess Passengers, Corrected

Station	7:40 8:00	8:00 8:20	8:20 8:40	8:40 9:00
68th and Lexington			41,680	15,688
125th and St. Nicholas	10,003	35,955	88,206	
High Street			41,598	
Manhattan Br. (Btn., WE, SB Exp.)		5,817	36,666	30,903
23rd and Ely		36,418	57,668	20,655
Vernon-Jackson			9,051	
Queens Plaza (4th Ave. Lcl.)			24,012	

The computation of Table 12 utilized the original cordon counts, corrected by the truncation adjustment. These counts are given in Appendix Table 15.

As shown in Chapter 6, however, the truncation adjustment does not provide a sufficient increase to
the actual cordon counts. The reconstructed cordon
count given in Chapter 6 represents the best estimate
of the actual number. To correct for the under-
stated count an adjustment must be made in the estimates of the equivalent excess passengers.

The adjustment is made by increasing the estimates through the use of the correction factors
given in Appendix Table 103. These factors are the
percentages by which the reconstructed cordon count
exceeds the cordon count used in computing the net
excess. The data employed in the determination of
these percentages are also given in Appendix Table
103. These percentage adjustments are applied to
the numbers of Table 12 to produce the final estimates of equivalent net excess passengers presented
in Appendix Table 102.

TABLE 103

Computation of Correction Factor

	7:40 8:00	8:00 8:20	8:20 8:40	8:40 9:00
Reconstructed cordon count	156,689	202,994	294,759	226,548
Adjusted cordon count	155,227	201,909	227,937	178,982
Reconstructed as % of adjusted		100.5	129.3	126.6

These correction percentages are conservative
estimates of the amount by which the excess equiva-
lents need to be increased. The amount by which the
reconstructed cordon count exceeds the actual

probably arises primarily among the congested stations. By including all the station counts into
this computation the percentage excess is undoubtedly reduced for the congested stations. In Appendix
Table 102, however, the percentages are applied precisely to the stations with the greatest congestion.
Accordingly, Appendix Table 102 probably underestimates the equivalent excess passengers.

THE REQUIRED REDUCTIONS IN TRAFFIC

Appendix Table 102 provides the basis for determining the required reductions in subway traffic
in order to provide comfort level conditions. The
amounts are rearranged by size in Appendix Table 104:
The equivalent excesses of each interval are listed
in order of amount, from highest to lowest.

TABLE 104

Equivalent Net Excess Passengers, Corrected, by Size

	7:40 8:00	8:00 8:20	8:20 8:40	8:40 9:00
Highest	10,003	36,418	88,206	30,903
Next highest		35,955	57,668	20,655
Third highest		5,817	41,680	15,688
Fourth highest			41,598	
Fifth highest			36,666	
Sixth highest			24,012	
Seventh highest			9,051	

The significance of Appendix Table 104 may be illustrated by reference to the 8:20-8:40 interval. To eliminate congestion during that interval, the total CBD count would have to be reduced by an estimated 88,206 passengers. If the total interval were reduced by this amount, then the 125th and St. Nicholas station would drop to comfort level (assuming it obtained its percentage share of the total CBD reduction of 88,206). The other stations would also be reduced--to below their comfort level capacities, since the 125th and St. Nicholas station was the maximum one. On the other hand, if the total CBD reduction were only 57,668 during this interval, 23rd and Ely and all other stations except 125th and St. Nicholas would have traffic at or below comfort level, not in excess of it. There would still be some excess at 125th and St. Nicholas. (The amount could be estimated as 88,206-57,668X the station's per cent of total CBD cordon count).

UNCONGESTED CORDON COUNTS

Appendix Table 105 gives estimates of the total CBD cordon counts which would yield comfort level conditions throughout the system during the four congested intervals. The estimates are computed by subtracting the equivalent excess passengers from the reconstructed cordon counts. The table gives the reconstructed counts and the results of the subtractions from the highest and second highest net excess amount of each interval.

Thus, if the cordon count during the 8:20-8:40 interval were reduced to 206,553 passengers, all stations would be at or below their comfort level limits. If the count were 237,091, again the maximum station would exceed comfort level, but all the rest would be at or below it.

TABLE 105

Estimates of Required Total CBD Cordon Counts to Eliminate Net Excess Passengers

	7:40 8:00	8:00 8:20	8:20 8:40	8:40 9:00
Reconstructed cordon counts	156,689	202,994	294,759	226,548
Reduced by high-est net excess	146,686	166,576	206,553	195,645
Reduced by second highest net ex-cess		167,039	237,091	205,893

CONCLUSIONS

The estimates of Appendix Table 105 may be employed as standards of comfort level subway traffic. The maximum estimates serve as the maximum standards of comfort conditions. If cordon counts can be brought to these levels, there is reasonable assurance that comfort level traffic (or better) will prevail during the 20-minute intervals at each of the twenty cordon stations. The higher cordon counts, based upon the second highest equivalent net excesses, may serve as a suitable relaxation of the maximum standard of comfort level traffic.

The only apparent way of evaluating the standards consists of reviewing the reasoning and the data from which they were produced. The substance of the reasoning was set forth earlier and need not be restated here. There is no cause to impeach or modify the essence of the argument supporting the standards. It

does however contain some assumptions which may affect their validity.

Foremost, is the assumption that the distribution of passengers by cordon station and interval
corresponds, in some systematic way, to the distribution of employees by industry, location, present
work schedule, and potential work schedule. This
means that if an interval is reduced by the required
number of passengers, the reduction will be distributed among the stations according to the present percentages, and that the percentages will neither be
affected by the industries whose schedules are changed
nor by the changes made in their schedules.

Another assumption is that the Transit Authority
will have the necessary equipment to operate the stations at required levels. This does not imply any
increase in the physical structure of the stations.
Principally it involves the availability of cars and
related equipment. Since the reductions in traffic
at many stations will be substantial, there is reason to assume that the equipment assumptions are
within the capability of the Transit Authority.

There is also an important assumption in the
actual computations. The system is assumed to operate at 100 per cent capacity during the intervals.
This is clearly invalid because it operates today at
an average of 97 per cent during the entire morning
period, and at lower percentages during individual
intervals. A more realistic efficiency figure would
reduce the comfort level capacities. Despite its
unreality, this assumption is not damaging to the
results. It imparts a desirable caution and conserv-
atism to the standards which will permit firmer
statements of conclusion and formulations of policy
to be made as a result of their use in subsequent
calculations.

The most critical data assumption rests upon
the use of the reconstructed cordon count and the
correction factors developed from it in Appendix
Table 103. It should be emphasized that these
reconstructed counts have not been evaluated by

the Transit Authority's experts, and hence have not
been approved (or disapproved) by the persons most
familiar with the measures and the system.   However,
if the reconstructed counts were not used, nor the
correction factors applied to the net excesses, the
resultant comfort level standards would be even
lower than they are on the basis of the reconstructed
data.   Appendix Table 106 gives the calculation of
the maximum possible standards (similar to Appendix
Table 105).   The table also gives the corresponding
standard taken from the reconstructed count.   The
result is apparent: At 7:40 the standards are about
the same, but at the later intervals the standards
(on the unreconstructed basis) would be lower than
those presented here by many thousands of passengers.

TABLE 106

A Comparison of Comfort Level Standards Based
on Adjusted and Reconstructed Cordon Counts

		Cordon Intervals			
		7:40 8:00	8:00 8:20	8:20 8:40	8:40 9:00
Adjusted cordon counts	(a)	156,689	198,934	225,249	186,824
Maximum excess, each interval	(b)	9,939	36,237	68,218	24,410
Comfort level standard, unreconstructed		146,750	162,697	157,031	162,414
Comfort level standard, reconstructed		146,686	166,576	206,553	195,645

(a) From Appendix Table 16
(b) From Table 12

APPENDIX

V

EFFECTS OF SCHEDULE
CHANGE ON THE
INDUSTRY GROUPS

The effects of schedule change on the industry
groups are calculated by modifying the present schedules and then determining the number of people who
have to be shifted. This involves a modification
procedure based upon the work schedule matrix as described in Chapters 4 and 5. The results are then
expressed in two ways. They give the net changes,
in the numbers of people, at each starting and
stopping time. They also show the numbers of people
who have to be shifted by each amount of time, ranging from 15 minutes and by 15-minute intervals.
Each of the alternative schedules of the groups is
evaluated by the numbers of people whose schedules
it modifies.

The question now arises: If a particular alternative is introduced--or is projected in the feasibility tests--how many people's work schedules will
be affected by the change? The number depends upon
the response to work staggering on the part of the
community. Two levels of response were defined in
Chapters 4 and 5. One level is based upon the functional capability of an industry to modify its schedules. At this level of response, all people in the
industry adopt the new starting time (within the
specific constraints described in Chapter 4). This
is the maximum response and expresses the fullest
amount of change which the industry could make on
functional grounds alone.

The second level of response implies a forecast
of what may be expected if the work staggering program is introduced. The forecast reflects the amount

630

of change which people are prepared to tolerate, as
discovered through the sociological investigations
which are reported in Chapter 5. The tolerance
level of response produced Table 49 which fixes
quantitatively the personnel constraints of schedule
modifiability. When this table is applied to the
modification of a work schedule--as described in
Chapter 5, particularly in connection with Table 50--
the result is a work schedule corresponding to the
forecasted or expected response by the industry to
the new starting time. The numbers of people who
are shifted according to this procedure constitute
the net changes on the basis of the expected response. It will be obvious that the net changes
according to the expected response will be smaller
than those of the maximum response.

These two response levels--and the net changes
calculated from them--furnish two significant points
in the ensuing computations of feasibility. Here,
they produce the essential data by which to show the
effects of schedule change.

The following tables give, for each industry
group, the numbers of people who would be shifted
from or to each starting and stopping time, by the
maximum and expected responses, respectively. In
these tables, the positive numbers are the net additions to the particular time (not including those
already at the time); and the negative numbers are
net subtractions for each time.

TABLE 107

The Net Numbers of People in the Production
Industries, by Start and Stop Times, Whose
Schedules Would Change, According to
Maximum and Expected Responses

	Maximum Response			Expected Response		
	7:30 Group	8:00 Group	Total	7:30 Group	8:00 Group	Total
Start Time						
7:30	213,760		213,760	61,803		61,803
7:45	-888		-888	-81		-81
8:00	-84,800	153,065	68,265	-38,513	99,950	61,437
8:15	-13,912	-9,397	-23,309	-3,277	-8,457	-11,734
8:30	-65,190	-54,592	-119,782	-11,734	-44,765	-56,499
8:45	-6,789	-15,716	-22,505	-1,439	-9,430	-10,868
9:00	-40,719	-68,048	-108,767	-6,759	-35,385	42,144
9:15	-398	-3,536	-3,934		-1,167	-1,167
9:30	-1,064	-1,776	-2,840		-746	-746
Stop Time						
3:30	50,022	2,885	52,907	11,553	1,607	13,160
3:45	-2,870	20,735	17,865	-7,140	14,922	7,782
4:00	53,200	94,591	147,791	4,329	58,065	62,394
4:15	24,758	-7,610	17,148	5,725	-6,487	-762
4:30	-14,190	-24,937	-39,127	5,614	-20,932	-15,317
4:45	-23,801	-9,341	-33,142	-5,751	-4,832	-10,583
5:00	-70,823	-57,504	-128,327	-18,544	-31,907	-50,452
5:15	-13,011	-4,728	-17,739	-2,362	-1,977	-4,342
5:30	-19,087	-12,484	-31,571	-3,468	-7,651	-11,119
5:45	-12	-53	-65	-4	-32	-36
6:00	-4,159	-1,554	-5,713	-1,284	-776	-2,060

TABLE 108

The Net Numbers of People of Central Administrative
Offices, by Start and Stop Times, Whose
Schedules Would Change, According to
Maximum and Expected Responses

	Maximum Response			Expected Response		
	8:00	8:30	9:30	8:00	8:30	9:30
Start Time						
8:00	133,827			72,144		
8:15	-633			-570		
8:30	-4,908	128,286	-4,908	-4,025	111,307	-1,963
8:45	-22,158	-22,158	-22,158	-13,295	-21,050	-11,522
9:00	-99,926	-99,926	-99,926	-51,962	-86,936	-76,943
9:15	-3,460	-3,460	-3,460	-1,142	-1,868	-2,976
9:30	-2,742	-2,742	130,452	-1,152	-1,453	93,404
Stop Time						
3:30	2,574			1,344		
3:45	21,653			11,545		
4:00	83,602	2,557	-17	43,733	2,225	-7
4:15	17,439	21,653		10,074	19,123	
4:30	42	75,538	-8,075	58	63,989	-4,604
4:45	-26,508	-8,773	-26,204	-14,781	-7,468	-18,049
5:00	-79,661	-72,159	-77,146	-42,733	-63,403	-56,335
5:15	-12,290	-12,033	9,363	-5,956	-9,527	-6,529
5:30	-6,768	-6,700	76,845	-3,252	-4,887	-56,940
5:45	-9	-9	17,422	-5	-7	10,726
6:00	-74	-74	7,487	-27	-45	4,635

THE TRANSPORTATION COMPANY OFFICES

TABLE 109

The Net Numbers of People in the Transportation
Company Offices, by Start and Stop Times,
Whose Schedules Would Change, According
to Maximum and Expected Responses

	Maximum Response			Expected Response		
	8:00	8:30	9:30	8:00	8:30	9:30
Start Time						
8:00	36,429			19,637		
8:15	−40			−36		
8:30	−1,469	42,807	−593	−1,205	37,392	−237
8:45	−3,577	−3,631		−2,146	−3,449	
9:00	−31,005	−38,757	−29,796	−16,123	−33,719	−22,943
9:15	−158	−158	−158	−52	−85	−136
9:30	−180	−261	30,547	−76	−138	23,316
Stop Time						
3:30	63			33		
3:45	132			44		
4:00	24,353	90		12,648	78	
4:15	5,998	159		3,405	86	
4:30	4,203	28,790	−63	2,503	24,925	−49
4:45	492	7,983		375	7,231	
5:00	−27,938	−27,961	−24,553	−15,108	−24,564	−18,698
5:15	−2,845	−4,419	−2,315	−1,594	−3,831	−1,773
5:30	−3,341	−3,418	21,150	−1,724	−2,910	16,288
5:45	−94	−94	2,421	−49	−82	1,864
6:00	−1,023	−1,130	2,706	−532	−983	1,864

RADIO, TELEVISION, AND MOTION PICTURE
COMPANIES AND ORGANIZATIONS

TABLE 110

The Net Numbers of People in Radio, Television,
and Motion Picture Companies and Organizations,
by Start and Stop Times, Whose Schedules
Would Change, According to Maximum
and Expected Responses

	Maximum Response		Expected Response	
	8:30	9:30	8:30	9:30
Start Time				
8:30	35,480	-829	28,664	-330
8:45	-3,164	-3,164	-3,006	-1,645
9:00	-25,085	-25,085	-21,824	-19,315
9:15	-192	-192	-104	-165
9:30	-7,039	29,270	-3,731	21,457
Stop Time				
4:00	571		304	
4:15	1,689		1,465	
4:30	21,016	-168	16,773	-67
4:45	-152	-2,218	61	-1,634
5:00	-9,238	-18,333	-8,651	-13,467
5:15	-576	1,053	-545	963
5:30	-11,050	9,680	-8,076	7,341
5:45	-36	2,030	-34	1,063
6:00	-2,224	7,442	-1,298	5,453

OTHER ADMINISTRATIVE OFFICES

TABLE 111

The Net Numbers of People in Other Administrative
Offices, by Start and Stop Times, Whose
Schedules Would Change, According to
Maximum and Expected Responses

	Maximum Response			Expected Response		
	8:00	8:30	9:30	8:00	8:30	9:30
Start Time						
8:00	52,983			28,500		
8:15	-9			-8		
8:30	-5,920	47,054	-5,920	-4,854	38,483	-2,368
8:45	-3,286	-3,286	-3,286	-1,972	-3,122	-1,709
9:00	-35,683	-35,683	-35,683	-18,555	-31,044	-27,476
9:15	-3,166	-3,166	-3,166	-1,045	-1,710	-2,723
9:30	-4,919	-4,919	48,055	-2,066	-2,607	34,275
Stop Time						
3:30	412			228		
3:45	350			233		
4:00	35,573	298	-114	18,188	190	-46
4:15	3,242	205	-136	2,246	177	-54
4:30	·4,943	34,781	-915	2,341	28,804	-418
4:45	-4,101	-1,771	-5,149	-2,993	-1,791	-2,442
5:00	-24,775	-21,422	-26,868	-12,336	-18,845	-20,648
5:15	-4,227	-3,179	-3,886	-1,847	-2,166	-3,157
5:30	-9,405	-6,900	26,291	-5,222	-5,115	20,164
5:45			3,378			1,860
6:00	-2,012	-2,012	3,846	-839	-1,254	2,819

BUSINESS PROFESSIONS AND SERVICES

TABLE 112

The Net Numbers of People in the Business Professions and Services,
by Start and Stop Times, Whose Schedules Would Change,
According to Maximum and Expected Responses

	Maximum Response				Expected Response			
	8:30	9:30	Total	9:30	8:30	9:30	Total	9:30
Start Time								
8:30	89,981	-89	89,892	-12,104	75,918	-36	75,882	-4,842
8:45	-31,409	-20	-31,429	-5,964	-29,839	-10	-29,849	-3,101
9:00	-44,133	-36,056	-80,189	-76,870	-38,396	-27,763	-66,159	-59,190
9:15	-3,116	-3,691	-6,807	-6,807	-1,683	-3,174	-4,857	-5,854
9:30	-11,323	39,856	28,533	101,745	-6,001	30,983	24,982	72,987
Stop Time								
4:00	521		521	-4	384		384	-2
4:15	430		430		364		364	
4:30	69,305	-42	69,263	-3,851	58,807	-17	58,790	-1,656
4:45	-20,424	-4,135	-24,559	-9,210	-20,846	-3,181	-24,027	-5,605
5:00	-23,394	-31,332	-54,726	-63,892	-20,308	-24,123	-44,431	-47,964
5:15	-3,593	429	-3,164	-5,958	-2,890	-1	-2,892	-4,315
5:30	-21,902	34,445	12,543	56,739	-14,808	26,849	12,041	43,239
5:45		4	4	9,818		2	2	6,792
6:00	-943	598	-345	11,204	-703	457	-246	7,129

637

THE WHOLESALE TRADES

TABLE 113

The Net Numbers of People in the Earlier Wholesale
Trades, by Start and Stop Times, Whose
Schedules Would Change, According
to Maximum and Expected Responses

	Maximum Response			Expected Response		
	8:00	8:30	9:30	8:00	8:30	9:30
Start Time						
8:00	120,549			20,676		
8:15	-64			-58		
8:30	-25,306	95,179	-25,306	-20,751	82,589	-10,122
8:45	-12,702	-12,702	-12,702	-7,621	-12,067	-6,605
9:00	-78,762	-78,762	-78,762	-40,956	-68,523	-60,647
9:15	-3,005	-3,005	-3,005	-992	-1,623	-2,584
9:30	-710	-710	119,775	-298	-376	79,958
Stop Time						
3:30	163			78		
3:45	842			434		
4:00	55,071	163		29,612	119	
4:15	17,463	822	-20	13,252	676	-8
4:30	39,518	52,061	-3,010	22,081	44,929	-1,243
4:45	-21,889	-5,042	-22,525	-15,937	-4,833	-10,311
5:00	-49,396	-8,977	-51,342	-28,041	-8,118	-35,753
5:15	-4,418	-3,846	-3,576	-1,720	-2,273	-3,020
5:30	-36,059	-33,886	19,012	-19,110	-29,453	12,203
5:45			17,483			7,825
6:00	-1,295	-1,295	41,233	-650	-1,046	28,749

TABLE 114

The Net Numbers of People in the Later Wholesale
Trades, by Start and Stop Times, Whose
Schedules Would Change, According
to Maximum and Expected Responses

	Maximum Response			Expected Response		
	8:00	8:30	9:30	8:00	8:30	9:30
Start Time						
8:00	70,298			40,132		
8:15	-595			-535		
8:30	-3,956	65,747	-3,956	-3,244	59,170	-1,582
8:45	-28,386	-28,386	-28,386	-17,032	-26,967	-14,761
9:00	-36,472	-36,472	-36,472	-18,965	-31,731	-28,083
9:15	-197	-197	-197	-65	-106	-169
9:30	-692	-692	69,011	-291	-367	44,596
Stop Time						
3:30	550			270		
3:45	377			196		
4:00	19,303	550		10,255	424	
4:15	28,587	377		16,955	328	
4:30	15,132	18,532	-771	8,368	16,190	-453
4:45	-1,243	26,627	-1,960	-645	25,107	-1,113
5:00	-42,096	-29,855	-44,968	-24,283	-28,099	-27,364
5:15	-2,501	-1,895	-2,124	-1,375	-1,629	-1,507
5:30	-15,132	-11,359	4,171	-8,219	-9,818	3,173
5:45	-199	-199	28,388	-101	-166	15,263
6:00	-2,778	-2,778	12,885	-1,421	-2,337	9,220

THE FINANCIAL INDUSTRIES

TABLE 115

The Net Numbers of People in Commercial Banks,
by Start and Stop Times, Whose Schedules Would
Change, Under Various Alternatives,
According to Maximum Response

| | Earlier Departments | | Public Departments | Later Departments |
	8:00	8:30	8:30	9:30
Start Time				
8:00	42,264			
8:15				
8:30	−5,541	36,723	21,997	−460
8:45	−2,267	−2,267	−10,546	−188
9:00	−33,096	−33,096	−10,999	−2,750
9:15	−252	−252	−84	−21
9:30	−1,108	−1,108	−368	3,419
Stop Time				
4:00	40,753			
4:15				
4:30	−5,541	35,212	11,702	−460
4:45	−2,267	−2,267	8,893	−188
5:00	−31,585	−31,585	−20,143	−2,624
5:15	−252	−252	−84	−21
5:30	−1,108	−1,108	−368	3,293

TABLE 116

The Net Numbers of People in Commercial Banks,
by Start and Stop Times, Whose Schedules Would
Change, Under Various Alternatives,
According to Expected Response

| | Earlier Departments | | Public Departments | Later Departments |
	8:00	8:30	8:30	9:30
Start Time				
8:00	23,662			
8:15				
8:30	−4,544	31,670	19,828	−184
8:45	−1,360	−2,154	−10,019	−98
9:00	−17,210	−28,794	−9,569	−2,117
9:15	−83	−136	−45	−18
9:30	−465	−587	−195	2,417
Stop Time				
4:00	22,877			
4:15				
4:30	−4,544	30,356	10,088	−184
4:45	−1,360	−2,154	8,448	−98
5:00	−16,424	−27,479	−18,296	−2,020
5:15	−83	−136	−45	−18
5:30	−465	−587	−195	2,320

TABLE 117

The Net Numbers of People in Business Credit
Institutions, by Start and Stop Times,
Whose Schedules Would Change,
According to Maximum and
Expected Responses

	Maximum Response 8:30	Expected Response 8:30
Start Time		
8:30	5,054	4,437
8:45	−497	−472
9:00	−4,557	−3,965
Stop Time		
4:15	3,727	3,242
4:30	80	70
4:45	−3,230	−2,770
5:00	173	111
5:15		
5:30	−750	−652

TABLE 118

The Net Numbers of People in Security Brokers,
Dealers, and Flotation Companies, by Start
and Stop Times, Whose Schedules Would
Change, According to Maximum
and Expected Responses

	Maximum Response 9:30	Expected Response 9:30
Start Time		
8:30	−815	−326
8:45	−289	−150
9:00	−29,555	−22,757
9:15	−1,181	−1,016
9:30	31,840	24,249
Stop Time		
4:30	−100	−47
4:45	−206	−112
5:00	−27,619	−21,241
5:15	−29	−25
5:30	27,840	21,367
5:45	88	46
6:00	10	4

LIFE INSURANCE COMPANIES

TABLE 119

The Net Numbers of People in Life Insurance
Companies, by Start and Stop Times, Whose
Schedules Would Change, According
to Maximum and Expected Responses

	Maximum Response			Expected Response		
	8:00	8:30	9:30	8:00	8:30	9:30
Start Time						
8:00	71,624			45,285		
8:15	-6			-5		
8:30	-19,271	52,347	-19,271	-15,802	46,515	-7,708
8:45	-28,294	28,294	-28,294	-16,976	-26,878	-14,712
9:00	-24,029	24,029	-24,029	-12,494	-19,624	-17,369
9:15	-24	24	-24	-8	-13	-21
9:30			71,617			39,810
Stop Time						
3:30	5,398			2,807		
3:45	6,535			3,798		
4:00	59,683	5,398		38,675	4,696	
4:15		6,529			4,794	
4:30	-29,702	29,987	-29,702	-21,629	27,548	-14,482
4:45	-24,732	-24,732	-19,334	-14,721	-22,097	-12,095
5:00	-17,182	-17,182	-10,653	-8,930	-14,941	-9,076
5:15			59,683			2,638
5:30						33,015

TABLE 120

The Net Numbers of People in Fire, Marine, and
Casualty Insurance Companies, by Start
and Stop Times, Whose Schedules Would
Change, According to Maximum
and Expected Responses

	Maximum Response			Expected Response		
	8:00	8:30	9:30	8:00	8:30	9:30
Start Time						
8:00	38,992			22,999		
8:15	-18			-16		
8:30	-5,357	33,617	33,617	-4,393	30,428	-2,143
8:45	-18,404	-18,404	-18,404	-11,042	-17,484	-9,571
9:00	-14,328	-14,328	-14,328	-7,451	-12,466	-11,033
9:15	-842	-842	-842	-86	-455	-724
9:30	-43	-43	38,931	-11	-23	23,471
Stop Time						
3:30	257			92		
3:45	6,808			3,914		
4:00	30,161	257		18,268	152	
4:15	1,130	6,808	-10,550	698	6,297	
4:30	-10,531	19,593	-14,569	-7,110	18,185	-4,556
4:45	-15,152	-14,005	-12,927	-8,887	-13,036	-8,476
5:00	-13,184	-13,184	6,721	-6,939	-11,220	-9,675
5:15	-60	-60	30,116	-25	-40	4,031
5:30	-27	-27	1,148	-11	-14	18,083
5:45			19		-224	583
6:00						10

TABLE 121

The Net Numbers of People in Government, by Start
and Stop Times, Whose Schedules Would Change,
According to Maximum and Expected Responses

	Maximum Response 8:30	Expected Response 8:30
Start Time		
8:30	34,266	30,295
8:45	-9,131	-8,674
9:00	-24,394	-21,223
9:15	-483	-261
9:30	-258	-137
Stop Time		
4:00	366	305
4:15	451	394
4:30	24,313	21,260
4:45	1,471	1,301
5:00	-22,743	-20,047
5:15	-2,647	-2,266
5:30	-1,116	-884
5:45	-9	-7
6:00	-86	-56

ABOUT THE AUTHOR

Lawrence B. Cohen is Professor of Industrial Engineering at the School of Engineering and Applied Science, Columbia University. During the academic year 1967-68, he was a visiting professor at the Israel Institute of Technology (Technion), Haifa, Israel.

Mr. Cohen has worked in industry and has served as consultant to United States Government agencies, business firms, and labor organizations. He is a member of the Labor Panel of the American Arbitration Association and of the Arbitrations Panel for The New York State Board of Mediation.

Mr. Cohen previously has published papers on industrial engineering, labor, and related subjects. He received bachelor's and master's degrees from the University of Pennsylvania and a Ph.D. degree from Columbia University.